A *Return to* PAGANY

A Return to

*The History, Correspondence, and
Selections from a Little Magazine*

BEACON PRESS

PAGANY

1929–1932

Edited by STEPHEN HALPERT
with RICHARD JOHNS

Introduction by KENNETH REXROTH

Boston

"Inspiration for Greatness," by Erskine Caldwell. Copyright 1929 by Macauley Company, renewed effective
1957, © by Erskine Caldwell. Appeared originally in
PAGANY. Reprinted by permission of McIntosh and
Otis, Inc. SOMETHING OF THE STING reprinted
with the permission of Manuel Komroff. Copyright
renewed 1957 by the author.

Grateful acknowledgment is made to Mrs. William
Carlos Williams for the use of the contributions to
PAGANY and the letters of William Carlos Williams,
M.D. Grateful acknowledgment is also made to all the
contributors for use of their materials and letters.

To MELINDA *and* SEAN

"The little magazine is something I have always fostered;
for without it, I myself would have been early silenced.
To me it is one magazine, not several. It is
a continuous magazine, the only one I know with an absolute freedom
of editorial policy and a succession of proprietorships
that follows a democratic rule. There is absolutely
no dominating policy permitting anyone to dictate anything.
When it is in any way successful, it is because it fills

a need in someone's mind to keep going. When it dies,
someone else takes it up in some other part of the country—
quite by accident—out of a desire to get the writing
down on paper. I have wanted to see established some central
or sectional agency which would recognize, and
where possible, support little magazines. I was wrong.
It must be a person who does it, a person, a fallible person,
subject to devotions and accidents."

WILLIAM CARLOS WILLIAMS

Foreword

IN SPITE OF THE ENTHUSIASM of Stephen Halpert, I was initially hesitant about making a biographical continuity out of my efforts in the 1930's at editorship and creativity. However, to have been a part of the organizing and editing of *A Return to Pagany* has been a most satisfying experience. It doesn't happen very often that one of the most rewarding periods of a man's life comes to actuality again.

RICHARD JOHNS

Contents

3. *Down and Out in Bethel and Redding*
   VOLUME III — 1932–1933

Introduction

As soon as I was invited to do this little introduction to Richard Johns' memorable literary magazine I got a complete, bound file of *Pagany* from the University of California library. As I looked through it, it was just like Proust's Madeleine. My own youth came back like a total hallucination of the senses, the very sight and sound and smell, taste and touch, of forty years ago. What affected me most poignantly before I had read any of it at all was the sight of my own typography for the ads of various and sundry other literary magazines of the time. They must have been the first examples of Bauhaus or Comfuturist typography in America done in the days when Rodchenko, El Lissitsky, and Moholy-Nagy themselves were young. It's not that my own youthful efforts were important in themselves; it's that *Pagany*'s lifetime spanned the breakdown of the international avant garde as the world economic crisis shut down and a quite different kind of literature emerged.

The earliest issues of the magazine are full of contributions by Americans who bear an apparent relationship to writers like Blaise

Cendrars, Pierre Reverdy, or the young Louis Aragon. Many of them are now unjustly forgotten. They believed and hoped that the arts would be the instrument of a fundamental revolution of the human sensibility as such. They believed that the word or the pictorial image could be used to subvert the dead syntax by which human self-alienation had been grafted into the very structure of the brain and nervous system. They believed that The Revolution of the Word would liberate a new life meaning for man and sweep away dead shells from which meaning had been exhausted or had turned malignant.

This does not mean Art for Art's Sake. Quite the contrary. The term itself had become a slander turned against its inventors by the squares—in those days the labor movement called them scissorbills —the guardians of conventional culture. Let's not forget that Oscar Wilde himself was a far saner and more trenchant critic of society than his disciple Shaw, an Oscar Wilde diluted with whey and hyped up with red pepper. The advance guard of international culture from 1870 to 1929 had already laid the foundations of what now we call the counter culture, and those foundations were certainly grounded in a maximum sense of responsibility to the people: "*paganus*—a person, or relating, or belonging to a person in civil life, a native, the opposite of *miles,* a soldier."

I would like to avoid singling out names because all of *Pagany* is important, but I would like to point out that its American writers were at least the equals of their European contemporaries. John Dos Passos' pieces that eventually went to form *U.S.A.* were sections from what is unquestionably the greatest achievement of *Unanisme,* certainly an incomparably greater work than the tedious, many-volumed production of Jules Romains, the inventor of the term. This is true of the poetry too. Many a long-forgotten or suppressed American poet was a far better writer than, say, Philippe Soupault, who already enjoyed a very substantial world reputation and who now seems pretty thin stuff. Long forgotten or suppressed but now being resurrected, ferreted out in libraries, by inquisitive poets of the present generation, ever becoming more conscious of their own ancestors, they were the first architects and bricklayers of a new Jerusalem that yet may never be built.

Then midway in the course of the short life of *Pagany,* the economic and social collapse of the dominant society began to make itself felt. As Louis Aragon was to say a few years later, "We do not need to manufacture our own synthetic apocalypses; we can find them every morning in the newspapers." Under the pressure of catastrophe, writers and artists all over the world began to turn to attack the specific social evils from which they had thought they had escaped by concentrating on the underlying, fundamental Lie. Richard Johns was especially sensitive to this great turn, and published some of the earliest and finest writing of the kind that was eventually to be debauched and destroyed by the slogans of falsification—Prolecult and Socialist Realism.

Only recently Stefan Heym said, "We will never have a true Socialist Realism until we are able, unafraid, to describe the boredom of Minsk." For this self-evident truism he was broken by the East German government and became a not person, like the folksinger, Wolf Biermann, who sings precisely of the soul of man under Socialism, the human self-alienation that still endures behind the interpersonal iron curtains of slogans and shibboleths.

Time was when the little toy dog was new and the soldier was passing fair. As the literature of social criticism and protest arose in America, it was still fresh, still undisillusioned. This freshness was not naïveté, but the voice of the unbroken heart of young men and women who were certain that the future belonged to them and the people for whom they spoke. Richard Johns was especially discriminating of the values of this kind of writing. There are no slogans, no stereotypes. He would not have printed them, and anyway it was before enforced stereotyping. It's sad to read over the work of some of these people. Where are they now? Only a handful of them are still left working away past the age of retirement in the skilled building trades, working on the walls of the New Jerusalem, their hair white or very gray, but still calling down to their tempters, "I'm working on the wall and I can't come down."

Pagany was a mirror, admittedly not the largest, of the conflicts and the communions, the victories and defeats, of a pivotal moment in the history of Western culture. Today when a whole generation has seceded from The Social Lie and has demanded the freedom to discover meaningful, significant lives in The Community of Love, it is good to have a collection of things where they can see, like notes in a sealed tin at the summit of a Himalayan peak climbers had believed hitherto inaccessible, that there had been others here before them.

Implicit in this piece is the idea, in case you haven't noticed, that Richard Johns was and is a very nice guy and a sensitive and perceptive one.

KENNETH REXROTH

Santa Barbara, California
April 21, 1969

Editor's Preface

SEVERAL YEARS AGO, I visited Richard Johns at his home in Vermont to buy some of his old books for my library. By chance, in his woodshed I came upon a number of musty cartons filled with old letters, manuscripts, and literary magazines. This was the archive of *Pagany: a native quarterly,* one of the most important and influential little magazines published in America during the early years of the depression.

In the past two years, I read the selections published in *Pagany* and sorted and correlated thousands of pieces of correspondence. What impressed me most in these letters was the warm friendship Johns extended to his contributors. He was an editor who not only loved the experience of literature but could touch upon genius without contracting the mania for owning it. This personal approach enabled him to publish an amazing cross section of writing and drew a sense of truth and respect from his contributors as reflected in their letters.

There was William Carlos Williams, corresponding with Johns

not as an established poet but as a soft-spoken doctor whose literary interests were second to his concern for life. It was for *Pagany* that Williams began his novel *White Mule*. There was Ezra Pound, not untouchable and restricted to intellectual discussion but a literary gadfly spreading his venom from the bushes in Bloomsbury to the swank experimental salons of Paris. There was Robert McAlmon, caustic, callous, yet, like a stubborn child, inwardly respectful and wanting to be of help; Sherry Mangan, effusive, rhetorical, and recently graduated from Harvard, who helped Johns in every way he could. There were the younger, lesser-known writers and poets of the day—Erskine Caldwell, fighting his private war against the censorship of his first novel *The Bastard*; Edward Dahlberg, smarting over the bowdlerizing by his English publisher of his first novel *Bottom Dog*; John Cheever, Albert Halper, Louis Zukofsky, and Carl Rakosi, trying to make ends meet while perfecting their craft.

A Return to Pagany is informal rather than critical or academic. Johns and I decided to let the original correspondence and the selections speak for themselves. In this way, we felt the inherent workshop quality of the little magazine genre would be better understood. This book reviews the highlights of *Pagany* and its accomplishments, it records its shortcomings and the measures taken to overcome them, and it recalls occurrences which will be useful to today's students of literature. I hope the history, correspondence, and reprinted selections from the twelve issues of the magazine will give the reader the unique experience of relieving a brief but vital period in American literature.

STEPHEN A. HALPERT

Boston, Massachusetts
May 1, 1969

Acknowledgments

I WOULD LIKE to express my deepest thanks to Richard Johns for his patience, generosity, and painstaking help. It wasn't easy for a contemporary, forward-thinking man like Johns to spend so much time in the past again. It was indeed a great privilege to have been able to work with him and to have gained his friendship.

I am greatly indebted to A. K. Workman, my friend and scholar in American literature, for his advice and assistance in the planning and preparation of the manuscript.

Also, thanks are due to Melinda Halpert, whose discriminating taste was invaluable in making the initial selections of the works from the twelve issues of the magazine.

I am also indebted to Miss Lisa Koch, Miss Denise Scully, and Miss Abby Solomon for their time and effort.

I wish to thank those authors, or their heirs, who readily granted permission to include works in this book.

Finally, I would like to thank Sassy who sang while we worked.

1.

*Toward
a Native Quarterly*

VOLUME I–1930

IN APRIL 1929, a youthful, energetic Richard Johns wrote a letter to William Carlos Williams. This event was the beginning of a remarkable odyssey—the preparation and the start of publishing in January 1930 of *Pagany; a native quarterly,* one of the most significant of the little magazines published in America during the early depression years of the Thirties.

> Box 93
> North Postal Station
> Boston, Massachusetts
> April 23, 1929.

William Carlos Williams

Dear Dr. Williams:

It is my intention to bring out a new Quarterly in January 1930. I should like to appeal to you for several things, and would appreciate any one of them you might be willing to do. First, I wish to call it "PAGANY" (this I feel demands both your permission and my request that you write for it a manifesto); secondly, I should like to consider you associate Editor; and thirdly, I should like to have a good bit of your work. I am appealing to you now, before anything is done. If you should be interested, I promise that the entire content shall be submitted to you for approval and decision. As yet I am not sure what I shall be able to pay for contributions, but intend to pay as liberally as finances will permit. There is room for a magazine such as I hope to have, there is nothing ideal in my conception; only it must not be the Dial, Blues, Transition etc. If you have any enthusiasm, any ideal in mind, do help me, for it is to you that I am appealing first, it is with you that I hope to fashion it. Can you not help me to get the people you would like to see printed, those you admire and whose work interests you? Your "Voyage to Pagany" first compelled me; won't you help? I offer you a place on the bridge.

> Very truly yours,
> *Richard Johns.*

WILLIAM CARLOS WILLIAMS, M. D.
9 RIDGE ROAD
RUTHERFORD, N. J.

July 1 , 1929

My dear Johns :

Nothing would please me more than a quarterly such as you suggest ; there is no project more difficult . I have seen enough of magazines which fail after the first four or five numbers . Any new magazine with which I would be associated must be in a position to continue for at least two years , come what may . This costs time and a large sum of money I am afraid .

Such a magazine , being a quarterly , must needs be of a good size, say a hundred and eighty pages . It had better not be published in Boston but in New York . You see what I mean .

But nothing - to revert - would please me more . It is only that I doubt seriously anyone's ability to swing such a thing in the U.S. unless he be himself wealthy and abler minded and more literary minded and phenomenally generous and enlightened of spirit more than any one I have ever seen on earth - that I hesitate .

You may be this person . If so the millennium is at hand .

Yes, I have what may be called ideals though they are curiously unlike anything that used to be called that . I have a vivid perception of something that might be done in the U.S. with literature as material . I should be instantly raised into heaven could I be sure that I would have a quarterly at my disposal that I could make the fulcrum by using which I would , in the course of the next ten years , pry things so loose here that we could breathe again in an enlightened air and not in this sink of stupidity and ignorance where we live now "saved" by science and philosophy .

Thus you see I take you seriously but so much do I pant for what you offer that I am doubly dubious of anyone's ability to make good . Yet what you envision IS the future - or rather the present if anyone could have the ability to put it across . I'd back it and it would be the center of every literary interest after a patient murderous ascent extending over several years of effort . I'd expect to give it my life - in short .

Yours

W. C. William

[handwritten in left margin: your letter dated April 23/29 just reached me today W.C.W.]

Johns, instinctively recognizing an important beginning, promptly followed up Williams' somewhat hesitant response; on July 11 he wrote:

July 11, 1929

William Carlos Williams

Dear Dr. Williams:

Your letter leaves me very much in a quandary. Are you with me or not? Not having heard from you (thanks to the Post Office) I have gone ahead, announced publication the first of January, 1930, accepted manuscript, etc. Little that I have accepted need be used, it has cost me practically nil. It amounts to two poems of Yvor Winters, a short story by his wife, Janet Lewis, two poems by Parker Tyler, one by Kathleen Tankersley Young, two essays by Gorham B. Munson and a short story by Manuel Komroff. As for demands and desires, I can promise two years of life, a hundred and eighty pages. Publication in New York is impossible, I have fled the town like a madman, hating it, hating literary gatherings, publishers' teas. Boston is quite free from such, those who would care to be interested are not too excellent, they may be crooned to and ignored. Printing and mailing will be done outside the city, away from the delightfully infantile censor. Another thing. You *have* got ideals curiously unlike any that used to be called that, your perception of literature and mine should have to be discussed, thrashed out. That you could pry things loose here, introduce an enlightened air here I sincerely doubt. The Quarterly must either be an expression of our personal preference in literature, or an attempt to combine that with stuff the people will buy and read. I favor the second, for were my taste the criterion there wouldn't be ten people to read the sheet with interest. Would yours be so very much more popular? How about it? It remains an adventure! I have started and will see it through. To know that you are enough interested to stand beside me, to quarrel with me over it, would be a sincere delight. All your dubiety I share: having read many manuscripts I believe mine may be deeper.

Faithfully,
Richard Johns

The reply came immediately:

> Yes, I am with you but I'd like best not to have any official editorial status—unless you prefer otherwise. I can't see that my name would help you.

Thus *Pagany* quickly gained the interest and concern of the man who would be its most steady contributor. At this time Williams was forty-six and a busy pediatrician in the burgeoning New Jersey town of Rutherford. Despite his devotion to medicine, he had already published more than ten books, including the poetry of *The Tempers* and *Spring and All,* as well as such prose works as *The Great American Novel* and *In the American Grain.* As editor, with Robert McAlmon, of the short-lived little magazine *Contact,* Williams had already made an impression on the little magazines of the early Twenties. The recipient of The Dial Award for 1926, this richly unselfish man was therefore an established literary figure when Johns first wrote to him. He was not, however, established in the sense of having made a financial success of his writing, but rather as a voice recognized and respected throughout the literary world. It is not only for the quality of his writing but also for his eagerness to be of service to literature that William Carlos Williams must be regarded as the most important contributor to *Pagany*—and indeed to the entire little magazine genre of his day.

Although the ensuing friendship between Johns and Williams, fused by a mutual enthusiasm for the work at hand, served as *Pagany*'s cornerstone, its real history began some four years earlier. At the age of twenty-one, Richard Johnson, soon to shorten his name to Johns, ended his frustrating years of formal education by dropping out of Classical High School in Lynn, Massachusetts. He began working at odd jobs that did not call for an education.

However, for Johns an interest in reading and writing had always been foremost. His first published piece was a poem, "Song Against Love," printed in 1926 in the first issue of the paperbound boxed quarterly, *Casanova Jr's Tales.* The publisher of this privately printed venture was the colorful Samuel Roth, a vender of erotica who later printed the first pirated portions of *Ulysses* and *Finnegans Wake* in America.

Johns enjoyed browsing at the two bookshops in the Boston area which stocked a variety of little magazines (Smith and McCance on Ashburton Place and the Dunster House Bookshop in Cambridge), and it was here that he discovered *Contact, transition,* and *The Little Review*, all published abroad, and *The Dial*, which he considered the most interesting literary periodical published in America. His own writings were published in such lesser-known magazines as *Greenwich Village Quill, Bozart,* and *Opportunity: A Journal of Negro Life* edited by Countée Cullen.

Johns' interest in writing was generally encouraged both by his father, Benjamin N. Johnson, a well-known Boston attorney and former student at Harvard of William James, and by his uncle, Arthur Johnson, then legal counsel to Isabella Stewart Gardner and author of a published collection of short stories, *Under the Rose*. His father had hoped Johns would follow the parental example of attending Harvard and Harvard Law School but was sympathetic to his son's desire to write.

After the death of his mother in July 1926, Johns accompanied his father on a long-contemplated visit to Greece. Together they explored this classic country leisurely and searchingly, even to the extent of riding horseback over obscure trails to see the Hermes of Praxiteles at Olympia. For both the older and younger man this distraction from deep grief had the added importance of bringing them even closer together in understanding and enhancing their respect for each other's interests.

After returning to the States, Johns spent much of his time between 1927 and 1929 in New York City. He studied comparative poetry and literary theory at Columbia. Many of his friends were young men starting their careers in publishing. Through F. Everett Abbott, a close friend from high school who was now a salesman for Doubleday Page, Johns met Stanley Rinehart and Edward Weeks. Two other friends, George and Julie Rittenhouse, let Johns and Abbott share the basement apartment of their 11th Street house. George Rittenhouse worked for *Publishers' Weekly*. His wife Julie, a reader for a number of publishers, had recently recognized the literary talent of McKinley Kantor and had placed his first novel *Diversey* with Coward-McCann. Frequently Johns would read and comment upon manuscripts, although the reports were always sent back to the publishers under the Rittenhouse name.

Having no responsibility to any job with regular hours, Johns shuttled back and forth between New York and Boston and its suburbs. He increasingly felt that his own writing was going to remain mediocre. Now and again, and generally with a good foundation of alcohol (after spending an evening with such writers as Sherwood Anderson and Lyle Saxton at Julio's), he could let himself go, but he soon recognized this state as a transitory seizure which would not develop into any sort of sustained drive. Gradually his writing moved more strongly into the area of criticism entered earlier when Frank Harris had sent him express from Nice his four volume *My Life and Loves,* on which Johns wrote an extensive commentary, "Truculent Revenant," published in the June 1927 issue of *Greenwich Village Quill.* Then he began working on a lengthy critique of Arthur Symons' poetry, an author he greatly admired and whose first editions he had assiduously collected. He first submitted "Arthur Symons: English Decadent" to the *Atlantic Monthly* and then to *Harper's;* both were little more than polite in returning it. Finally Johns sent the piece to the newly announced *Poetry World,* and it was used as the lead article of that magazine's first number. After his success with the Symons article, Johns became increasingly interested in the prospect of developing an independent little magazine, which by Spring of 1929 was to be *Pagany; a native quarterly.*

As the idea of a magazine became more and more a reality, Johns began to look analytically at the existing literary publications. With the immensely influential *Dial* no longer on the scene, there were three magazines which would have a major impact on the editorial policy of *Pagany.* Eugene Jolas' *transition,* first published in 1927, was running James Joyce's *Finnegans Wake* when *Pagany* came into being. *transition*'s main contention was that the conventional language of patterns had become inadequate and new literary forms needed to be developed.

Hound and Horn, self-styled inheritor of the new-humanist *Dial* traditions, was by contrast to *transition* quite academic, originally calling itself "a Harvard miscellany." In its early development its co-editor, Lincoln Kirstein, was somewhat pedantic and prudish in his selection, but after moving the magazine in 1930 to New York City, he broadened his editorial policy.

Blues stated that it was a magazine of new rhythms, and under the editorship of Charles Henri Ford its tone was daring and enthusiastic, although highly self-conscious in its experimentalism.

While *transition, Hound and Horn,* and *Blues* expressed the wide variety of the existing little magazines, Johns observed that they wasted a great deal of space attacking one another and over-amplifying personal literary gods. What Johns set out to find was the best and most exciting writing being done, primarily from the experience of American writers, regardless of their affiliation with constrictive literary camps, whether new-humanist, proletarian, or the self-consciously experimental.

Johns' impressions of what would make a good magazine began to take more solid form during the early part of 1929 while he was in Lynn. His father, already impressed with the strength of his literary convictions, was inclined to support a serious literary effort. It was soon agreed that Johns was to have fifteen hundred dollars on loan as working capital for a magazine.

With his magazine project now funded, Johns began to search for a key concept that would unify his main purposes and give him the basis for a title. He thought about the writers he admired whose work was not yet widely known and whose writing might give him a focal point for gathering the work of other unrecognized writers.

When William Carlos Williams' book *In the American Grain* was published in 1925, Johns had been deeply impressed by the brilliant portraits of the individuals involved in the expanding American civilization. Despite its impact on many readers, the book had no success, and became a common title in the remainder section of many bookstores. This had been followed in 1928 by *A Voyage to Pagany,* Williams' first venture into fiction. The novel was a lightly veiled summary of a trip to Europe by Williams and his wife, with subtle evocations of the people and places of Europe, which Williams found "largely pagan" in comparison with the New World of *In the American Grain.* Although Williams used the term "Pagany" as a synonym for Europe, the phrase stuck in Johns' mind. He went to the dictionary and presently worked out a paragraph:

Pagus is a broad term, meaning any sort of collection of people from the smallest district or village to the country as an inclusive whole. Taking America as the *pagus,* any one of us as the *paganus,* the inhabitant and our conceptions, our agreements and disagreements, our ideas, ideals, whatever we have to articulate is *pagany,* our expression.

This seemed a sound derivation from the Latin and expressed succinctly what Johns wanted his magazine to articulate.

At this point, Johns began writing to those who might help with the start of a magazine, and addressed his all-important request to Williams. He had already become deeply involved in plans for the magazine when he received Williams' commitment to the project. This support gave an increasingly clearer definition to the "Pagany" concept. On July 12, 1929, Williams wrote to Johns:

*11-12

I think I begin to see what you are at. . . .

13-16

Meanwhile, Johns had carried his publication plans quite a bit further through soliciting some advertising and some good contributions from such writers as Gorham B. Munson, Yvor Winters, his wife Janet Lewis, and David Cornel DeJong.

Perhaps one of the most important persons who gave early support was Johns' near neighbor in Lynn, Sherry Mangan. Both Johns and Mangan had grown up in Lynn, but there had been little more than a casual nodding acquaintance until Mangan printed a poem by Johns, "Mazie Marston," in the final issue of his little magazine *Larus,* which he printed on his small Lone Gull Press. Johns had been a high school dropout, whereas Mangan had graduated from Harvard in 1925 with honors in Greek and Latin literature. During 1926, he assisted his father, Dr. John Joseph Mangan, in the completion of *The Life, Character and Influence of Desiderius Erasmus of Rotterdam.* But now, with a magazine of his own to launch, Johns felt Mangan would be both interested and valuable in contacting those writers whose work Johns knew should appear in the early issues of *Pagany.*

The imminent demise of Mangan's *Larus* could have been a depressing factor for Johns, giving him a pessimistic outlook for his own opening venture. But Johns visualized *Pagany* as something far

---

*The page numbers appearing in the outer margins refer to those letters and selections under discussion in the text.

WILLIAM CARLOS WILLIAMS, M. D.
9 RIDGE ROAD
RUTHERFORD, N. J.

July 12, 1929

My dear Johns :

Yes, I am with you but I'd like best not to have any
official editorial status - unless you prefer otherwise . I
can't see that my name would help you . Besides , I am now
american representative for a french quarterly and <u>Blues</u> has
my name on its stationary - meaning nothing . Yet, <u>if</u> you want
my name you may use it .

I think I begin to see what you are at,"A Native
Quarterly" gives me the hint . Your references in your first
note to my narrative "A Voyage to Pagany"completes the picture
for me . You believe then that we must build up from what we
have before we shall be able to do more . In this you are
opposed to <u>Blues</u> which is in your mind, perhaps , just a loose
end . In a measure I agree with you that this is so . You
would perhaps begin low , fasten to the native shale or
sandstone or what have you . Splendid , I say - but full of
danger . Yet the work must be done . Perhaps things like
Blues can never make headway until that underground work has
<u>first</u> been done . It may be that Europe can permit itself
a fling once or twice in a century because that underground work
has been done . But all this is merely to attempt to feel
your pulse , take your blood-pressure, etc.

<u>The Dial</u> , it strikes me is precisely what you do
not want to imitate .

You want a basis for an advance , do you ? And you
accept the proposition that the basis is always that which is
native . You want to consolidate your position and not fly off
and think to reach an end before that end is defined . Or why
did you leave New York for Boston ? And what is your experience
with publications ? I am tempting you , attempting to annoy
you .

If I motor up to Boston three weeks from now may you
be seen ?

My suggestion is that I write for each quarterly a
few pages , five to twenty , in which I shall be permitted to
develope a theme , slowly and steadily , the native theme and
its implications . In addition you may occasionally accept a
poem , or a prose bit now and again . But the pages I write
will be signed and published on my own responsibility , not that
of the magazine . You could then attack me in the same issue
as you may care to . Is that what you want ?

(over)

But why "Pagany" ? I used the term as a pseudonym for Europe
present day Europe . But how, exactly, will you apply it to
America ? Mind you it <u>does</u> very much apply , in my own mind , but
how will you placate a possible group of readers when the
implications of such a name comes home to them . And there is a
Washington Squarish conotation too that aint so good . There used
to be a magazine , <u>The Pagan</u> published there . Pretty bad .

And what will Ivor Winter's say ? He is already ill over my
lack of godliness or eclesiastiel organization or evil nature or
general cussedness .

The things you have accepted for the first issue suit me well.
Go to it . I have some others I can appeal to for work if you
like . But the magazine must #### something more than a mere appeal
to the stodgy well meaning reader . Sales are important but not
at the cost of tempering the wind to them .

Le's see more of your mind relative to the undertaking .
Then I'll write the manifesto , yes I will , after which you may
open the screen down and point to the exit if you wish to
without in the least offending

Your humble servant

W. C. William

But I'm for you and I like your deliberation . I'll do everything I
can to further your project which may be important if it can be
organized on some basis of decency (not moral)

Write freely of yourself, please ; I am still in the stage of trying
to formulate exactly what you may have in mind .

Grand Rapids, Mich.
May 14, 1929.

Mr. Richard Johns,

Editor, Pagany,

Boston, Mass.

Dear Editor,

I received your address from a
friend, and not knowing what the character of Pagany will be like
I am submitting the enclosed material, which may be exactly what you
want, or precisely the furthest removed from it. However, I judged
by the title, and its connotation. If nothing of the enclosed is
of any value to you, I will gladly send other material. If on the
other hand I have misinterpreted your editorial wants completely, I
apologize for having taken all this your valuable time.

Perhaps you may be interested to know, that I have contributed to
Poetry, Forge (of which I won the poetry prize, winter, 1929 number)
Free Verse, Carmelite, Gypsy and several other magazines of this type.
Furthermore, that I am a college senior, and have only during the last
few months sent out my work to magazines. This will account for the
amateurish flavor of this letter no doubt, if you are able to detect
anyhting like that in it. I hope not.

If for any reason my stuff is not elligible, as for not being a
subscriber, living too far west, being foreign born and having spent
my first thirteen years abroad, I beg your pardon for submitting this
material and for this lengthy letter.

Yours very sincerely

David Cornel DeJong

YADDO Box 395
SARATOGA SPRINGS
NEW YORK

July 10, 1929

Dear Mr. Johns,

Mrs. Munson has been ill, and owing to that I shall probably not get back to N.Y. before July 20. We must however leave Yaddo on the 15th and board in Saratoga until my wife is well enough to travel. Therefore, I shall be delayed in getting hold of the <u>Secession</u> list. That is now five years old and may not be of much use to you. I am, however, enclosing a list of a few writers, some of whom you may wish to invite to contribute and all of whom ought to be your readers. You may use my name, if you wish, in writing to them. Thanks for the cheque for the second Sword paper.

Faithfully yours,
Gorham B. Munson

✱ *Indicates authors who make it a rule not to give material gratis. Should be offered a minimum payment.*

YADDO

SARATOGA SPRINGS

NEW YORK

✱ John Riordan, ℅ McIntosh & Otis, Inc., 112 West 42 nd St., N.Y.C. Editor of Salient, contributor to the American Caravan, New Student, author of On the Make (short stories) to be published this fall.

Hansell Baugh, ℅ U.S. Rubber News, U.S. Rubber Co., Broadway & 58th St., New York, N.Y. Contributor to Freeman, Bookman, Reviewer, translator of Rimbaud's prose (some of which might be published) has an unpublished article on Scriabin, editor of Frances Newman's letters.

Elva de Pue, 136 East 67th St., N.Y.C. Contributor to Seven Arts, New Masses, Figure in the Carpet.

Oakley Johnson, 76 Horatio St., N.Y.C. Professor at Michigan and Long Island Univ. Contributor to Salient, New Republic, Book League Monthly, New Student. Uneven

Edwin Seaver, ℅ McIntosh & Otis, Inc., 112 West 42 nd St., N.Y.C. Critic, poet, short story writer. Macmillan has taken his book of stories. Editor of 1924.

-2-

YADDO
SARATOGA SPRINGS
NEW YORK

✳ Lawrence S. Morris, Huntington, Long Island, N.Y. **Critic** for the New Republic and the Bookman.

R. Ellsworth Larsson, ℅ Muriel Draper, 24 East 40 St., N.Y.C. Poet and critic. Has a number of unpublished poems in a volume forthcoming by Payson & Clark.

Kenneth Burke, R.D. #1, Andover, New Jersey. May have some more Declamations with no place to publish them now the Dial is gone.

✳ Jean Toomer, 1447 North Dearborn St., Chicago, Illinois. Author of Cane, contributor to Dial, Broom, American Caravan.

William Troy, 78 Horatio St., N.Y.C. Critic and short story writer. Contributor to The Figure in the Carpet, New Republic and Bookman.

Hart Crane, ℅ Guaranty Trust Co., 1 & 3 rue des Italiens, Paris, France. Poet.

broader and more inclusive than this somewhat precious publication. Johns also had the cash advance from his father to start *Pagany,* and the added assurance of a reasonable sum for living expenses. Surely, it looked as if only success was ahead.

Sherry Mangan answered Johns' request for assistance with enthusiasm and when Johns visited Mangan in his home for the first of many informal conferences, the editorial wheels began to turn. Mangan wrote to friends in England and to Virgil Thomson, the former European editor of *Larus* in Paris, on the possibility of receiving contributions from Mary Butts, Gertrude Stein, and Robert McAlmon.

Mangan was an eager Irishman, full of spontaneity and gusto while at the same time insecure and unnecessarily defensive of his bogtrotting ancestors. Arrogantly sure of his intellect, he worked fervently and with no desire for personal recognition during the assembling of material for the first issue of another man's magazine. Johns, grateful for this help and given a lift by much intellectual blarney, was happy to take over the balance of all *Larus* subscriptions, which were few.

Johns had sent out letters announcing the impending publication to all magazines and newspapers as well as to such trade journals for the free-lance writer as *Publishers' Weekly, The Writer,* and *Writer's Digest.* After they were printed, contributions began coming in from all directions.

> Richard Johns sends in a modest announcement that he is about to launch a quarterly to be called "Pagany" in Boston, on the first of January, 1930 . . . He says it ain't going to have no policy . . . Any sort of fiction, criticism, or poetry, seriously intended, will be given serious consideration . . . 94 Revere Street is the address . . . Don't make a noise while passing the Watch and Ward headquarters. . . .
>
> —Isabel Paterson, *New York Herald Tribune*

Now faced with what he should accept for the first issue, Johns considered the editorial possibilities and ramifications created by *Pagany*'s subtitle, *a native quarterly.* Johns' original intention was to limit his contributors to those who, whatever their ethnic back-

THE OLD HOUSE • BEDSOR ROAD • UPPER BOURNE END • IN BUCKINGHAMSHIRE

Dear Dick:

I proved the truth of the epigram that 'many Americans are wintering in
England this summer' by getting a miserable and rather grave influenza
on the river here which dumped me into bed until a week ago. Since then
I have been progging around seeing what England has in the way of literature. After considerable discussion with James Wood as to who knew most
(and knew it most accurately) about the genuinely important doings in London, I applied myself to C K Ogden, whom you perhaps know as the author
of *The Meaning of Meaning, The Foundations of Aesthetics* (in conjunction
with Wood and I A Richards), etc. I wrote him, informing him that a London
letter, precise, unbiased, critical, and dealing not chattily with developments of genuine importance, was contemplated, but binding you to nothing.
He expressed interest and willingness, so that I am turning him over to
you by giving him your address. In all this I am careful not to tie you up
to anything, by the way: I simply hook the fish, and it is for you to determine, after you look them over, whether they go in the creel or back in the
river. You should hear from Ogden within a short time. I.A.Richards has
taken himself off to no less than Pekin, and is uncommunicable by all
means. D H Lawrence has gone to the Pyrenees, but I am getting hold of
his London agent, Rhys-Davies, who can act for him; and I think we may
expect some action from that quarter. As for Liam O'Flaherty, however, I
fear I misled you. The friend of Kate Foster's was Sean O'Casey, which is
quite a different matter. But I have a lead through Augustus John, which
I shall endeavor to work. Ran into John and Wyndham Lewis the other night
at the Eiffel, but they were somewhat pie-eyed, occupied with two sweet
young things, and in no mood to talk sense. These are all the people you
spoke of in England.
In Paris I am lining up engagements with Mary Butts, Robert McAlmon, Djuna
Barnes, and Gertrude Stein. Tommie tells me that Djuna is getting very
snooty, but may be approachable. The others are quite sure. He also highly
recommends someone unknown to me by the name of George Davis. I shall see
him also and look over his stuff, bringing some for your examination if it
seems worth while. Tommie also says that he can probably get us things by
James Joyce and Glenway Westcott if you want them. I forget whether you were
handling those personally. If you were not, and do want them, cable me as
Mangan Hottinguer rue Provence Paris, and I'll see them too. With these I
shall make no guarantees in your name, unless, as with Joyce, the person
is so distinguished that it is necessary; but simply explain that I am
acting as agent, and must have your confirmation on any acceptances. That

will, I think, make it easier all around. I have asked Tommie his advice
as to someone who can do a really good Paris letter, and shall report on
that as soon as anything is decided. It seems to me that most letters of
that sort are cliquey, chatty, biased, and generally empty. And I think
that a letter which would be terse, filled with solid information and
acute criticism, with as little bias as possible, would be a real advantage to an American periodical.

Excuse the illiteracy of this letter. I am having to dictate it, being
still pretty weak and lying down, and I fear I haven't mastered the
technique of dictation. But perhaps you can extract some information
from its ramblings. I am having my secretary copy some poems of Norman
Dodge, which I shall send you within a few days.

I hope everything on your end is going smoothly and successfully. Best
greetings...

28 August
1 9 2 9

Paris address, by the way, is:

> c/o Virgil Thomson
> Hottinguer et Cie, Banquiers
> 38 rue de Provence
> Paris

--for mail, that is, though I sail back about the 20th September. The
briefer address will do for a cable--use a weekend letter if you need
to cable.

ground, were essentially Americans. One dictionary definition of native, "belonging to, or natural to, by reason of the circumstances of one's birth," would certainly include such writers as Ezra Pound, Gertrude Stein, Mary Butts, and Emanuel Carnevali, who despite their present expatriate status were born and bred in this country.

18-19

Sherry Mangan's suggestion for a Paris and London letter did not contradict this original intention. These letters spoke only of contemporary activities in two world centers and were primarily informative and critical rather than creative. To write them, Mangan recommended George Hugnet, a contemporary French poet and friend of Gertrude Stein, and Kate Foster, an English writer he met while traveling through England and whom he eventually married. The one clear snapping of the elastic boundary was the printing of Jean Cocteau's "Laic Mystery" in 1932, made available to *Pagany* by Ezra Pound. Johns felt it of sufficient importance to have it translated and appear in an American magazine.

21-23

It is important to note that for the most part the first issue of *Pagany* was comprised of material submitted directly to Johns by solicited contributors. Though all unsolicited material was read with great care, most of it came from aspiring amateurs and was doomed to be rejected by any publisher approached. Just what constitutes errors in editorial judgment is impossible to assess, but it is interesting to consider what might and might not have been.

For instance, on the 10th of October, 1929, D. H. Lawrence wrote from England expressing regret that he had nothing new to submit, but offering "The Risen Lord," which had been published in an English newspaper. Johns read this attentively. Certainly, despite the fact that he was primarily interested in native American expression, it would be noteworthy to have the name D. H. Lawrence appear on the cover of the first issue. On the other hand, if all that was available from an established and honored author was an unimportant Sunday Supplement sort of piece, should space be given in preference to something fresh, exciting, and young in imagery? The article was returned with thanks and regret that it would not be used. Thus the name of Lawrence never appeared as a contributor, for he died soon after *Pagany*'s inception.

Villa Beau Soleil . Bandol . Var . France

10 Oct 1929

Dear Mr Johns

I had your letter today. There's
nothing on hand I can find for Pagany - my health has
been so bad lately. But if you are a "sincere speculative venture"
and not a new flower of literary artifice, you might like
the Risen Lord article - which has not appeared in America -
at least I suppose not. Edwin Rich - Curtis Brown Ltd
116 West 39th St. New York City
will tell you for sure. They are my agents. It is an article
most magazines would jib at. If you want it, tell Rich
I accept your terms. And if you do take it, would you be so
good as to tell Mrs Maria Cristina Chambers. 43 Hillside Rd
Elm Point . Long Island
N.Y.
But you may not want a thing that has appeared
in England. - I might send you a couple of poems.

Yours sincerely
D H Lawrence

R.F.D.
Patterson, New York
Aug. 2, '29

Dear Mrs. Johns:

Your letter, written to Paris,
has been forwarded to me here since
my return. As I haven't a single poem
to send anyone at present there is not
much use in responding to your letter except
to mention that I appreciate your courtesy
in asking me to contribute.

Please accept my thanks for that
and my best wishes toward the success
of *Pagany*.

Sincerely yours,

Hart Crane

Dear Mr. Johns:

I am asking Meridel Le Sueur to contribute something to your magazine. Perhaps you know her work. I think it is excellent. Now that the Dial has been discontinued she has no place to publish, or rather, no regular place. You can find some of her work in the American Mercury, New Masses, and a story has been re printed by O'Brien in, I think, the 1927 book. Her husband, Yasha Bbbonoff, is a writer too and I am suggesting that he send something to you.

I'm awfully pleased with the cordial letters you write to my friends. I have asked several to send things to you. But I was dismayed at a line you wrote about me to the Kelm boys. You said that I seemed deliberately neurotic in some of my work. Since you were good enough to ask me to contribute I am going to tell you that you have me wrong. My definition of neurotic is – aimless, dark, dismal, horrid, miserable, rat-like, futile, and without any life or energy to change and be something more alive. I was very hurt.

When you print my story "Monday Morning" will you please put in fine type somewhere below the title – "To Blanche Matthias." Please don't forget.

Cordially yours,

Margery Latimer

August 27, 1929.
Portage, Wisconsin.

348 Carl St.
San Francisco.
December 3, 1929.

Editor,
The Pagany Quarterly,
Boston, Mass.

Dear Sir:

    If The Quarterly appears on
the local newsstands I shall be sure
to purchase your first issue.

    I am attaching for your con-
sideration a short story entitled When
In Rome. I am 21, and anxious to get
get some of my short stories published
in literary journals of national scope.
I have succeeded in getting them into
the other kind.

    With best wishes, I am,

    Sincerely yours,

    William Saroyan.

Very different was the reading of "When in Rome," submitted by then unknown William Saroyan, who was indeed young in imagery. Although this contribution may have been fresh and exciting, it was quickly read and returned. William Saroyan never submitted anything else, which was surely a loss to *Pagany*.

24

Both Mangan and Williams provided valuable assistance to Johns with their editorial suggestions and author's communiqués. Yet another editor, Charles Henri Ford, must also be considered of great importance to *Pagany's* early development. By informing fellow writers, especially his own camp of *Blues* contributors, about the existence of a new little magazine, Ford was instrumental in putting such literary hopefuls as Kenneth Rexroth, Erskine Caldwell, Norman Macleod, Parker Tyler, Kathleen Tanksley Young, and Forrest Anderson in touch with Johns.

26

28-31

This action, which might have been regarded as editorial suicide by the staffs of larger magazines like *The Smart Set, Saturday Evening Post,* or later, *Vanity Fair* and *The New Yorker,* reflected the methods and thinking of the little magazine "underground." Despite many disagreements over content and policy, little magazine editors recognized the necessity of communications within their own genre, dependent on one another as they were, to the point of free exchange advertising during the depression. They were a simple band of builders, each constructing part of the new literary foundation, and in such an atmosphere all were equal. Financially established celebrities were unknown commodities, a part of another world. Johns, like other young editors, was as dependent upon this system as he was a part of it, and monetary compensation became secondary to the literary body itself.

27

Indeed, it was exceptionally good luck for Johns that at Ford's suggestion both Rexroth and Caldwell, as well as other *Blues* contributors, submitted works which appeared in *Pagany's* first issue. Ironically, it was Caldwell, currently fighting a censorship suit in Maine over the suppression of his first novel, *The Bastard,* whose short story, "The Strawberry Season," prevented Johns from scoring a 100% by Edward J. O'Brien's critical selections. O'Brien had tremendous influence in determining the quality of the American short story of the period. He had first published his annual collection

CHARLES HENRI FORD, EDITOR

BLUES

A MAGAZINE OF NEW RHYTHMS

ROOMS 227-228 GILMER BLDG.
COLUMBUS, MISSISSIPPI

Aug. 5, 1929

Dear Mr. Johns,

thank you for your letter, poems, and check
(which will do nicely for gin i am leaving
for Chicago this week back soon).

Glad you liked arrangement of advertisement
and No. 6. . . I don't understand why you
would hesitate to publish RAY ON THIS SURFACE
if you liked it. Besides there are too too
few magazines that DARE. Maybe youll like
the enclosed PARAGRAPH which is another
"excerpt". . . Your poems are good. I'm
retaining ROBERT IN BERLIN which i like
very much for use in BLUES. I'm sorry as
hell that i can't pay you for it. Pagany,
in paying, is doing something good something
i wish to god BLUES could do and may do later.

With best wishes, i remain,

faithfully yours,

[signature]

charles henri ford

p.s. maybe you could send a photograph
for blues rogues gallery i'd like one.

[signature]

over

JANUS

**A Quarterly Review of Letters
Thought, and the New Mythology**

EDITORIAL OFFICE
Apartment 2, 800 Eighteenth Street, N.W.
WASHINGTON, D. C.

Solon R. BARBER, Editor
T. Swann HARDING, Dissenting Editor
Harry Francis CAMPBELL, Art Director
Barbs FARRELL, Contributing Editor

September 17, 1929.

Mr Richard JOHNS
Editor, Pagany
94 Revere Street
Boston.

My dear Mr JOHNS,

I take pleasure in sending you an announcement of
the forthcoming natal number of JANUS: A Quarterly Review of
Letters, Thought, and the New Mythology, and in cordially inviting
you to join our list of contributors which includes: T. Swann
HARDING, Nelson Antrim CRAWFORD, V. F. CALVERTON, John Lee HIGGINS,
Charles Henri FORD, Joseph UPPER, Norman MACLEOD, Muriel WRIGHT,
and numerous others.

Would you care to exchange from one-fourth to one-half page of
advertising space with us? In case this is agreeable to you, the
announcement of PAGANY would appear in our October 31 number and
we would expect a like space in your first number which will be,
I understand, January, 1930.

With all best wishes to you and to your Quarterly, I am,

Sincerely yours,

Solon R. Barber.

Editor, JANUS

Dear Mr. Johns,

      Ch. Henri Ford writes me to be sure and send
something to your new magazine. Perhaps the enclosed poem would
be appropriate. Just now i have nothing else i care to send out.
I have sent a copy to Williams for his OK. Between now and winter
other opuses will undoubtedly be born and i will send a selection
of them. I f you are to publish drawings etc. or care for a cover
design my wife and i could sumbit something. If you care to i
would be glad to hear from you and would welcome the opportunity
to form a clearer idea of the polices of your project.

      faithfully

      Kenneth Rexroth

      kenneth rexroth

October thirtieth 1929.

Richard Johns, Editor of
PAGANY, A Native Quarterly,
Boston, Mass.

Dear Mr. Johns:

Charles Henri Ford has written to me that you expect to be
in New York in the near future. I do not know whether you are interested
in meeting the new writers of your magazine or not, but I am always interested
in meeting editors of new magazines, and listening to their slant on things.
If you do have time and care to see me, a note to my present address
will find me any time before the 22nd of November. At that time I am
starting to find a tropical winter in Christobal, Panama, to return to
New York in the early spring.

What do you think of the New Caravan? I think that parts of it
are splendid, and that the poetry as a whole is very bad. Have you seen
the last TAMBOUR from Paris? I was disappointed beyond words as this
issue. I dislike the work of my American contemporaries in there more
than I can say. In a few days BLUES will be off the press as a quarterly,
and there'll be something more to criticise. I am afraid that my criticisms
of the last issue of BLUES might seem harsh. I do tremendously like the
word ARTICULATE in the Pagany announcement.

Cordially Yours,

Kathleen Tankersley Young
605 West 113th Street
New York City.

668 Congress Street Portland Maine October Fourth Twenty Nine

Dear Mr Johns: CharlesHenri Ford has told me about the work
you are doing with a new magazine to be called PAGANY and that
you may use contributions in it. The two pieces I'm enclosing
are for you to consider. You don't know me and neither does
anybody else. I've been working for seven or eight years unsuc-
cessfully, though several of my pieces are comibg out this fall.
Short stories in TRANSITION, BLUES, and THE NEW AMERICAN CARAVAN.
And a novel called THE BASTARD, which I hope doesn't shock you.
In case you should want to see anything else by me I'll be glad
to send what I have that you would consider. That's about all I
have to say.

                        Sincerely

                        Erskine Caldwell

IN DEFENSE OF MYSELF

The charge brought against Helen Caldwell, my wife, by County Attorney Ingalls, of Cumberland County, for selling a copy of *The Bastard* in her bookshop, and, curiously, against me for being the author of the novel, has resulted in official suppression of the book in Portland without trial before a judge, or before a jury. Not having the opportunity to defend myself or my novel, means that with the consent only of County Attorney Ingalls himself *The Bastard* contains an impure word, or words. No attempt was made to isolate these words in my hearing by the c o u n t y attorney and neither was the offer made to permit my defense of them as being thought necessary in the construction of the story. With this comedy of justice bowing from the stage, the novel was blanketed with this brand of obscenity and hustled out of town. In the City of Portland and in the County of Cumberland, one superimposed upon the other in the State of Maine, *The Bastard* is obscene, lewd and immoral; likewise the author, by command of County Attorney Ingalls, is obscene, lewd and immoral in the City of Portland and in the County of Cumberland, all imposed upon the State of Maine. Therefore, it is a crime in this county to sell the n o v e l, give it to my friends and, tomorrow perhaps, read it.

All of which gives me an involuntary urge to vomit profusely.

The Bastard was conceived and written as an important and untouched phase of American *mores*. That this custom of life in the nation had previousy been unknown outside its own sphere was its own necessity for expression and valuation. It so happens that this sphere is at times realistically uninhibited. Among those who live there and die we find a man who, when his belly is content, and when he feels no immediate fear of violent death, takes a female of his own stratum for relaxation, beauty and contentment. He plays no golf, he has no club; the churches were not built for him. He cannot read.....Here is a woman, a girl in years, who has no friends with whom she can play bridge. She works in a cotton mill. She is a lint-head. She earns eleven dollars and fifteen cents from one Saturday to the next. The mill lays her off six weeks. Neither her mother, nor her father, if either she has, can afford to give her money to buy a pair of stockings and a hat. Somebody else can. A man. She goes with him and he buys her the clothes she wants so much. A week later he is in New Orleans, in Chicago, in Detroit. She gets along the best way she can. We all do.

I did not write this novel with obscenity, lewdness and immorality in mind. I wrote it the book it is because I have a deep sympathy for the people in it. I hoped it would be a good novel. I know it is not perfect. It has faults, grave faults. For ten years I have tried to overcome them. Ten, twenty, thirty be years from now I hope to be still trying to overcome faults But I have not finished what I have to say about the people in this novel that has been suppressed: I have an intense sympathy for these people. I know them and I like them. I have slept with them in jails, I have eaten with them in freight cars, I have sung with them in convict camps, I have helped the women give birth to the living, I have helped the men cover up the dead--- but I have said enough. I have said that I know these people, that I love them. That is why I could not stand silent while the story of their lives was branded obscene, lewd and immoral; because this story belongs to them even more than it does to me. It is of no concern to me that I, too, have had this same brand placed upon me by Cumberland County. But these friends of mine----I shall defend them until the last word is choked from me. I cannot disown them.

Honi soit qui mal y pense

ERSKINE CALDWELL

Portland, Maine

WILLIAM CARLOS WILLIAMS, M. D.
9 RIDGE ROAD
RUTHERFORD, N. J.

Aug. 30 , 1929

Dear John :

An interesting bunch of script , it should make a
readable and saleable first issue of your quarterly . And it
justifies you in your attempt . I wish you luck and I'll do
all I can to help . Don't give up the ship !

Naturally some of the work is better than the rest .
Some need criticism and some need chucking out . I'll mark
what I like - the rest you will make up your own mind about .

I wouldn't print all that you have . I wouldn't
print too much of any one person . I'd print only the two
stories I have marked of Riordan . I'd print only the one
essay of Munson's . I'd print both stories, though , of Janet
Lewis . She has something -##

The skeleton story of Manuel Komroff is splendid in
most places but the end is ridiculous . I mean that it is
quite out of character . The only possible end is for Death
to give the Fool the only thing he has to give , that is a
good grip of his hand - which would kill him . For the love
of Pete speak to Komroff about that . And the Mayor's death
is rather too dramatic .

Best of luck . I'm sending the script back to
you under spearate cover . It may# not come for a day of
two .

Yours

The Best Short Stories as early as 1915, and by the time *The Best Short Stories of 1930* was printed, the volume also included The Yearbook of the American Short Story and its Roll of Honor—those stories O'Brien felt worthy of consideration as part of American literature. For many authors his assessment of quality meant acceptance not only by other little magazines but by the larger commercial publishers as well. There are many examples of writers whose work was first brought to national attention by the O'Brien polls; let three women suffice—Janet Lewis, Katherine Anne Porter and Kay Boyle.

September 24, 1929

William Carlos Williams

Dear Williams:

Many, many thanks for the excellent Manifesto. I am enclosing *50* a check, the best I dare do.

I was very much pleased with your liking for the material you *32* took along with you. I am carefully weeding it more, and will try to show you my completed idea when I get down to New York, which I hope will be about the middle of October.

I wrote Komroff your suggestion and have heard nothing from him. I rather have an idea the story is to come out in a limited edition with the original ending. He sent me more work which was quite impossible. How I wish I might get another "Thumbs" out of him.

I shall get in touch with you as soon as I get down to Manhattan. I look forward to knowing you better. Also I have the very embarrassing task of letting you look over my work in the hope that there will be something you consider possible to include.

Until I see you, then, my thanks and best wishes.

Faithfully,
Richard Johns

With enough publishable material on hand to fill the first issue, Johns began thinking about the physical appearance of *Pagany*. *Pagany*'s format became less a matter of aesthetics than one of practical need to fit as much material as possible into each issue. A forty-two-line page was decided upon with a long running line of type along the margin. All contributors would be listed in the same type on the cover, making none appear more important than another.

As to the design of the magazine, Johns decided to consult his close friend Virginia Lee Burton for some professional advice. This young artist, then doing free lance designs from her Joy Street studio, would soon gain prominent recognition for writing and illustrating a number of children's classics (including *The Little House, Choo Choo,* and *Mike Mulligan and His Steam Shovel*) as well as for creating many portfolios of excellent commercial designs and paintings.

Quickly perceiving the situation and following Johns' initial design concept, Miss Burton sketched a sturdy tree flourishing within a circular enclosure. This sketch readily pleased Johns, and she proceeded with a stylized pen and ink drawing which was reproduced on both the front cover and first page of *Pagany* throughout its existence. Since it was also used in most advertising copy, this design came to be as much a part of *Pagany; a native quarterly* as the title itself.

Johns decided to print *Pagany*'s cover in one ink on colored stock, a different color for each issue. Although *Hound and Horn* and *The New Masses* frequently designed their covers with two and sometimes three inks and printed on either white or pastel stock, Johns realized that while this made a more attractive presentation, he should stick to a more simplified approach, following the economical example set by such editors as Charles Henri Ford and Norman Macleod.

With a general layout in mind, Johns' next step was to secure the services of a printer. Since he was quite familiar with the work being done by private presses in New England, and wished to keep the printing in Boston for convenience, it was logical that his first choice would be the celebrated D. B. Updike, eminent head of The Merrymount Press and considered by publishers and printers alike the best typographer in town, and possibly in the country. Updike expressed a complete lack of interest in the project.

Research into the types of jobs handled by different Boston printers finally led Johns to the C. H. Simonds Company, a lesser-known print shop, which agreed to set into type, print, and bind one thousand copies of a 120 page magazine at a sum not to exceed $350. *Pagany* would be sold for fifty cents a copy, or two dollars for a

Eftablifhed *Mdcccxciij*

D. B. UPDIKE THE MERRYMOUNT PRESS, 232 SUMMER ST., BOSTON MASS^{TTS}

CABLE ADDRESS UPDIKE BOSTON: TELEPHONE LIBERTY 1922 September 30, 1929

Dear Mr. Johns:

Your letter of the 26th has been received, but I am sorry to say that we are too busy to undertake, or even make an estimate on the work you suggest. Furthermore, we have no Granjon type.

In regard to specifications of this sort, I cannot at all tell whether with the materials you indicate the book would turn out well or not, as we would go to work in a little different way. But that is neither here nor there - we have not, as a matter of fact, any time to go into it.

Very faithfully yours,

D. B. Updike

Richard Johns, Esq.,
    Pagany,
        94 Revere Street,
           Boston, Mass.

one-year subscription. After considering his own budget and studying what other little magazines paid their contributors, Johns felt
three dollars a page and a minimum of three dollars for a half-page
poem was fair compensation to contributors. A full page advertisement would be fifty dollars, and after a rate sheet was printed and
mailed to a number of Boston firms (including a list of his father's
local clients), the first issue was assured checks for full page ads
from The Atlantic National Bank of Boston; Lucius Beebe and
Sons, Leather Merchants; The United States Leather Company;
F. Knight and Sons, Contracting, Forwarding, Rigging; The Boston
Woven Hose and Rubber Company; The Carver Cotton Gin Company, as well as others. At this point, even Benjamin N. Johnson had
to admit that the magazine seemed a practical undertaking.

Once the Simonds Company was selected and production under
way, Johns began to feel the pressures of an editor. Although the
pressmen made few mistakes and the Simonds proofreaders were excellent, there still remained a number of contributors who demanded
extensive changes upon reading their manuscripts in galley proof.
It took a great deal of diplomacy on Johns' part to keep these demands at a minimum.

Johns' personal friends rallied to the task of rereading proofs
from manuscripts while he cut and pasted together the first issue.
One amusing incident took place when two girl friends read the
clear typescript "goddamned wings" in Dudley Fitts' "Crucifier,"
delicately rendering it as "g—d—— wings." Since the compositor had
the same personal reservations as to what was proper, the galley was
printed in its censored form and Johns did not recognize the discrepancy between typescript and print. When the galleys were sent
to Fitts, who spent so much time making revisions in the text that
the piece had to be held until the next issue, Johns was told quite
soundly not to prissify his words. Later, when Fitts was again censored he wrote to Johns:

> can't I have son-of-a-bitch, instead of son-of-a-b——? The latter
> gives me the Willies; the former appears, without expurgation, in
> the current number of the *Forum;* has recently not shocked the
> readers of the *Nation* (review by John Dos Passos); & is a conven-

tional Connecticut term of endearment. The emasculation, wch gives the whole a faintly facetious air, rather spoils the tone of the passage. df.

Despite an earlier direct mail appeal consisting of a printed broadside and mimeographed letter sent to the old *Larus* subscription list, some customers of the Dunster House Bookshop, and the collectors of the day whose names appeared in *American Book Collectors,* the number of paid subscribers was small and distribution of the first issue depended upon single copy bookstore sales.

❡ LARVS IN PAGO NIDIFICAT

LARVS having taken refuge within the confines of PAGANY: *A Native Quarterly*, those of its subscriptions which remain unexpired, through the courtesy of Mr Richard Johns, its editor, will be filled pro rata in lieu of rebate by the numbers of the new periodical, the first of which accompanies this announcement.

PAGANY is not a continuation of LARVS, but a completely new magazine; nor does the editor of LARVS expect Mr Johns to be responsible for his former editorial policies. He does, however, strongly recommend the new magazine to those who liked LARVS, on the grounds that they will find, not only what in LARVS used to please them, but much else and different which should also give them pleasure. It is with regret that the project of indices had to be abandoned.

LARVS *by* MANGAN

WILLIAM CARLOS WILLIAMS, M. D.
9 RIDGE ROAD
RUTHERFORD, N. J.

Oct. 24, 1929

My dear Johns :

 I read over the new batch of script last evening
for the first time . Some of it is excellent stuff , in fact
I am beginning to grow enthusiastic about this venture of
yours . I had no idea there was so much really new writing
going on about me . It may not be devastatingly beautiful
composition , any of it, but it is diverse and full of vigor
and thrust .

 At the same time there is some God awful tommy rot
in this that you have handed me down . That's good too ! in
a way . Some of it is funny as a crutch .

 I'm returning the mass of script at once - marked
as well as I have been able to mark it .

 Yes, come on out when you are in the city , take a
bus at the Hotel Astor : Rutherford . Call up Rob'T McAlmon
at the Hotel Lafayette , 9th. St. and University Place . He
is worth talking to .

   Best luck

   Yours

   William

WILLIAM CARLOS WILLIAMS, M. D.
9 RIDGE ROAD
RUTHERFORD, N. J.

Nov. 7, 1929

Dear Johns :

Give me a few more days - even hours ; I am
for the moment knocked off my feet with trouble over the
acute illness of several children .

I do want the Stein piece to go into the first
issue . I'll have it for you within a week .

The manifesto will be very brief , it will take
no more than half a page , reserve that much room for it
and go ahead , I'll have that much in your hands in a day
or two .

Yours

William

Announcing

PAGANY

A Native Quarterly

which will be published upon the first of January, 1930.   Here is a sincere speculative venture, filling in the middle scene between the excellent conventional magazines and those which are entirely experimental in content.

Pagany will publish vital writing, articulate and important.

Among the contributors to the first issue are:

William Carlos Williams
Kenneth Burke
Gorham B. Munson
Mary Butts
Robert McAlmon
Witter Bynner
Margery Latimer
Yvor Winters
Janet Lewis
Manuel Komroff
Norman Lewis Dodge
Parker Tyler
William Closson Emory
Leon Srabian Herald
Edwin Seaver

Anyone interested in American expression, in an unbiased account of literary developments in this country, in London and in Paris, will be disappointed not to be certain of possessing this first issue of Pagany, publishing the important fiction, poetry and criticism of our time.

Richard Johns, *Editor*
109 Charles Street
Boston, Massachusetts

As the bookshop sale will be strictly limited and all collectors of the first editions of these writers eager to obtain the first printing, it will be wise to assure yourself, through subscription, of participation in the discussion of this unique collection of native literature.

$2.00 *yearly*   *50 cents the copy*

109 Charles Street
Boston, Massachusetts

Gentlemen:

I am enclosing an announcement of Pagany: A Native Quarterly, which has been sent out to 2000 individuals interested in our American literature. There are many thousand more, and they will come to you. Upon the initial appearance of the Quarterly, reviews of it will appear in the book-sections of all the leading newspapers throughout the country.

Among the contributors to the first number are William Carlos Williams, whose "In the American Grain" has called forth universal praise for a beautiful and sensitive style; Gorham B. Munson, whose books on Waldo Frank and Robert Frost have been followed by "Destinations", considered the most searching estimate of our present-day literature. Munson contributes an argumentative essay in which Adam Sweord, long familiar to readers of the Bookman, discourses pungently on Humanism. Witter Bynner, the nationally esteemed poet, contributes a superb translation from the Chinese; Margery Latimer, whose two books, "We Are Incredible" and "Nellie Bloom" have been hailed by Zona Gale and others as masterpieces, contributes a representative story. Mary Butts, Harry Crosby and Robert McAlmon are of international importance; Mary Butts' two novels, one the exquisite "Armed With Madness", have introduced her to a select audience in this country; Harry Crosby's beautifully designed books from the Black Sun Press in Paris have become better known through the publication of his own "Mad Queen"; Robert McAlmon's "Village" and "Portrait of a Generation" have never been overlooked in any important estimate of American expression. Manuel Komroff, whose widely heralded two-volume novel "Coronet" is to be published in January with a first printing of 100,000 copies, contributes a moving little masterpiece entitled "Something of the Sting." Also in the first issue are John Riordan, whose "On the Make" has been receiving superlative reviews; Edwin Seaver, whose new book appears on Macmillan's Spring List, as well as many new writers who are sure to become important. For instance, Erskine Caldwell, whose stories in the New American Caravan have been highly honored.

You are interested in the support of good literature. I feel sure you will find Pagany to be an important center of literary discussion. Let us all profit together, you, the reader and myself. Business arrangements are most simple. There is no book-keeping necessary as catalogue-cards will be enclosed with each order. Unlimited returns may be made at Pagany's expense, each unsold copy being returnable upon the receipt of the following issue. Pagany retails at 50¢; you send me 35¢ for each copy sold when you return the unsold ones. Display-cards will be enclosed with each order. To make a special display of the initial number will, I feel sure, react favorably for yourself and the magazine. There is bound to be interest in this unique Quarterly. Profit by it!

Very truly yours,
Richard Johns

Many sets of 5, 10, 25, and 50 copies were scheduled to be shipped to a number of bookshops that received a similar letter and replied by placing orders. They included: Smith and McCance, Boston; the Dunster House Bookshop, Cambridge; Brentano's, Dauber and Pine, and The Gotham Book Mart, New York City; Koch's Bookshop, Detroit; and Walter Kraus' Bookshop, Chicago. All booksellers had agreed to return thirty-five cents for each copy sold. Johns had agreed to pay return postage on all unsold copies.

November 27, 1929

William Carlos Williams

Dear Dr. Williams:

I fear that my preoccupation with printers etc. has kept me from acknowledging your paper on Stein. It, and everything else for the first number, is here in proof.

Now, at the last moment, with no chance of changing anything, I feel that my quarterly may quite honorably go out and find a place for itself. To you and some few others I owe much. I hope you can guess my very real gratitude.

Faithfully,
Richard Johns

By the middle of October 1929, the first issue was ready to be printed, and Johns studied the total presentation with a tremendous sense of pride. His own "Announcement" stated exactly what he intended the magazine to be, and William Carlos Williams' "Manifesto" set the tone for the challenge this new decade brought to the

50

writers of the day. Williams' article "The Work of Gertrude Stein" was both compact and pertinent. The philosophically critical "The Artist's Stone" by Gorham B. Munson seemed a step forward from his excellent book *Destinations: A Canvass of American Literature Since 1900*. For the present, this article, along with Williams' article on Stein, would suffice as critical appraisal, since so many other little magazines devoted much space to it.

54-59
85-87

As for fiction, the range was both exciting and diverse, from the polite sensualities of Mary Butts' mannered "The House Party" to the sensitivities of Margery Latimer's "Monday Morning." Mary Butts, the red-haired wife of John Rodker, English poet, critic, and publisher, had already had three novels, *Speed the Plough, Ashe of Rings,* and *Armed with Madness,* published in France; and like them, "The House Party" epitomized the amoral living of some of the wealthy English and American expatriates on the Continent. In contrast, Margery Latimer, who was gaining popularity with such books as *We Are Incredible* and *Nellie Bloom,* searched the souls of simple-living Midwest American characters.

68-73

Another example of the variety of fiction in the first issue lay in the comparison of the earthy simplicity of Erskine Caldwell's "The Strawberry Season" with Edwin Seaver's searching portrait of "The Boss" directing his company toward the future.

62-67

Also included was Manuel Komroff's excellent short story "Something of the Sting," simple in design and therefore very different from the pageantry of his new novel *Coronet,* which was then leading all best-selling fiction lists. Having already published *The Grace of Lambs, The Voice of Fire, The Fantasy of Quest,* and *Juggler's Kiss,* Komroff like so many other contributors to the first issue was well established as a major literary voice of the times.

Although there was a wide variety in the prose selections, the poetry was even more diverse, from Gertrude Stein's "Five Words in a Line," to John Holmes' graphic salute to Carl Sandburg in "Who That Has Heard Him," and Grant Code's "Religion at 2 A.M.," which might have taken place in Harvard Square any night. Howard Baker contributed a salute to the gothic English Ann Radcliffe in "North Atlantic," and Robert McAlmon's "New England Victorian Episodes: Pennythinker" was among his best poems.

60-61
83
77-82

74-76

Johns questioned the lasting quality of such exercises in making typography seem erotic as Parker Tyler's "Kingdom of the Rose," but it was expressive of one facet of the period's foibles and therefore printed. And it was sad, after having accepted Harry Crosby's "Assassin," to have to ask the printer to add the statement of his recent death in New York City to the Notes on Contributors section. Johns did not print the facts—that this ex-Back Bay Boston renegade to Paris had died back in America in a violent suicide pact with a woman other than his wife Caresse. What was important was that this poet, who had founded the Black Sun Press in Paris, had written one of his richest salutes to the Sun, worshiped in all his writings. "Assassin," one of his final poems, was the only contribution which foreviewed the tragic last act of Harry Crosby.

51

Johns was proud to publish the poetry of Kenneth Rexroth and Norman Macleod. He was confident that Rexroth's brilliance with words and images would develop even more as he matured. His "Into the Shandy Westerness" was regional in concept but its pervasive Joycian meaning spread outward in rings, like the impact of a stone on water. Norman Macleod's *Morada,* to which Johns was a Contributing Editor, was one of the very best of the new little magazines. Opposite Rexroth, Macleod's "Behavioristic at a Trading Post" brought the wider meaning into a single place. Yvor Winters' "Three Poems" was beautifully articulated, as was Louis Zukofsky's single "Poem." Both of these men were poets whose work Johns had admired in *The Dial,* and he had particularly wanted contributions from them for the first issue.

During those memorable October days of 1929 when the stock market crashed, the presses at Simonds' pulled final sheets of one more little magazine. There was no reflection in the writings about the tragic events reported by the newspapers and weekly journals. But the full-page advertisements, paid for in cash by large Boston corporations, were missing from all following issues. There would be no more profit by advertisements except for the personal considerations of credit in a few small Beacon Hill restaurants for food and a Cambridge bookstore for certain first editions which might have value for the future if well selected.

For the balance of its years *Pagany* carried advertisements only for books and food plus a free exchange of notices with other little magazines printed at home and abroad.

In order to be of assistance during this time of financial crisis, William Carlos Williams, long accustomed to receiving no payment for his contributions to little magazines, returned his check to Johns. For Williams, the value of being printed far outweighed the token check received from this newly established outlet.

December 15, 1929

Dear Williams:

Correction made. Proof-read and make-up finished. I am embarrassed to say how excellent and important a magazine I believe has developed from my original little idea.

My many thanks to you for all you are doing.

Faithfully,
R. Johns

And so *Pagany; a native quarterly* in its bright orange and black cover was released to the public during the first week of 1930.

PAGANY

A Native Quarterly

VOLUME ONE
NUMBER ONE

WINTER
1930

50 *cents a copy*

$2.00 *the year*

RICHARD JOHNS · LEON SRABIAN HERALD · HOWARD
BAKER · ROBERT McALMON · KATHLEEN TANKERSLEY
YOUNG · NORMAN LEWIS DODGE · HAROLD J. SALEM-
SON · KENNETH REXROTH · SIDNEY HUNT · MORISON
FYFFE · JOHN ALBERT HOLMES · GRANT CODE · WITTER
BYNNER AND NIEH SHIH-CHANG · BRAVIG IMBS · JOSEPH
MacSHERAGH · FORREST ANDERSON · PARKER TYLER
NORMAN MACLEOD · CHARLES HENRI FORD · LOUIS
ZUKOFSKY · YVOR WINTERS · HARRY CROSBY · GREGORY
MOORE · WILLIAM CLOSSON EMORY · LOUIS GRUDIN
WILLIAM CARLOS WILLIAMS · **MARY BUTTS** · GORHAM
B. MUNSON · SHERRY MANGAN · ERSKINE CALDWELL
GEORGES HUGNET · GERTRUDE STEIN · MANUEL KOM-
ROFF · JANET LEWIS · DAVID CORNEL DeJONG · EDWIN
SEAVER · MARGERY LATIMER · JOHN RIORDAN · JOSEPH
VOGEL

NUMBER 1 *January—March*

CONTENTS

CONTENTS

PROSE

PAGANY

A NATIVE QUARTERLY

Edited by   *Richard Johns*

VOLUME I . NUMBER 1   JANUARY-MARCH 1930

ANNOUNCEMENT

"A new magazine should announce a reason for existence": PAGANY, perhaps, more than another, for it will avoid any attempt to seek a standard, it is neither entering into connexion nor competition with any magazine trying to make a point, to formulate a policy. There is much danger in such freedom, in leaving unarticulated one or two precepts of editorial limitation. Yet even a hint of regimen is made impossible by the connotations of the title.

Pagus is a broad term, meaning any sort of collection of peoples from the smallest district or village to the country as an inclusive whole. Taking America as the *pagus,* any one of us as the *paganus,* the inhabitant, and our conceptions, our agreements and disagreements, our ideas, ideals, whatever we have to articulate is *pagany,* our expression.

This *Native Quarterly* is representative of a diverse and ungrouped body of spokesmen, bound geographically. Wary of definite alliance with any formulated standard, PAGANY (as an enclosure) includes individual expression of native thought and emotion.   RICHARD JOHNS

MANIFESTO:

William Carlos Williams

"The ghosts so confidently laid by Francis Bacon and his followers are again walking in the laboratory as well as beside the man in the street",* the scientific age is drawing to a close. Bizarre derivations multiply about us, mystifying and untrue as — an automatic revolver. To what shall the mind turn for that with which to rehabilitate our thought and our lives? To the word, a meaning hardly distinguishable from that of place, in whose great, virtuous and at present little realized potency we hereby manifest our belief.

*Scott Buchanan, *Poetry and Mathematics,* p. 18.

For W. C. W.

INTO THE SHANDY WESTERNESS
Kenneth Rexroth

a

Do you understand the managing?

Mornings like scissors.

Leaves of dying.

Let event particle e. Point track m-n.

Congruence. Yes? that's what you thought it would be?

A flag waves, a kite climbs. Clouds climb, advancing impalpable edges. The whole mottled sky turns slowly on its zenith, the same clouds go round and round the horizon.

As A is.

A triangular chessboard squared in two tones of grey. P to K3, Kn x B. It's very cold under the table. A cold window.

When he was little he used to go out to the barn and put his cheek against a cow and cry and cry. When he swam in the pasture creek the little fish tickled his legs.

Something is going to cut.

Something is going to break.

I don't see it I can't hear it but it's swinging.

One goes swiftly back. One goes forward. Two move to the left. A Voice. The steel column bores and bores into the ground. Presently the air is filled with ammonia fumes.

We will sing hymn number 366, "Art thou weary, art thou languid" 366, MY number, MY bleeding number. So I ups and tells 'em WHY I was weary WHY I was languid.

b

As B is.

Orange green yellow blue red violet.

Is there anybody there said the stranger. Is there any reason why after all these difficulties we should be subjected in this particularly humiliating manner?

Orange. Row after row of shining minute faces. Green. A slight lurch and then the floor begins to climb smoothly steadily up up everything clatters against the altar. The celebrant is embarrassed.

White disks fly from the cylindrical heads of the spectators and disappear out of the windows. Presently only their palpitating necks are left; hollow, dark purple inside.

It's pleasant to think of the cottages along the mountain side. The alfalfa ripening in the afternoon. The thin smoke of evening. The chill nights.

Assorted solutions, neat packages of peace were distributed by officious archangels. There was much unemployment, long breadlines everywhere in the dusty cities, quiet, no traffic, much patience. We came on, collecting visas, wasting our substance in bribes, asking, Who is king in this kingdom, who is your ruler, by what do you measure?

c

Whenever I think of England I see Wyndham Lewis standing in a high freezing wind on the plain where Mordred and Arthur fought, dressed only in his BVDs painfully extracting thorns from his chapped buttocks. It grows dark rapidly.

When I think of France I see Marcel Duchamp on Michigan boulevard in a raccoon coat and a number of young americans praying before a roller-coaster from which middle aged frenchmen strapped to bicycles leap into tubs of coca-cola.

Ta-tum-ta-tee* I love you
There'll ne'er be none above you
Even when you do
Fa down and go boom
BOOM boom BOOM boom   boom

d

Now the blue flowers return the gravel mornings.
Now the immaculate mistresses
And those we loved from afar.

It's yellow in the sunlight and blue around the corner and it's all been so simple. The grey furry plants and the white hands. The considerations, the ablatives. The conversation about death. The lace parasol.

He was naturally very neat.

He was particular about his neckties and very proud of his razors. They gleamed on maroon plush. His watch lost sixty seconds every four weeks neither more nor less. He sat on the screen porch smelling faintly of citronella and spoke slowly and distinctly about love. Then he died. And she hadn't made up her mind. So she walked under the lace parasol avoiding the decayed catalpa blossoms that littered the sidewalk.

e

It grows dark. A shitepoke flies up from the canal. That's a shitepoke he

---

*The reader may substitute any four syllable word he chooses.

says to the boy. For supper hasenpfeffer. The rabbits are getting at the tomato sets, bad. Tourists are camping down at the wood lot at the corners. You can see their fire from the back door. When they came for water Nero snapped at the man. Now he looks over at their fire and barks every few minutes. On both sides of the walk about every ten feet all the way to the gate bushel baskets are turned upside down over the peonies. As it gets darker they disappear.

THE WORK OF GERTRUDE STEIN

"Would I had seen a white bear!
(for how can I imagine it?)"

William Carlos Williams

Let it be granted that whatever is new in literature the germ of it will be found somewhere in the writings of other times; only the modern emphasis gives new work a present distinction.

The necessity for this modern focus and the meaning of the changes involved are, however, another matter, the everlasting stumbling block to criticism. Here is a theme worth development in the case of Gertrude Stein — yet signally neglected.

Why in fact have we not heard more generally from American scholars upon the writings of Miss Stein? Is it lack of heart or ability or just that theirs is an enthusiasm which fades rapidly of its own nature before the risks of today?

* * * * * * * * * *

"The verbs auxiliary we are concerned in here, continued my father, are am; was; have; had; do; did; could; owe; make; made; suffer; shall; should; will; would; can; ought; used; or is wont, — . . or with these questions added to them; — Is it? Was it? Will it be? etc. . . Or affirmatively, — Or chronologically, — Or hypothetically, — If it was? If it was not? What would follow? — If the French beat the English? If the Sun should go out of the Zodiac?"

"Now, by the right use and application of these, continued my father, in which a child's memory should be exercised, there is no one idea can enter the brain, how barren soever, but a magazine of conceptions and conclusions may be drawn forth from it. — Didst thou ever see a white bear? cried my father, turning his head round to Trim, who stood at the back of his chair. — No, an' please your honor, replied the corporal. — But thou couldst discourse about one, Trim, said my father, in case of need? — How is it possible, brother, quoth my Uncle Toby, if the corporal never saw one? — 'Tis the fact I want, replied my father, — and the possibility of it as follows."

"A white bear! Very well, Have I ever seen one? Might I ever have seen one? Am I ever to see one? Ought I ever to have seen one? Or can I ever see one?

"Would I had seen a white bear! (for how can I imagine it?)"

"If I should see a white bear, what should I say? If I should never see a white bear, what then?"

"If I never have, can, must, or shall see a white bear alive; have I ever seen the skin of one? Did I ever see one painted? — described? Have I never dreamed of one?"

Note how the words *alive, skin, painted, described, dreamed* come into the design in these sentences. The feeling is of words themselves, a curious immediate quality quite apart from their meaning, much as in music different notes are dropped, so to speak, into a repeated chord one at a time, one after another — for itself alone. Compare this with the same effects common in all that Stein does. See *Geography* and *Plays*, "They were both gay there." To continue —

"Did my father, mother, uncle, aunt, brothers or sisters, ever see a white bear? What would they give? How would they behave? How would the white bear have behaved? Is he wild? Tame? Terrible? Rough? Smooth?"

Note the play upon *rough* and *smooth* (though it is not certain that this was intended), *rough* seeming to apply to the bear's deportment, *smooth* to surface, presumably the bear's coat. In any case the effect is that of a comparison relating primarily not to any qualities of the bear himself but to the words *rough* and *smooth*. And so to finish —

"Is the white bear worth seeing?"
"Is there any sin in it?"
"Is it better than a black one?"

In this manner ends Chapter 43 of *The Life and Opinions of Tristram Shandy*. The handling of the words and to some extent the imaginative quality of the sentences is a direct forerunner of that which Gertrude Stein has woven today into a synthesis of its own. It will be plain, in fact, on close attention, that Sterne exercises not only the play (or music) of sight, sense and sound contrasts among the words themselves which Stein uses, but their grammatical play also — i.e. *for, how, can I imagine* it; *did* my . . . . ; *what would, how would,* compare Stein's "to have rivers; to halve rivers" etc. It would not be too much to say that Stein's development over a lifetime is anticipated completely with regard to subject matter, sense and grammar — in Sterne.

* * * * * * * * * * *

Starting from scratch we get, possibly, thatch; just as they have always done in poetry.

Then they would try to connect it up by something like — The mice scratch, beneath the thatch.

Miss Stein does away with all that. The free-versists on the contrary used nothing else. They saved — The mice . . under the . . . . .

It is simply the skeleton, the "formal" parts of writing, those that make form, that she has to do with, apart from the "burden" which they carry.

The skeleton, important to acknowledge where confusion of all knowledge of the "soft parts" reigns as at the present day in all intellectual fields.

Stein's theme is writing. But in such a way as to be writing envisioned as the first concern of the moment, dragging behind it a dead weight of logical burdens, among them a dead criticism which broken through might be a gap by which endless other enterprises of the understanding should issue — for refreshment.

It is a revolution of some proportions that is contemplated, the exact nature of which may be no more than sketched here but whose basis is humanity in a relationship with literature hitherto little contemplated.

And at the same time it is a general attack on the scholastic viewpoint, that mediæval remnant, with whose effects from generation to generation literature has been infested to its lasting detriment. It is a break away from that paralyzing vulgarity of logic for which the habits of science and philosophy coming over into literature (where they do not belong) are to blame.

It is this logicality as a basis for literary action which in Stein's case, for better or worse, has been wholly transcended.

She explains her own development in connection with "Tender Buttons" (1914) "It was my first conscious struggle with the problem of correlating sight, sound and sense, and eliminating rhythm; - - - now I am trying grammar and eliminating sight and sound (transition No. 14, Fall, 1928).

Having taken the words to her choice, to emphasize further what she has in mind she has completely unlinked them (in her most recent work) from their former relationships in the sentence. This was absolutely essential and unescapable. Each under the new arrangement has a quality of its own, but not conjoined to carry the burden science, philosophy and every higgledy piggledy figment of law and order have been laying upon them in the past. They are like a crowd at Coney Island, let us say, seen from an airplane.

Whatever the value of Miss Stein's work may turn out finally to be, she has at least accomplished her purpose of getting down on paper this much that is decipherable. She has placed writing on a plane where it may deal unhampered with its own affairs, unburdened with scientific and philosophic lumber.

For after all, science and philosophy are today, in their effect upon the mind, little more than fetishes of unspeakable abhorrence. And it is through a subversion of the art of writing that their grip upon us has assumed its steel-like temper.

What are philosophers, scientists, religionists; they that have filled up literature with their pap? Writers, of a kind. Stein simply erases their stories, turns them off and does without them, their logic (founded merely on the limits of the perceptions) which is supposed to transcend the words, along with them. Stein denies it. The words, in writing, she discloses, transcend everything.

Movement (for which in a petty way logic is taken) the so-called search for truth and beauty is for us the effect of a breakdown of the attention. But movement must not be confused with what we attach to it but, for the rescuing of the intelligence, must always be considered aimless, without progress.

This is the essence of all knowledge.

Bach might be an illustration of movement not suborned by a freight of purposed design, loaded upon it as in almost all later musical works; statement unmusical and unnecessary. Stein's "They lived very gay then" has much of the same quality of movement to be found in Bach — the composition of the words determining not the logic, not the "story", not the theme even, but the movement itself. As it happens, "They were both gay there" is as good as some of Bach's shorter fugues.

Music could easily have a statement attached to each note in the manner of words, so that C natural might mean the sun, etc., and completely dull treatises be played — and even sciences finally expounded in tunes.

Either, we have been taught to think, the mind moves in a logical sequence to a definite end which is its goal, or it will embrace movement without goal other than movement itself for an end and hail "transition" only as supreme.

Take your choice, both resorts are an improper description of the mind in fullest play.

If the attention could envision the whole of writing, let us say, at one time, moving over it in swift and accurate pursuit of the modern imperative at the instant when it is most to the fore, something of what actually takes place under an optimum of intelligence could be observed. It is an alertness not to let go of a possibility of movement in our fearful bedazzlement with some concrete and fixed present. The goal is to keep a beleaguered line of understanding which has movement from breaking down and becoming a hole into which we sink decoratively to rest.

The goal has nothing to do with the silly function which logic, natural or otherwise, enforces. Yet it is a goal. It moves as the sense wearies, remains fresh, living. One is concerned with it as with anything pursued and not with the rush of air or the guts of the horse one is riding — save to a very minor degree.

Writing, like everything else is much a question of refreshed interest. It is directed, not idly, but as most often happens (though not necessarily so), toward that point not to be predetermined where movement is blocked (by the end of logic perhaps). It is about these parts, if I am not mistaken, that Gertrude Stein will be found.

There remains to be explained the bewildering volume of what Miss Stein has written, the quantity of her work, its very apparent repetitiousness, its iteration, what I prefer to call its extension, the final clue to her meaning.

It is, of course, a progression (not a progress) beginning, conveniently, with "Melanctha" (from *Three Lives),* and coming up to today.

How in a democracy, such as the United States, can writing, which has to compete with excellence elsewhere and in other times, remain in the field and be at once objective (true to fact) intellectually searching, subtle and instinct with powerful additions to our lives? It is impossible, without invention of some sort, for the very good reason that observation about us engenders the very opposite of what we seek: triviality, crassness, and intellectual bankruptcy. And yet what we do see can in no way be excluded. Satire and flight are two possibilities but Miss Stein has chosen otherwise.

But if one remain in a place and reject satire, what then? To be democratic, local (in the sense of being attached with integrity to actual experience) Stein, or any other artist, must for subtlety ascend to a plane of almost abstract design to keep alive. To writing, then, as an art in itself. Yet what actually impinges on the senses must be rendered as it appears, by use of which, only, and under which, untouched, the significance has to be disclosed. It is one of the major problems of the artist.

"Melanctha" is a thrilling clinical record of the life of a colored woman in the present day United States, told with directness and truth. It is without question one of the best bits of characterization produced in America. It is universally admired. This is where Stein began.

But for Stein to tell a story of that sort, even with the utmost genius, was not enough under the conditions in which we live, since by the very nature of its composition such a story does violence to the larger scene which would be portrayed.

True, a certain way of delineating the scene is to take an individual like Melanctha and draw her carefully. But this is what happens. The more carefully the drawing is made, the greater the genius involved and the greater the interest that attaches, therefore, to the character as an individual, the more exceptional that character becomes in the mind of the reader and the less typical of the scene.

It was no use for Stein to go on with *Three Lives.* There that phase of the work had to end. See *Useful Knowledge,* the parts on the U. S. A.

Stein's pages have become like the United States viewed from an airplane — the same senseless repetitions, the endless multiplications of toneless words, with these she had to work.

No use for Stein to fly to Paris and *forget* it. The thing, the United States, the unmitigated stupidity, the drab tediousness of the democracy, the overwhelming number of the offensively ignorant, the dull of nerve — is *there* in the artist's mind and cannot be escaped by taking a ship. She must resolve it if she can, if she is to *be*. That must be the artist's articulation with existence.

Truly, the world is full of emotion — more or less — but it is caught in bewilderment to a far more important degree. And the purpose of art, so far as it has any, is not at least to copy that, but lies in the resolution of difficulties to its own comprehensive organization of materials. And by so doing, in this case, rather than by copying, it takes its place as *most* human.

To deal with Melanctha, with characters of whomever it may be, the modern Dickens, is *not* therefore human. To write like that is not, in the artist, to be human at all, since nothing is resolved, nothing is done to resolve the bewilderment which makes of emotion an inanity. That, is to overlook the gross instigation and with all subtlety to examine the object minutely for "the truth" — which if there is anything more commonly practised or more stupid, I have yet to come upon it.

To be most useful to humanity, or to anything else for that matter, an art, writing, must stay art, not seeking to be science, philosophy, history, the humanities, or anything else it has been made to carry in the past. It is this enforcement which underlies Gertrude Stein's extension and progression to date.

FIVE WORDS IN A LINE

Gertrude Stein

Five words in a line.
Bay and pay make a lake.
Have to be held with what.
They have to be held with what they have to be held.
Dependent of dependent of why.
With a little cry.
Make of awake.
Five words in a line.
Four words in a line.
They make it with it being please to have withheld with with it.
Four words in one line.
If to pay by postage.
At all to delay to pay by postage.
If he is he then he will follow me but will he. With them. With will he.
Really. Five words in a line.
There is every way to-day to say in with a whitened end with it.
Pardon there with ours.
It is very little that will. That in that in that will.
Four words in one line.
Have withhold. Have withheld.
Six words in one line.
They were alike. With them. They went with wish. If they had the
possibility of annoyance.
Six words in one line.
They are as well as alike.
Three were by theirs allied.
If they were true to usual. A refusal. Made carriage with a weeding.
Without varied vary roses.
But with them.
Withhold.

They look at him and they know what he thinks.
Now they could when they look at him.

When they were married by him this made away.

Barred to be barred.

Why little a long a lain made with a piled with adapt.

Very benevolently she left for him.

If she could with and did dazzle.

Why were they changing two in yet or all day.

It is very happily that it is with added that it is as it is a gold or is told.

Commence again that we like waving.

Once every day once a day they make it do. By this time a part of it is impressed favorably with keeping. If not by and with allowance. They mean that if they know.

What does it look like if it looks like it.

They came to the country and they asked them not to and they did a little at a time with whom with flourishes.

Jenny Solomon
Matter pan has acuteness in return she said with they did.

Only now nearly known names a press with them.

A Sofa
Married a presently for them and known. It might be larger.

It might not be as high as with them.
To come back.
If it looks like it.
Without it.
With it.
If it looks like it with it.
Four words in each line.
If it does it looks as it does it looks like it.
Does look like it.
It does look like it.
Five words in a line is right.
By never being suspicious and always being careful she has never been robbed.

THE BOSS

Edwin Seaver

The boss is a little man about as wide around as he is high. He has several extra chins that almost hide his wing collar. His hair is thin and grey and it is patted down in a funny little bang on his forehead. Sometimes it makes him look like a big baby with his hair coming down that way in a point between his eyes. You can almost see him stroking it with his chubby hand when he sits up in bed in the morning. Only the boss' eyes are not at all bright and dewy like a baby's. They are very grey and very still and they look right past you when you meet him in the corridor.

The boss only smiles when he is having his picture taken. The boss likes to have his picture taken and so he has it done lots of times. Sometimes it is as the director of a great Safety Drive and the newspapers tell how he has helped to save thousands of lives. Sometimes it is as chairman say of the 34th Street Centennial Celebration and the newspapers tell how the boss is working for a bigger and finer 34th Street. And sometimes it is just as one of the country's great big business men. But always it is the same old boss with the softly smiling face, the satisfied quiet lips and the eyes that look right past you.

When the boss poses for his picture he sits in a comfortable chair with his fat hands folded over his belly and he looks very contented. He looks as if he has just had something good to eat. His little legs hang down quietly from his paunch. His spats look quite expensive. To see him sitting there, his head inclining just a little to his broad right shoulder, his mouth full and happy, you would hardly think he was an important business man.

The boss does not stop smiling when the photographers have fired their flash. His smile lingers for a moment even after the cameras have clicked. Then gradually the chins relax and the boss gets up from his chair heavily. He always carries a little cane for on some days he limps quite badly.

Sometimes I think this is because he likes to eat too many good things. Once when I was in the ante-room to his office I heard his secretary talking over the telephone to the chef at the Waldorf. The chef said that he was awfully sorry but he had shopped all over town and could not find the kind of peaches the boss would like to have served to his guests. The secretary told the chef to hold the wire a minute please and hurried gravely into the boss' office. In a little while she came out looking quite relieved and told the chef the boss said he was also very fond of figs and cream and should like to have that served the guests since good peaches could not be found.

Feeding his face, the clerks call it. Only in our office the clerks are not called clerks, they are called Junior Executives. Our office is the Editorial Bureau and everybody in it is a writer. Naturally, a writer can't be a mere clerk.

The junior executives do not like the boss very much. They say he has bluffed his way to the top and that's why he has no understanding of those who work under him. They tell how he began as an office boy in the Company forty years ago. You can always tell a self-made man they say sarcastically. He gets there by using others as a step-ladder. But you never can tell. Maybe they're jealous and envy the boss his place.

Maybe that's why they're always telling stories about him. One of their stories goes like this and they claim it's true, every word of it.

They say that once the employment manager reported to the boss that the negro doorman was a college graduate, an A.B. It was a shame, the employment manager thought, to be wasting such good equipment merely because the fellow was colored.

The boss didn't think so. I don't see why you consider it a shame, he said. I think the man has a wonderful opportunity in his job. In a way, he acts as host for the Company. Just think what a real privilege it is to be able to greet every one that visits us and extend the cordial greetings of the Company to all. Why, I almost envy the man his job.

Yes, he does like hell, one of the junior executives says bitterly. The pot-bellied hypocrite. But the others only laugh uneasily. No one likes to be thought a grouch around the office. After all, if we don't like our jobs we know what we can do.

The boss sits behind a big mahogany desk in a spacious office. He is one of the vice presidents of the Company. There are six vice presidents altogether. The Company is divided into six departments and each of the vice presidents has a department all to himself. But the boss is really the big boss of the Company because his department is the biggest.

In the boss' office there is a thick carpet that entirely covers the floor. Your feet sink into the carpet when you walk across it. The boss does not look up when you come in even though he has rung for you. He is always very busy with some papers. Behind him is a great window that reaches from floor to ceiling. Looking over his head you can see the power house, belching smoke from eight enormous chimneys.

Your eyes wander back to the boss and rest on his head. Under his thin grey hair his head looks very old and fragile and suddenly you feel that you could crush it easily between your fingers.

At last the boss looks up and hands you two letters. One of them is from the Rotary Club of Newark who would like to have the boss talk to them on every worker becoming a capitalist. The other is from the Yonkers Bulletin of Commerce and asks for an article from the boss on public relations.

In writing on public relations I always like to have the point made that in the last analysis public relations are human relations, the boss says. Then the telephone rings and he looks past you with his grey still eyes. You cannot hear your footsteps on the thick carpet. The door swings after you without a sound.

Sometimes one of the junior executives opens the *Who's Who* to the boss' name. It's an old trick in our office. We read over the names of all the clubs the boss belongs to and you can feel resentment clogging the air. But it does not burst out until we read how the boss is author of numerous technical and financial articles. Then some of us laugh sarcastically as if we knew all along what was coming and some say if he were decent enough to acknowledge who wrote his articles and speeches we might get somewhere.

Occasionally the boss calls us in for a conference. The boss likes to hold conferences. He says it helps to keep up the morale of the staff. But sometimes I think he likes them because it makes him feel important to have us grouped around him like the host at the feet of God.

When we come in he sits behind his big mahogany desk looking over some very important papers. Chairs are already arranged for us in a semi-circle around his desk and we sit down. By his side, facing us, sit several of the bureau managers. They are the archangels in the scheme of things, as you might say. The clerks call them the boss' yes-men.

When we have all been seated for some time the boss finishes with his papers. Once he took a cigar from the top drawer of his desk and cut off the end with a little silver cutter. Then he put the other end between his quiet lips and struck a match. You could see from the way he handled his cigar that the boss was not what you would call a smoker. He took a few short puffs, rolled the big cigar between his fat fingers and took it out of his mouth.

You understand, he said, no smoking is allowed in my department. This afternoon I am doing the smoking for the Company. His lips turned up at the ends. We looked at each other and some one coughed.

The boss seemed to feel that his little joke had fallen flat. He did not put the cigar in his mouth again. He leaned back in his swivel chair and turned to the manager on his right. Mr. Pope will tell you why I have called this conference, he said and looked past us.

Mr. Pope explained that there had been too many latenesses in the department. Lateness was becoming a habit and must be stopped. The boss had decided that from now on all considerations for advance in the department would have to depend on the employe's attendance record.

The boss nodded. The Company had a right to demand loyalty in little things like this of its employes, he said. The boss always speaks of the Company as if it were some immaculate conception quite outside of him and of us to which we both owe equal devotion.

When the boss had finished speaking he turned to the manager on the left. He was the chief clerk. I have asked Mr. Bishop to stand by me in this decision and he has promised me his full support, the boss said. Am I right, Mr. Bishop?

Yes sir.

That will be all, said the boss, pressing the button on the side of his desk. The door opened and his secretary came in carrying a note-book and pencil.

Mr. Roger Phillips, Secretary,
The Broadway Association,
New York, N. Y.

My dear Mr. Phillips:

It is a great personal pleasure for me to be able to accept the chairmanship of the Committee of distinguished business men who are to speak on the air on the greater Broadway of the future. I feel that the public not only of our great city but of the entire country is deeply interested in the changing history of our great thoroughfares of commerce.

I wish to particularly recommend your idea of binding the various papers read in book form and hereby gladly subscribe to one hundred (100) copies at two dollars ($2.00) a copy. As you say, so much of the daily tasks of business men like ourselves passes unnoticed by others and this should be a splendid opportunity for us to bequeath some record of ourselves to our children.

Your plan to present copies of the book to the public libraries throughout the country is sound and should prove of great educative value.

I am free to speak on March 17th and choose for my subject, "The Busiest Little Street in the World."

Yours for a greater Broadway

The boss does not look past the secretary as her rapid fingers make swift neat marks on the pages of her book. The boss has neither wife nor daughter. After he has dictated his letters he will go down to the street in the elevator reserved for executives. Henry will be waiting for him and throwing away his half-finished cigarette will jump down from his seat at the wheel to open the door. Then Henry will close the door quietly and drive him to the club. There the boss will rest in a deep leather arm chair and read the evening papers. He has an appointment with his friend the Judge for dinner. After dinner . . .

The boss pats the bang of thin grey hair on his forehead. He does not like to think of after. It makes him feel lonely.

His secretary sits by the desk, her strong legs crossed, the notebook resting lightly on her knee. While her pencil glides swiftly across the page and down, the boss thinks of many things. That is what a big business man is able to do even while the words he is dictating fall easily from his lips. He thinks of how that day he bested another vice president of the Company in the honor of a particular piece of business. He rubs the chubby palms of his hands together. He was getting old but he could show them a few tricks yet.

Other thoughts come and go in the boss' head as the words are caught and fixed by the capable fingers of his secretary. She has vigorous white hands and under the tight sleeves of her blouse her arms are sturdy. They are warm and shapely like her breasts that erect themselves so firmly under the snug blouse. The boss cannot keep his eyes from following the vigorous line of her leg, firm as a pillar from ankle to knee, and above the knee where her skirt is drawn tightly over the swelling thigh. His eyes rest on the mar- celled waves of her hair and follow them around the bent head to the neat nate upon the neck. And the neck itself, so strong and white, and the vivid shoulders, like ripe figs and cream in the mouth.

The boss passes his tongue nervously between his lips. They are very dry and suddenly he feels hot and cold all over. It makes him think of a narrow escape he had that morning. Henry almost ran down an old woman when they were driving to the office. Even now the boss winces when he thinks of it. Henry must be more careful in the future. Especially with this being Safety Week and he head of the New York division.

The boss trembles when he thinks of the unfavorable publicity it would mean. It was wonderful though how the public appreciated civic service. His name was in the newspapers all over the country since he had agreed to act as chairman of the New York division of the National Safety Drive. It was remarkable what publicity could do to bring your name before the entire country. Here he was sitting in his office dictating letters and out in California citizens were reading of how he was doing his bit to promote human welfare. He must not let any chance slip by to interest himself in public services.

Deep in the corner of his car the boss sinks back into the cushioned seat. He feels snug as a bug in a rug. Outside a biting wind whips the dust against the windows and the bent faces of the passersby, but inside the car it is warm and comfortable. The purring of the motor, the broad back of Henry, his steady hand upon the wheel, the deferential salute of the traffic officer, the thought of an excellent dinner coming — all this makes the boss feel secure and contented. The confusion and tumult of the traffic outside the windows of the car and the flocks of people who stand on the curbs patiently awaiting the signal to go increase his sense of well being.

The tall buildings stride past him, majestically on parade. New buildings are mounting and high up on the steel girders the riveters are busily at work. The steady hammer of the riveting irons falls soothing upon the boss' ears. His hands caress the leather seat and his eyes rest satisfied upon the upholstered interior of the car. Underneath, strong steel. The car rocks gently as a cradle on its springs as it crosses the trolley tracks. Everything is so sure, so real, like these steel frames upon which the workers will shortly dress the new skyscrapers. Prosperity in every rivet.

To Blanche Matthias

MONDAY MORNING

Margery Latimer

"Dear, it *is* a rose bug."

She turned the gas low under the coffee and ran in.

"Is it, dear?"

"Look. It is!"

"Where? Oh, but it isn't, dear."

"But, did you ever see a rose bug?" he asked. He straightened up and put his arm around her, laying his face against her hair. She turned to him quickly and pressed her lips on his ear. "Oh, God, I had a quake," she said, drawing back. "It seemed as if my cheeks flashed white. Just as if I'd turned the light on and off."

"I like the way you arrange flowers, dear," he said. He began kissing the same place on her cheek, as if he were absent-mindedly eating something good.

"Oh, listen, it *is* a bee. That zzzz comes right out of its stomach. Oh, the coffee!" She ran into the kitchen and poured a little cold water down the coffee spout. "Eggs, darling?" she called. "Both sides? A little cinnamon on your toast?"

He came running to her, his rather firm short legs stiff, as if he were running on a track. He pushed back his cuffs and stood there by the stove, smiling and smoothing his ring. His body was so alive, she thought proudly, and his large mouth was generous, and sometimes when he tried to make her understand things all his eagerness and honesty seemed to push out of his pores. He would get close to her if she could not understand. He would bend over her, examining her eyelids, her face in its very center.

"I say, dear, can't I get the water?" He sprang for the pitcher before she could say, "Don't bother." He jerked the empty water pail then and went out the door whistling as she flopped the eggs. She heard him pushing the handle up and down, then the splash of water came as he emptied out the first bucketful. She shoved the hair up from her forehead.

O that little room, that sodden bed. The broken chair in the corner. O the body beside hers. The white restless hands. "You want courage, don't you? You want life, don't you?" O the agony and glory of that face pressed on hers, the agony and glory of that giving. O the light that came from their skin. All never ending. Life never ending. All around them the great world of tenements, sorrow, rage, bricks, joy, old brooms, cats, all — all never ending. The great world in whose body they lay, whose arms arched their heads, the roof of the house, whose hands put rain and snow and sun in their faces, brought money and took it away, ate them slowly, smiling, as they ate it,— that world, never ending.

She put the eggs on a platter. Parsley. She turned the bacon with a black spider-fork. She laid it crisply, rolled like little blankets, round the side. She shook cinnamon over the pale toast and spread it, watching it mix brownly with the butter; and bubble under the heat. "Oh, I love my life." She took off her apron that was like a yellow Easter egg and laid her hand on her brooch. Then she glanced down, turning the pin up — a white dove in a basket of roses.

"Margot, the radishes are up, dear."

He set the pail down and filled the pitcher with a long dipper. He went in and filled their glasses. Then he dashed back for the food. "You take the coffee, dear. I'll take the platters. Go ahead."

She stood by her chair, gazing at the ceiling. She raised both hands quickly, her head pressed back against her shoulders. "Dear God, thank you for our life." As she felt the cool chair, the hard cool wood under her hand, that other voice shot through her, "Margot, you're never polite to me." And her answer, "I know it. I love you. I can't be polite. I want the whole world from you."

She sank down, smiling at her husband. "Oh, I forgot the fruit. We were going to have casaba melon. It's in the ice box. Let me get it, dear."

He was serving the eggs. "Don't want it." The clean way he placed the egg on the plate, just to the side of the gay French couple, made her open her mouth a little as if she were already putting the first precious taste on her tongue. He laid the bacon gently beside it. A bit of parsley.

She took it. "Thank you, darling." Now it came again, filling her head, her ears, now the room came again, the bare walls, the papers. Now the little windows opened behind her eyes, the lighted shops, the stars at night over city roofs, the sky at night above those cold white streets, those towers that went into the deep blue evening sky. "I won't let you lock me up. I won't. No. You can't. Cry then. Cry all you please. No, I'm not a monster." Girls holding their jackets together in front, a window of cloth roses. A card — Dinner .35.

"Oh, I forgot to pour the coffee."

"You're absent-minded, dear."

She lifted the proud silver pot. "Oh, I forgot the sugar, dear. I'll just put it in now. Three?"

"Why, no, dear," he said sharply, a wrinkle coming down his nose. "You know I don't take sugar."

"Of course, dear." She handed him the cup. "Shall I order fish for dinner? They're going to have trout today. Hollandaise? Of course I can. Why, I can too make it. I did last Wednesday and it was good." She closed her eyes for a moment, lifting her head the way she did when everything suddenly came to life, the chairs on their polished legs, the old table, the cloth, the silver, the big bowl of roses opened full. "Oh, husband, I love my life." She leaned over the table toward him, smiling, holding a piece of toast, a tiny buttered crumb on her red mouth. "I love you. I love my life."

He always sprang up, his very blue eyes almost closing too. He always choked her with his arms, bending over her face, pushing it back, back into his hands, kissing her then so gently, his hands, his body seeming to say — "Thank you, thank you, wife."

"You smell so good," he said. "You always smell that way." She felt his nostrils quivering over her cheek. She felt the melting joy of her arms as his swept hers. "Oh, I love my life," she cried, rising away from him, looking strangely into his face. "I love the world. I'm in the world with you." She pressed her hands against her womb, looking full at him now. "I love our baby. I wish there were three of them inside me." She laughed, her head far back.

"You'll have three," he said. "I promise. You'll have twelve if you want. Two dozen. A gross."

They ate, smiling at each other.

"I decided in bed last night that he will have to be named Wren."

"That's a silly name," he protested. "My poor mother couldn't think of anything else for me. . . ."

"Wren, I love your name."

He shrugged. "Have it your own way." He laid the top off the toast-plate and took another brown piece. "Oh, say, Margot, I'm just joking. I'd be tickled pink to call him Wren. I just feel more manly not liking it. You know."

"Wren, Wren, Wren," she said rapidly.

"Dear, that is too a bee. Look it's getting ready to sting you. See. It's sharpening its hind legs to sting you with."

O save me now. O master, save me now. Let him come. Let everything be the way it was at the beginning. Make him come, God. Make him come now. Make him, make him. "I'll always love you, Margot. I'll make one million babies for you." There is the train pulling out. There is his head in the window, his body, both arms waving. There are his eyes, sad, accepting all — every separation — every sundering — all, all. O run, run by the train, run faster, faster, run by the train, O run, run. Catch at the window, catch at the arms, hang, hang, be drawn up, lie forever near that face.

She ran into the kitchen. What is it? she thought. I don't really want to go back. I love this. I love him. I don't want to go back. It was like a clock striking in her stomach — "That was divine." She remembered the great wrenchings she used to have to understand, to enter the world outside, the pain of love, of giving, the rockets that would break in her body when they sat together, then the soft gush of light through her pores.

"What *are* you doing, dear?"

"Heating the coffee."

"All right, I'll bring the pot," he called.

She bent over the stove, the lighted match in one hand, the other on the white knob. "Thanks, dear."

He took out his watch. "I ought not wait for it. I'll miss the bus again."

She stood with her back to him. "Why is anything — anything at all — always so good when you look back at it?"

"My dear, only the present is good," he mumbled. "What we do with our bodies in the present is good. What we say to each other and look. What we can express now, this minute — that's good."

"But, darling, the past becomes the present and the present seems the future and both are equally real. You know that."

"No, I don't."

"Well, it's ready."

They went in arm in arm, trying to squeeze themselves past the narrow cupboards with the rosebud china and the pewter. "Oh, my whole self is open to you, Wren," she said. "I — I look back. I think of him. I can't help it."

"Of course not, dear," he said instantly. "It's all right. Why not?"

"Oh, those quakes. They come before I think of him. Just like turning on the light, Wren."

He forced her into her chair. "You drink the coffee, dear. Here goes the sugar. Here goes the cream. Here goes the spoon to stir it. Here it all goes into your red mouth. Isn't that silly, dear?"

"Thank you — thank you." She closed her eyes, pressing her lips against his hand, but there was space between. She laid her ear against his mouth but she heard that other mouth, that other voice, as if that rainy night were happening now, the cold wind blowing open the little window, rain pelting their clothes, the clean cruel lightning crashing and blazing on the bare wall above them. In that little space between her ear and his mouth she heard those other words as if it were now. "Today I don't want a million babies, Margot. I'd kill them all. You bore me. I want to go one million miles away from you, angel. I'd soon choke you and the kid as well. I'd murder you after six months. I'd be in the penitentiary and you'd be bringing me cigarettes and stale cookies. Don't talk. Every word you say you've said one million times. You bore me. Keep away. I haven't anything at all for you — ever. No, you've got me crazy. I swear any woman in the streets has more than you. They have bodies. They have senses. They don't hang on a guy for love all the time. Oh, shut up for a change."

She stood up, grasping the edge of the table, leaning over the fresh opened roses to him. He was standing there looking young and lonely. "What did I say to you, Wren, that day I told you all about it?"

"What? Which?"

"That day I told you how I lived with him. What did I tell you?"

"I can't remember."

"Think. Try."

He went to her. He laid his hand on their child, on her breast. His warm arms held her. He looked then into the center of her face, all of him pressed toward her, something inside him making all his particles seem loose and open, as if all his eagerness were spinning out to her from the tumult inside him.

"I said, 'What I am looking for is not in life. I can never have it.' I said — I said — 'Now I want to give. I want to serve. I want to love. I want to understand.' "

Wack-ack-ack-ack-ack-yeek!

"God, I can't miss it on Monday. Where's my case? To hell. Where did I put the damned thing anyway? Take a nap, dear, won't you. You're pale. I'll phone. . . ."

"What about the trout? Shall I order. . . ."

"Water the radishes, dear."

"Don't forget the receipt this time, dear."

Now he was climbing into the bus, reaching out to shake hands with his friends in grey hats and canes and crushed gloves. He was turning to smile back at some one as he straightened his tie, his big generous mouth very pleased and boyish.

Wack-ack-ack-ack-ack-yeek!

Now he waved at her as the bus was moving, making one of his hideous faces just for fun. Then he smiled quickly and lifted his hat. The long orange bus went.

"West End 2039-W." She fingered the telephone book. "No, operator, I said West End 2039-W. Yes."

O to be nothing but a tree, to spread cool branches over grass and flowers, to let children climb my body and lie in my boughs, to shake off my leaves and fall asleep, making a soft zzzzz under the fallen snow. O to be born again, to be new, to blossom.

"Hello, this is Mrs. Henshaw. I want you to send me a very nice lake trout. About one and a half pounds. I want half a dozen lemons. A dozen of the best eggs. A pound of the best butter and two casaba melons — no, not any melons. Cross that off. I have melons. Yes, that's all. No, I must have a bottle of prepared mustard. That's all this morning."

She went upstairs, singing, shaking her bright hair. Then she stood before the opened windows, her hands on their child, her face light and beautiful as she looked down into the garden, then up to the branching trees that sprayed the house. She saw the bright perfect sky, the white clouds. It was all still. She leaned out to make sure she was seeing right. But the clouds, the air, even, the great trees, all were still, gleaming in the sun.

The soft lavender quilt was half on the floor. The white mark of their heads had creased the pillows, dented them softly. There was her orange robe with the pale yellow flowers breathing softly out of it, shaking soft petals down it, vibrating on the cloth as if a little wind were underneath. She sat down on the hard cool chair near the desk. Instantly ice spread over the skin of her feet. It spread up and they turned hard and dead. They broke apart with lightning from that night and it ripped her open in long clean cracks.

"For God's sake marry some one else, not me not me not me, for God's sake, where's my tobacco, marry some one else, please, I want you to be happy, you're the one I love best of all, Margot, marry some one else. I can't bear to see you unhappy, get that match over there for me, where the hell did I throw my pouch, I'll find some one for you, I love you, I love you, it will make me jealous, I want you to be happy, Margot, Christ, can't you see I'm cold, close the window, don't you ever see what I need, no, I won't regret it, don't fool yourself and that's the truth, don't reproach me for the truth, I won't regret it, I love you best, give me a dime, damn it I want a dime, I do too love you."

She went downstairs and gathered up the cups and saucers. She threw the Easter egg apron over her head and turned water into the dish pan. Then she carried the plates into the kitchen, into the sunny window by the gleaming pan. She pushed the parsley aside so that she could look down on the gay French couple, hand in hand, laughing in their big shoes and funny peasant hats.

"I have a child inside me," she whispered to them softly. "I love my husband. I love the world. Thank you, God."

ASSASSIN

Harry Crosby

(voici le temps des assassins —Rimbaud)
(unleash the sword and fire —Shelley)

I exchange eyes with the Mad Queen

the mirror crashes against my face and
bursts into a thousand suns
all over the city flags crackle and bang
fog horns scream in the harbor
the wind hurricanes through the window
and I begin to dance the dance of the
Kurd shepherds

    I stamp upon the floor
    I whirl like dervishes
colors revolve dressing and undressing
I lash them with fury
stark white with iron black
harsh red with blue
marble green with bright orange
and only gold remains naked
columns of steel rise and plunge
emerge and disappear
pistoning in the river of my soul
    thrusting upwards
    thrusting downwards
    thrusting inwards
    thrusting outwards
      penetrating

    I roar with joy
black-footed ferrets disappear into holes

the sun tattooed on my back
begins to spin
    faster and faster

whirring whirring
throwing out a glory of sparks
sparks shoot off into space
sparks into shooting stars
shooting stars collide with comets

Explosions
Naked Colors Explode
into
Red Disaster

I crash out through the
window naked, widespread
upon a
Heliosaurus
I uproot an obelisk and plunge
it into the ink-pot of the
Black Sea
I write the word

SUN

across the dreary palimpsest
of the world
I pour contents of the
Red Sea down my throat
I erect catapults and
lay siege to the cities of the world
I scatter violent disorder
throughout the kingdoms of the world
I stone the people of the world
I stride over mountains
I pick up oceans like thin cards
and spin them into oblivion
I kick down walled cities
I hurl giant firebrands against governments
I thrust torches through the eyes of the law
I annihilate museums
I demolish libraries
I oblivionize skyscrapers
I become hard as adamant
strong as battle

indurated in solid fire
rigid with hatred

I bring back the wizards and the sorcerers
the necromancers
the magicians
I practise witchcraft
I set up idols
with a sharp edged sword
I cut through the crowded streets
comets follow in my wake
stars make obeisance to me
the moon uncovers her
nakedness to me

I am the harbinger of a
New Sun World
I bring the Seed of a
         New Copulation
I proclaim the Mad Queen

I stamp out vast empires
I crush palaces in my rigid
         hands
I harden my heart against
         churches

I blot out cemeteries
I feed the people with
stinging nettles
I resurrect madness
I thrust my naked sword
between the ribs of the world
I murder the world!

NEW ENGLAND VICTORIAN EPISODES
PENNYTHINKER

1922

Robert McAlmon

PENNYTHINKER'S DECISIONS

I

Spring brightened the village campus
while students strolled on grassy lawns midst trees.
Elders and weeping willows cast string shadows
on bright frocks that young girls wore.
Boys played rampantly with boisterous glee on sidestreets.

Pennythinker strolled, and thought the scene
"So young, fresh, and exquisite.
Just too much the last word in young and carefree beauty.

"How Watteau would have revelled in this.
Young things romping, agile and unafraid,"
he reflected, and mourned, "So unlike my own young years
spent companionless with old maid aunts in a great box house.
Those were times of tremulous terrors and sleepless nights.
I moved too fearfully surrounded by spectres
of an untaught imagination to tire myself daytimes with play.

"It would be all I could ask to have always
a number of young things about to care for;
only to have them running to me with their troubles.

"Life as an idea is all right. I want no reality.
Give me the divine trivialities,
the little, exquisite emotions over flowers, perfumes,
sounds, movement, color,— and youth."

II

Moonmusing in palliative balcony darkness
Pennythinker heard her oboe-toned laughter.

"I've been told she likes me more than well," he sighed,
"but again I must give up to finding to what extent.
That is one of the things I can't afford.
But she compels me.   She is the kind of flesh that I adore."

Behind his glaciated stare was no steeled resignation,
but a look carnivorous, hunted and hunting,
a stare of terror gone stale.

"I know so well what it is I want, in flesh,
and in the quality of things and people about
which are to be intimate with the inner me.
I feel released from New England now
but for this ghastly poverty.   I shudder
at the idea of some fanciful god who cares what we do.
He gives no indication then, unless he likes suffering.
I must get away to Europe where they understand, and accept.

"I must look into this matter though;
find out to what extent she is attracted to me.
Good God! If that is only another illusion!

"I suppose one's only way is to die.
Then recognition, and perhaps
some sort of decent appreciation follow —
when it can no longer matter.
I get so sick of those who ask for everything
and give nothing in return."

III

Having plucked flowers on the mountain sides
Pennythinker was fatigued.
"My stomach drops down on me
because of that accident — stepping into a manhole —
years ago . . . . This atmosphere!
This clarity of space, hill lines, and foliage tonalities!
If I had consulted my emotions I would go on forever,
but one eventually learns one's limitations."

Pottering about his room he arranged flowers
to judge their color schemes.
A lavender hyacinth above narcissus and black pansies

pleased his design senses.
"This is just too exactly the thing
to have made Cezanne know he must paint it,"
he declared, giving the vase a background
by draping a blue and orange tie about it.

"It's too wonderful being an artist
so that one has nothing to think of
but a line, a bit of color, or a mass formation.
How sick I get of the gas about profundity,
sentiment, reality, and truth.
Such concepts should be barred from the language
along with ideas about beauty and nobility and the sublime.

"I must begin painting tomorrow.
I am so tired trying to create for myself the illusion
that people have affection for me.
Ugh! When they speak of my "intellect" and "austerity",
even you — as if I ever looked forbidding!

"If I ever did let myself go!"

Ceasing to speak for a moment he gazed
with carnivorous connoisseuring eyes at the room's spacings.
"Lovely, just too lovely, today has been.
When it takes so little to make one happy
it seems one might be permitted that little, always."

IV

News filtered in on gossip.
A lad, whom Pennythinker knew, was drowned at sea.
In the café square before the moon arose
a Frenchman strangled at a shrieking lady,
and Pennythinker knew "that if the moon were out
those two would likely be at something different.

The Finnish boy with theosophic tendencies
had suicided since his wealthy older woman had left him.
He could not live a poor man, so his note read.

Pennythinker sat, complacent, gay,
for the youthful painter with him thought him a master.

"Do they think I still have emotions about such things?"
he asked.   "People will copulate and fight;
someone is always being born or dying.
Can we waste sympathy on such final things?
My God, after all these years, what I've been through!
As if it were coldness to accept what happens!

PENNYTHINKER'S FRUSTRATIONS

I

"Indeed," Pennythinker was gay and facetious,
"I could arrive at the ball looking a high Rajah,
or an Indian potentate smothered in jewels thick as onions
over a well grilled steak.
Wouldn't I be the luscious dish too?

"But — I shall simply wear my evening suit
with one great orchid pinned to the coat lapel.
That will nullify the triteness of a boiled front;
and I assure you, I shall be aloof and much to myself.
All I wish is to sit and watch proceedings
so as to become in no way a part of the jam.
That sort of plunging into the riot is bye for me.

"I'm almost reconciled to the realization
that neither my personality nor my intestines —
(They will drop down in me if I over-exert) —
are of the sort that let me abandon myself
to the excesses that people attempt to amuse themselves.

"And even in the most riotous gatherings
there are always a few that come to sit and converse
or be quiet.   They find my *repose* a variation.
If they only knew! If I ever did express myself!

II

Wind, vulgarly blowsy, swirling,
blew elemental tang upon bourgeois streets
in whirlpools of dust, paper, and odors
stenched with a kitchen nostalgia.

"His lovely legs are just too wonderful,
the last word," Pennythinker declaimed,

as gazelle-bodied boys, shy and pink,
ran in flamboyant diffidence through his conscious.

Stars pricked the sky's impalpable flesh
and a quiver of tender ecstasy
swept the night's arena.

Incontrovertibly more commanding
as an iceberg, revealing
"the slopgullion of emotion
frozen to clarity in his centre,"
Pennythinker deigned to melt and beam.
"Eagle without a cliff" he descended from thwarted heights
to smile on gorgeous youth.
Some passion glances are better jewel-glittering,
and Pennythinker, slipped from his throne of arrogance,
lacked his camel-haughty fascination of dignity.

Antelopes now limped across his imaginings,
their horns crumbling.
Gazelles fattened and shed hair with love season by.
Pennythinker was deciding to paint
something abstract, and hard and cold.

"I'm through with being human," Pennythinker asserted,
glaring at the daughter of love drinking his boy's coffee,
coquettishly sure of her conquest.
Glaze rather than jewel-glitter
was the scintillant light in Pennythinker's eyes.

III

Economically safe for a time
Pennythinker enjoyed charming humanity.
He did not drink but he loved the scene
of wild things being reckless.
Night was soothed with a subdued cosmopolitan throb.

Reboantly, murmurs of city noises dissolved
into lengthening lapses of late night quiet.
Fervor for years withheld re-glowed in Pennythinker.
"He's just too sweet and clean-minded
for all his affectation of tough pugnacity,"

he confided, speaking of an amateur boxer.
"The most sensitive person with his intuitions,
if he never does have an idea beyond the moment's emotion.
Indeed, why should he?"

The boxer, catching a French girl's eye,
departed saying, "So long, mamma wants papa."

Pennythinker, slumping back into his chair,
glared with vulturish eyes of life-hate
into the abyss of time, of maddening, detail-filled space,
of people passing and of incidents unemphasized.
Only after two days of austere intellectualization
to freeze his sensibilities to disdain of human pastimes
could he comment, "Christ, how I detest personal relationships."

WHO THAT HAS HEARD HIM
John Albert Holmes

A Swedish boy worked on a milk-wagon, and washed dishes, shifted scenery, and went away to Porto Rico to the war.

Later a Mr. Sandburg published twenty-two poems.

A poet out in Chicago wrote, "Hog-butcher for the world, Player with Railroads and the Nation's Freight-handler; stormy, husky, brawling City of the Big Shoulders," and all over the country people turned to listen to a new voice.

His black hair turned slowly gray and Time carved sadness on his face, the eyes ached, the heart ached with love and pity for the conscripts, the good losers, the hungry and the lonely of the world.

And who that has ever heard him can forget his voice?

Who that has ever heard him say, "Everybody loved Chick Lorimer, no-body knows where she's gone," — who could be content again with ordinary words from ordinary human throats?

"The Prairie Years" had waited for a man to write it, a man with enough laughter, enough sun and soil in him, enough pity and love and hate.

And all the time the voice. Carl Sandburg's voice.

Like a 'cello, like an organ? More than that.

Like a great actor with "Tomorrow and tomorrow and tomorrow creeps in this petty pace from day to day?" More, more than even this.

The wind. Making its own music for its own voice to sing.

The sea. Beating on all the shores of the world the same.

Life gathered in a word, and the word spoken . . . the heart stirred and troubled . . . and the Sound of poetry.

THE ARTIST'S STONE

MR. SWEORD SEARCHES FOR A MEANS TO TRANSMUTE HUMAN EXISTENCE INTO AN ART

Gorham B. Munson

I

"Munson," said Adam Sweord, "the trouble is that you're identified with the Tortoise. That is the result of your damned New England education." His elephantine countenance loomed through the wreaths of cigarette smoke and the alert eyes held steadily on me. I did not glare back, not even when he outraged Aesop's fable and reversed its meaning, but bowed my head in reflection. That cursed habit of reflection! How often it has hamstrung the natural wish to defend myself.

I had been trying to renew a former discussion with Mr. Sweord on American Humanism, the only movement, by the way, in contemporary American thought that is of international importance. But he would none of that. Humanism was plodding, and plodding didn't win the race — at least not in one man's short existence. With great energy Mr. Sweord finally ejaculated something about "the art of life" and then announced his departure to keep an appointment.

I stayed for another cup of coffee with the phrase still sounding in my mind. Strange! I had often heard people speak of "the art of life" and, of course, I had read Pater and had even tried to select my experiences as he counselled. But unfortunately no good had· come of it: life seemed a higgledy-piggledy welter of experiences and the pursuit of the exquisite had to be abandoned whenever the wind blew. But Mr. Sweord by his intonation, the light in his eyes, the evidently personal meaning he had for the words, had revivified the phrase. It was now as if I had heard it for the first time and with a thrill.

It was, however, old thoughts, not new ones, that I turned over that afternoon. Did the art of life consist in securing an attractive shelter from the streets, pleasingly furnished and decorated with charming paintings? Did it show itself in one's grooming, in dress carefully selected and well-tailored? Was it based upon the pleasures of reading, of concerts, of art galleries? Or upon travels and luxuries for the senses? Or upon the cultivation of courtesy and minute discriminations in social relations? Was love the key or philosophy or the practice of one of the ordinary seven arts? No, all this was Paterian: "stirring of the senses, strange dyes, strange colours,

and curious odours, or work of the artist's hands, or the face of one's friend."
I had tried them all and in retaliation for Pater's refined language I now
pronounced my own life a mess, its gratifications coming by chance and not
enduring and its flow having no ordered pattern.

But this time I more clearly perceived than I had ever before that I had
mistaken the medium. The artist of life works not in things external to
himself but attempts to mould his own experience. I had been chiefly looking at a library and not at myself. My daily behavior: there was the place
to begin.

At once I succumbed to the phrase-making habit of the literary man. I
tore off the back of an envelope and scribbled:

> O pursuer, not the objects you chase
> Will give to you that sense of harmony you seek.
> Emptied of energy, you will lie down without satisfaction.
> But in the composing of the motions of the hunter,
> There is your secret!
> Learn then: to regard the pursuer and not the pursued.

I was looking this over with a view to revision when Mr. Sweord re-
appeared at my table. The coffee house was again filling up with late afternoon visitors, I noticed. He glanced at my lines, said something disparaging,
and then twinkled.

"Come on in, the water's hot!" he exclaimed. "Guaranteed to boil you
hard if you stay in it. But look before you dive. . . . You are a scribe of
sorts: you have a home, a country, and no doubt a benevolent God who is
especially interested in you: your imperfections don't bother you very much
and your illusions are priceless. Bewitched by words, you'll trot home now
and write an essay on the art of living. Hopeless! However, I shall profit,
for if your essay is any good, I shall live it, whereas you, my pen-hypnotized
friend, will only write it."

II

I did write an essay that night which I entitled *The Unknown Art* and
from it I now extract an analogy.

"An artist in any of the commonly recognized media — paint, stone,
sound, words, and so on — must first know the nature and the real possibilities of his medium: second, he must have some method for working in it:
and, third, he must by practice attain control of the medium and his method
so that he can achieve the results he wishes. Hence, a long apprenticeship
is necessary just for the sake of learning what the medium is like. And
teaching is needed, so that methods may be accessible to the pupil's choice
and he be not compelled to repeat the history of fruitless experimentation

which each art has traced. Again, time is required for the ripening of the artist's power of directing the medium to obey his plans. This is platitudinous in the studios. There people who think that quickly, by inspiration, without study or instruction, they can qualify as masters are butts for laughter.

"So should the man be derided who decides, 'I shall become a living work of art,' and thinks that it is not necessary to be self-knowing and self-directing, and above all not necessary to acquire a 'way of life'. For how can he work intelligently on his own self when it is material of which he is grossly ignorant? How can he organize and display what he is unfamiliar with? How can he even begin the task since he refuses to take thought on *how* to reach the results in himself that he deems desirable?

"Harmony is the keynote of a work of art, but show me a harmonious life. Mastery is the attitude of the artist toward his medium, but show me a man with a masterful attitude toward himself."

After this challenge I developed my points in a rather negative fashion. One's life, taken as a medium of creation, was, I said, so electrically swift in its processes, so complex and fluid, so *continuous* and never remaining still, that one might very well despair of doing anything with it. Yet people did try and even offered various technics, and some of these I examined (among them were introspection, theosophy, Yoga and Catholicism) but one and all they signally failed to put the object — one's self steadily transforming impressions into expressions — in complete focus for impartial study. Indeed, I had great difficulty to conceive, in the absence of a comprehensive method for working the medium, what the Good Life could really be. What effects, for instance, would an artist of life bring to pass in his own psychology? Had there ever been any such artists, for I could not quite admit that Socrates and da Vinci qualified as more than advanced students of the ways and means of developing self-harmony? At the end I threw my hands up when I had written:

"The ordinary artist is distinguished by his consciousness of the material he manipulates. If he is a dramatist, he is aware of far more about the people he puts on the stage than he is about his own roles in the odd melodrama called Life. Sensations, emotions and ideas rise constantly in him, and he recognizes not a tenth of them. A tenth? The case is far worse. At a minimum rate of ten thousand per second, he is bombarded by impressions and of these he is sometimes aware of two or three, chiefly the disagreeable ones. That is the pitiful measure of the self-consciousness of the man whose plays are no doubt hailed as revelations of life's occult significances. Thus, the problem of living one's days as an art is, *au fond,* the problem of increasing one's consciousness, and that is a baffler.

"Science of Psyche, thou art our hope, and to thee we turn!"

III

I read the entire paper one evening to a club of literary men. It was coldly received and one critic, well known for his dependence on the latest lecturer from Vienna, sneered at it. "You have a Messiah-complex," he remarked afterwards in pity.

When I showed it to Mr. Sweord some time later, he said: "It's pretty theorizing, and you'll make no impression with it."

"Why," I said, "I should think that at last I have formulated an important problem and that people who read it will be less glib in talking about the Good Life."

"You didn't paint the difficulties black enough," he returned. "Man definitely has no will. That doesn't matter in the ordinary arts which he practises mechanically. But it does matter in the mythical Art of Living, which absolutely requires will. And though I have searched for it more than most men, I know of no means for acquiring will."

"My paper implies what you say."

"Implies! But you have to bang your reader on the head with it. Life implies death, too, but most of us successfully ignore the implication until a gun points at us. You see, you haven't carried your theme to the place where it seems to have real personal application for the reader. Your reader, like you but not like me, is aimless a good part of every day: he indulges himself in trivialities: he is lop-sided in his growth, being strong mentally, let us say, weak emotionally, and mediocre physically (you write for the intellectuals, you know): his behavior according to circumstance is so variable that he is as unreliable as a fluttering leaf. Well, try to read a book through that is purposeless, ill-proportioned, uncertain. You will curse the author's lack of artistry, and a man should curse the sloppy way he gets through his twenty-four hours."

"Perhaps the whole discussion is futile."

"Not futile!" Mr. Sweord flared up. "Why, in Heaven's name, didn't you draw a few practical conclusions? We can't wait for the psychologists. We must search, search like demons. Perhaps somewhere in the experience of the race is what we want. But I know that it won't drop on our laps. You at least indicate a direction to look. Sound the horn and let's go. We must experiment! Get out of our grooves! For us the Good Life is a dream but through experiment and search we may hope — only hope — to find the key to the dream. We can't be artists of life — we don't know how — but we can be gymnasts in life. There's an essay for you."

"I have a better idea," I replied. "I'll write your biography."

"Ass! You'll be better employed if you imitate it."

JANUS

Solon R. BARBER, Editor
T. Swann HARDING, Dissenting Editor
Harry Francis CAMPBELL, Art Director
Barbs FARRELL, Contributing Editor

**A Quarterly Review of Letters
Thought, and the New Mythology**

EDITORIAL OFFICE
Apartment 2, 800 Eighteenth Street, N.W.
WASHINGTON, D. C.

January 5, 1930.

Dear Richard Johns,

        I have just finished looking through *Pagany*
number one and I want to write and say that you have done an
excellent piece of work. I am looking forward with pleasure
to reading it through this evening.

The magazine is somewhat reminiscent of *The Dial*, but to me,
it is more vigorous, closer to the pulse, nearer the earth
than *The Dial* was in its later years. Perhaps *Pagany* will
carry on the quite excellent traditions which *The Dial*
established in its earlier years. At any rate, you have
a running start.

I am greatly pleased with the quantity of material printed
in number one and, for the most part, with the quality. I
am of the opinion that a magazine sets up a terrific handi-
cap for itself at the start when it chooses a size represented
by JANUS, for example. Of course that is usually a matter
of money. I notice you have some advertising to start with:
a good thing. The format, the type, the paper are all
pleasing. *Pagany* is very readable in a mechanical way.

How readable in a literary way, I have yet to judge. As I
say, I have not had time to read much of it yet. But I
have learned by experience that Williams, Winters, McAlmon,
Crosby, Butts, Caldwell, Stein, Komroff, DeJong, Latimer,
Riordan, and some of your other contributors, generally
have something to say. . . . At any rate, congratulations
and the very best wishes to you. *Pagany* is needed and you
have made an impressive start.

                   Cordially,

                   Solon R Barber

Richard Johns
Boston

668 Congress Street Portland Maine January 7th 1930.

Dear Johns: You probably have already had and will continue
to have for the next several weeks so many letters telling you
how damn good PAGANY is that you will soon be a little sick of so
much praise. And too much praise is like too many roasted sweet
potatoes. But you mustn't think that because I'm not saying how
damn good it is it's not good. It stands at the head of the list
by all methods of count and recount.

I hope(this is a personal prejudice I have had for a long time)
you never go in for names. To hell with "names". If I were king
and could run a magazine and, let's say for instance, Dreiser,
Anderson and Joyce sent me some pieces I didn't like and I thought
were rotten I'd stick a one-cent stamp on each piece and shoot
them back like a bad check. Let Happers and the LHJ and the PR
buy the names and let PAGANY print the stories. From the point
of view of business management that is pretty rotten as policies
gom butfrom the eye-view of the reader who has tastes like mine
it is the only possible way to make a quarterly worth paying for
a year in advance. And paying a yers subscription in advance is
a pretty good test of value, don't you think?

And you have partially exploded the folkway that women can't write.
Janet Lewis can and Margery Latimer can. Ninety % of the stuff
written by women is junk, but when you find the ten % you have
work well worth reading. Janet and Margery so-and-so can write as
well as a man. But don't try to find many others---they are not
to be found. *You shouldn't stop looking for them just because they
are scarce, however* ⊙
And the contributions are intelligible. Experiment is sometimes
necessiarily unintelligible, in a shell like a green walnut; but
any man who consciously covers up his work in difficult technicalities
is robbing himself and his readers. The easiest way the reader's
emotions can be reached(the hardest way to write however is the
perfect way. The work leaves a deeper and more/incere impression
on the mind.

A quarterly like PAGANY shouldn't be the mouthpiece of a group or
a collection of groups. It shouldn't be ~atholic or Methodist,
Surrealist, Republican, Single-Tax, New England, or dogmanic. As
it turns out to be PAGANY is exactly what it should be and never
what whould it should not be. It will become the target of every new
magazine beginning hereafter. Most of them will miss, a few will
hit, and possible one or two will score. None however will surpass
what PAGANY NO 1 VOL 1 is. I'm sure of that. And I hope PAGANY
will never slip within reach of any of them. PAGANY should never
becĂome a sort of national privy where every body with dissentary
makes a dash for. There are too many toilet-paper magazines already.

You see I have talked about the stories only. I leave the poetry
and essays for others who work with poetry and essays. The fiction
ranks, I believe, one hundred %. I am not counting the story by
Seaver and the one by myself. I have not yet read Seaver's story
because I did not care for the title, for some unknown reason. That
is merely foolishness on my part because it may be the finest in the
entire issue. Honestly, you have passed, as far as fiction goes,
every magazine printed in the english language. There are no
exceptions whatever. I believe those fellows who work with poetry
and essays will say the same thing when you hear from them.

I would like to hear from you when you have time. Best wishes, sincerely

Erskine Caldwell

note Will: Often re-working what I have written and sent that I have intended say, may—I do try again some time and word difficulty—E.C. and perhaps I had

COVICI, FRIEDE INC · PUBLISHERS

386 Fourth Avenue · New York

January 8, 1930

Dear Johns:

I'll try to find time to write you in detail
about the first issue of Pagany--it's astonishingly good.
First thing that struck me was that it is too generous;
there's a week's reading in it. I liked the variety,
which is excellent and promises that Pagany will never
be dull. Williams' essay on Gertrude Stein, in particular,
is fresh, original, first rate criticism. Can you get
him to do more? I won't mention any of the other items,
having thus far read only about half the issue. Incidentally,
I might suggest a few slight typographic changes. First,
to omit the decorative tail-pieces--both the little centered
square, which is meaningless, and the printers' flowers, which
are in character with nothing at all, and are found in every
printshop in the country. Second, to omit the horizontal
rule across the bottom of the type page--it is redundant
and the extra margin it uses up is precious. Third, to
use Pagany as a running head only on left-hand pages; and
text title as running head on right hand pages, to avoid
the monotony. Fourth, to make the length of line on
the type page one pica less--you would lose only about
thirty words by the narrower page--and it would increase
the legibility of the page at least 50%. I had a suggestion
to offer for the cover, but have left my copy home and
can't remember. But the cover is quite good.

By the way would you like a remarkable group of
translations from Catullus, and a few original poems, by
Horace Gregory? Also, I can get you a few photos of
paintings by the most interesting painter in America--
Myron Lechay (Jane Heap printed some in Little Review);
he has a one-man show on at Valentine Dudensing this Fall.

Twelve-gun salute to the first Pagany, and best
wishes for the issues following.

Yours,

Lou Grudin

Closing time on second issue?

cable address: covifri, new york

norman macleod

220 North Maple St.
Albuquerque, N.M.

Dear Richard Johns:

I want to congratulate you upon
PAGANY: it is one of the best numbers of
any I've seen in years. Your "Moonblind"
I enjoyed particularly; and "the glove",
"religion at 2am", ivor wintors, closson
emory and others.
one issue of PAGANY has enough blood
to invigorate a department store of Dials.
PAGANY is perhaps the only comprehensive collection of modern writing in
America.
if i can be of assistance in any way,
please let me know.

fraternally,

macleod.

did you get MORADA 2?

the morada

28 Billingham St.
Somerville, Mass.
Jan. 12, 1930

Dear Dick,

It might please the Boston Herald to know that their gracious note on Pagany caused me to spend two cents for another copy of the paper, surely only a little more than it was worth.

Not that I could sincerely champion each and every piece in this first issue, but I certainly do the magazine itself, and congratulate you on its splendid appearance - as one who has met and conquered various linotypes and presses and their problems. I have seen copies of it in several places, and have had word of it's being in others. Depend upon it, it goes to hundreds of persons who will never report the fact. A very large part of any public is silent, but interested.

I'd like to hear some opinions that have come your way. Who beside the Herald will pronounce upon the magazine?

Now about the MacLeish article. Please tell me just when it must be in your hands, and what the limits in number of words, maximum and minimum, are to be. And are there any suggestions as to how much of his work other than the Hamlet you think is to be touched on?

Yours sincerely

John Holmes

WILLIAM CARLOS WILLIAMS, M. D.
9 RIDGE ROAD
RUTHERFORD, N. J.

1930

Jan. 6, 1929

Dear Johns :

    The format is first rate, the contents mediocre
but representative of what is being done in America today -
nothing to be proud of . But the magazine itself is a
splendid gesture .

    It is what it should be : a bulletin of method .
It should not grow or be controvertial, thoughtful or
take on burdens or righteousness or policy . It does what
it should : presents an extant practice of the art of
writing .

    The Mary Butts story is somewhat out of place . I
have not finished reading it . But I can see, I think ,
why you featured it - for it has the most prominent place
in the layout and is the longest work used - probably
because it deals with Americans in a certain way . I'll
tell you more of this later .

    I'm returning the check , not because it is small
for that would be all right but because I don't want you
to think of paying me for what I send you . I want to
help, in fact, in every way I can to make PAGANY a success.
I'd even help share the expense if I could .

    Go on with your second number . The first is a
thing of the past now , to hell with it . See if you can't
get some better poetry (in general) than the first
number contained - tho' I liked the McAlmon thing and
one or two other bits . My contribution, if you want me
in this time, will be a short group of poems .

    Sorry about the damned printer . But I like what
you have done and wish you the best luck in the world
for the New Year .

      Yours

      W. C. Williams

88-93

ON JANUARY 5, 1930, letters of criticism and approval came in from many directions. Reading the comments of Solon R. Barber, Erskine Caldwell, Louis Grudin, Norman Macleod, Robert McAlmon, Gorham B. Munson, and William Carlos Williams, all expressing a variety of opinions, Johns recognized that what he had undertaken was much more than one young man's slightly impertinent appearance on the literary scene with a magazine expressive of his own personal taste and judgment. *Pagany* was regarded as a serious literary effort, serious enough that in some quarters it was thought to be the new replacement of *The Dial*. Johns, perhaps now for the first time, realized that the content of future issues would fall under the critical eye of an extremely intelligent public.

Now it was important for Johns to balance the variety of critical opinions received and use them for the best interests of *Pagany*. He experienced no sense of personal confusion from the mixed responses to the first number; indeed, for as long as the magazine survived, Johns' clear intention would be to keep *Pagany* essentially a literary medium for individual expression. Johns welcomed critical comment and assessment of the contributions, for he felt this made an encouraging atmosphere for creativity in both fiction and poetry. However, never would diverse opinions be given editorial approval one above another; there were enough journals where editorial policy controlled and limited the freshness of words. There would never appear a "typical *Pagany*" story or poem.

It now seemed that setting up each future issue, planning what should be printed immediately and what might better be held for a later issue, was much like planning a superior vaudeville, for as piece followed piece, whether fiction, poetry, criticism, painting or photograph, instead of being regimented, as would have happened in most periodicals of the period, it was delegated to its proper though limited space.

Pagany was designed for the desultory reader, jumping from one subject to another with no rational connection. Individual works stood completely apart from each other, and the reader could choose what he wanted to read at will. Although it was clearly stated at the outset of the publication that this was the intended format, some critics, used to departmentalized magazines, felt *Pagany*'s lack in this regard made it appear both aimless and unsubstantial, which was certainly not its purpose. Each contribution was to be judged as a single entity.

Johns' interest remained always in the quality of the individual's personal words for the world, and *Pagany* never aligned itself with any one group banded together in a common cause. The disagreements, the sharp critical comments on the purposes and accomplishments of others never came to influence the magazine's content, for Johns was always able to withstand external pressures. The letters of varied opinion are of lasting interest for tomorrow's readers as well as today's, for it is on account of William Carlos Williams' and Sherry Mangan's intellectual disparagement of T. S. Eliot and Robert McAlmon's fury at the humanism of *Hound and Horn,* that the magazine stayed robustly alive in opinion, besides remaining an open market for all sorts of prose and poetry of the period.

In *Pagany*'s second issue Johns allowed more space than usual for critical writing, for he believed that the "Preface" to Louis Grudin's *A Primer of Aesthetics,* which he had read in proof, was a fresh approach to a fascinating subject as well as an excellent introduction to an important book. And certainly Sherry Mangan's "A Note: On the Somewhat Premature Apotheosis of Thomas Stearns Eliot" was *105-118* an amazingly astute commentary on a great poet's lesser side, with many well thought out opinions on a number of other writers as critics. Johns was pleased that Mangan wished it to appear in *Pagany.* There was also Harry Alan Potamkin on "The Future Cinema: Notes for a Study," which developed further the earlier pieces Potamkin had done on the new cinema for such publications as *Pool, Close-Up, The New Masses,* and *transition.*

The poetry in this second issue took up less space than in the first. The "Three Poems" contributed by R. P. Blackmur, who had *123* recently resigned as an editor for *Hound and Horn,* had the creative sharpness and imagery which graced his well-respected critical writing on such poets as T. S. Eliot and e. e. cummings.

103-104

Very different, Horace Gregory's "Longface Mahoney Discusses Heaven" made a fusion of slang phrases with delicacy of feeling to construct a most down-to-earth though sensitive poem. The light and skilled rhythms of Alfred Kreymborg's words gave an enchanting delight to his "Neighborly Narrative," a lilting relaxation bringing sheer pleasure. The masterly touch of this author of *Troubadour* and *Funnybone Alley* was true and sure.

In the same issue were three stories by three very dissimilar but sensitive women. There was Margery Latimer's "The Little Girls,"
120-122
Meridel LeSueur's "Holiday," and Janet Lewis' "The Still Afternoon." Johns had earlier been charmed by Janet Lewis' poems in *A Wheel in Midsummer,* which Sherry Mangan had printed on his Lone Gull Press.

Other fiction ranged over many subjects: gregarious loneliness in Joseph Vogel's "Neighbors," the portrait of a shy, creative proletarian trying to make contact with the earthy girls of a tenement rooming-house; the "doctor–family of a young patient" give-and-take in William Carlos Williams' "Four Bottles of Beer"; the social North Shore community of Ipswich, Massachusetts, is probed in the wealthy Churchly family atmosphere where Dudley Fitts' carefully mannered "Crucifier," a lengthy work of both prose and poetry originally slated to appear in the first issue.

To Johns each contribution seemed to shine from its own carefully constructed frame. With the second issue of *Pagany* under his belt, he now felt even more confident of his ability as an editor.

P.S. My books of poems "Chelsea Rooming House" will be published in Sept; please let me know whether or not you like the present group of poems before Sept 1 st. HG

Dear Johns:

This is a belated appreciation of the
check for MAHONEY and the Spring issue of Pagany.
I liked M Latimer's piece immensely and I believe
Sherry Mangan looks very promising indeed. As for
Louis Grudin, I'm already predjudiced in his favor.
His is perhaps the most intelligent and sensitive
minds in our generation. He is our latter day
skyscraper Spinoza. I sincerely hope that Pagany
survives a difficult period for experimental
magazines. What about the Summer number? Will it
arrive? Could you send me a copy?

I'm enclosing a couple of new poems
of my own and a selection from the typewriter
of Edward Dahlberg. Dahlberg, as you may remember is
the author of "Bottom Dogs" an excellent first novel
written in the American vulgate. I think that he will
develop into an artist of extraordinary vigor and power.
His sense of the American lingo is remarkably accurate;
I hope that his stuff falls somewhere within the
policy that you have adopted for publication in Pagany.

Thank you again for your appreciation

of MAHONEY .

Horace Gregory

3932 44th St
Long Island City
N.Y.

2024 Bay Ridge Ave.,
Brooklyn,N.Y.
Apr. 29, '30.

Dear Richard Johns:

A word in reply to your letter of the 28th. Particularly to "the
artist against the world should seem a better artist...the poem is
poor and not helped by the admission..." The story "Neighbors" is
of course a fragment, as you must have seen, and it is a fragment,
not to depict the artist therein as better, but as an ass. You will
admit that there are artists who are jackasses.What more fitting
than to show that this artist, who makes such a fuss over little,
trivial things, writes rotten poetry...in other words, is a rotten
artist.

The piece Neighbors should have been longer. Then you would have
seen that the character depicted...you would have sensed it...as
a vain, proud, silly ass. You would have known, before confronted
with a sample of his work, that he wrote rotten stuff.

Therein lies the danger of publishing uncompleted work. On the other
hand I find a certain fascination in fragments, and wish more were
published.

Neighbors in its complete form will be a satire on a poet. As editor
you know what loads of poetry are written, awful stuff. Every editor
I know is flooded with reams of this kind of poetry and has a hard
task shifting sifting the good from the bad. I have already told you
that, in my opinion, there is very little good poetry written today.

Your manifesto in Pagany No. 1 was excellent...like most other
manifestos. But you will find...rather, others will find, that Pagany
will not achieve its worthy goal of presenting a cross section of
Amer. literature. No magazine can...as long as it has to be edited
by one man or a group with similar ideals.

As an editor of an important magazine you should not shun satire.
American needs loads of it...and it is difficult to get, because
political events, as well as literary business, is so crude, that
treatment of it with tongue in cheek turns to burlesque. You need
subtlety for satire. That is, you need a subtle people...more like
the French.

"Peace Conference" ---regardless of its merit--- satirized modern
poets as well as politicians. Perhaps that is why you don't take to
the piece. More likely, that is why it doesn't fit in Pagany, which
publishes a number of artists who lend themselves to satire. Study
the modern scene. Study the relation of a Carlos Williams to his
surroundings. You will find that, not the surroundings are ridiculous, but Williams. In my eyes Williams, a doctor who comes in
intimate contact with life, is awfully ridiculous...considering the
kind of work he writes, and his childish horror of present day life.
Williams is weak. What we need more than ever today is strong artists.
And strong, vivid writing.

I am glad that Munson, for instance, has a vehicle in Pagany to express
his ideas. Mr. Miller, to whom you sent a copy of the magazine, likes
Munson's work the best. Mr. Miller, however, is not an artist. He is
a liberal business man. For artists, on the other hand, Munson and
the humanists are deadly. No artist could produce great work under
their rule. What happens, under their influence, is a Thorton Wilder,

who might just as well be a mummy. That's what the new literary
humanism tends to.

Take my word for it. It won't be long before the tradition of
"transition" will be a laughing stock in the eyes of the world.
It is so today among uncomprehending people like Isabel Paterson...
but it will some day be so among people who understand too well.
At that time this tradition will arouse sympathy...equally as bad as
laughter.

The editor who encourages satire and has the nerve to publish it,
will be far ahead of his time.

Sincerely,

Joseph Vogel

NUMBER 2 *April–June*

CONTENTS

103-104

105-118

119

120-122

123

LONGFACE MAHONEY DISCUSSES HEAVEN

Horace Gregory

If someone said, *Escape,*
let's get away from here,
you'd see snow mountains thrown
against the sky,
cold, and you'd draw your breath and feel
air like cold water going through your veins,
but you'd be free, up so high,
or you'd see a row of girls dancing on a beach
with tropic trees and a warm moon
and warm air floating under your clothes
and through your hair.
Then you'd think of heaven
where there's peace, away from here
and you'd go some place unreal
where everybody goes after something happens,
set up in the air, safe, a room in a hotel.
A brass bed, military brushes,
a couple of coats, trousers, maybe a dress
on a chair or draped on the floor.
This room is not on earth, feel the air,
warm like heaven and far away.

This is a place
where marriage nights are kept
and sometimes here you say, Hello
to a neat girl with you
and sometimes she laughs
because she thinks it's funny to be sitting here
for no reason at all, except perhaps,
she likes you, daddy.
Maybe this isn't heaven but near
to something like it,
more like love coming up in elevators
and nothing to think about, except, O God,
you love her now and it makes no difference
if it isn't spring. All seasons are warm
in the warm air
and the brass bed is always there.

If you've done something
and the cops get you afterwards, you
can't remember the place again,
away from cops and streets —
it's all unreal —
the warm air, a dream
that couldn't save you now.
No one would care
to hear about it,
it would be heaven
far away, dark and no music,
not even a girl there.

for Doctor John Joseph Mangan

'A NOTE':
ON THE SOMEWHAT PREMATURE APOTHEOSIS OF THOMAS STEARNS ELIOT

Sherry Mangan

'Ah, vous autres américains! vous êtes tellement intelligents, vous avez beaucoup de talent, même de génie, mais vous manquez presque complètement le courage d'être vous-mêmes.'

I

It is not without diffidence that one protests against the Eliot myth, not only because an unknown young man feels a certain lèse majesté inherent in caviling at an older and established writer, not only because Mr Eliot, critic, is able, admirable, plausible, and above all formidable, but most especially because his critical station is in opposition to so many objectionable camps with which one is in fear a casual reader might identify any adversary that there seems scarcely to be left any tenable ground save Mr Eliot's own. Yet this cannot be so; and this little paper is partially concerned in a search for that position from which one may point out certain evils resultant upon Mr Eliot's consecratio without being classed in with certain 'modern' ergo dating movements (or rather fluxes) from whose pretensions and inadequacies we have all long since turned.

Our ability to define this position with sufficient precision to satisfy the tastes of those for whom this paper is especially intended, of those who have reacted from the critical looseness of these post-war years into a need for precision that has become an addict-like craving for the soporific of exact rightness — our ability to do this is limited by the very nature of the position we seek. It is impossible to fight 'criticism' (in the sense in which we shall treat it in this article) with its own weapons, by setting up an antithetic corpus of the 'non-critical' or 'creative', because it by nature cannot be made into such a corpus. Unless we point, without comment but not perhaps without malice, to those who were simply great poets and wrote no criticism; and (it is as tenable as its contrary) were not 'critical' at all save in their personal canons relating to their own work.

That Mr Eliot, as a poet, has not only established himself as a master (whether major or minor we must leave to time), but has, to borrow one of his own tropes, slightly readjusted the entire body of poetic art, one can scarcely doubt. And we moreover think that his influence will be of a permanence, though it will be difficult to accurately situate this until the present vogue for him has diminished. At the moment, of course, so many unauthorized disciples are pilgrimaging across the waste land that one expects daily to hear of some critic opening a roadside refreshment stand near the rocks where there is, unless Mr Eliot is mistaken, no water. But when all the more obvious mannerisms, of technique, of thought, and of emotion, have been exploited by the camp-followers, we make no doubt that English poetry will betray, however minutely, the fact that a genuine poet has passed. For which fact we render thanks to Apollo and respectful homage to Mr Eliot himself. No, it is Mr Eliot qua critic whose influence we wish to counteract.

Now it is no more our intention to concoct a polite 'note' upon Mr Eliot's curious style or failure to recognize Artemis-Selene in Shelley's *Skylark* or possible underestimation of Beaumont and Fletcher or any similar fiddling with trivia and rattling of dead bones than it is to dilate on our useless regret at Mr Eliot's apparent poetic dessication and intemperate demise. The latter is his private affair (and we all eagerly embrace the hope of a resurrection); the former we can safely leave to the literary jugglers or unpretentious scholars whose defensible métier it is. We have slight quarrel with Mr Eliot as a capable critical scholar, nor is what slight quarrel we have closely germane to this essay. Our real quarrel with Mr Eliot is that he insists on delivering post-mortem oracles to those whom admiration for his poetry has put in too receptive an attitude; it is that a man of his genius, past accomplishment, and influence is a mere critic at all. In fine, we accuse Mr Eliot (and related precisians) simply and solely of the classic crime of corruption of the youth. And if we thereby put Mr Eliot in the enviable position of Socrates, and ourselves in the position of that worthy's stupid accusers, then so much the better for Mr Eliot — and so much the more characteristic of the impregnability of his position. We hold indeed that this position should be, not so much attacked, for the fault of its almost invariable dead rightness is its very strength, but avoided, just as one would avoid the vicinity of a deadly upas-tree. Or, to change our figure and attempt to turn Mr Eliot's thunder against him, let us, quoting that heresy is a truth carried to excess, charge Mr Eliot with the related crime of heresy. And if it be justifiably argued that Mr Eliot may not want or countenance his disciples, we may, while politely suppressing our doubts, reply that this paper constitutes rather a lay warning to the faithful than a bull to Mr Eliot, since we are after all not the Pontifex Maximus, and Mr Eliot will be quite justified in regarding these strictures with a smile as polite and condescending as Tertullian's. But we strongly believe it to be high time an objection was made to Mr Eliot's somewhat premature (and — may we maliciously suspect? — not wholly unwilling) apotheosis; and we, though perhaps ill-fitted, venture to raise the first voice.

II

Before we proceed to the amplification of the formal charge against Mr Eliot, let us take up a perhaps less important related subject, a few remarks on which, opinions rather than pronouncements, may elucidate the attitude with which we protest the Eliot myth: let us, that is, essay a few hesitant remarks about the popular idol and literary mode of the moment, precisian criticism itself; and in specific about the elevation of the critical faculty, which subsists relatively in all men, to the detriment and stunting of its twin, the creative faculty. It seems unnecessary to undertake a demonstration of the simultaneous existence of these two faculties, when, under various terminologies and in various aspects, they have been recognized and argued about since the beginnings of literature, in recent years having formed the subject for disquisitions by such dissimilar writers as Friedrich Nietzsche and Matthew Arnold. Indeed, for all its lack of proportion, Nietzsche's laudation of the Dionysian spirit remains of intelligence and stimulation.

The precisians themselves concede, if we do not misunderstand them, a delicate balance in the mind of the artist between the creative (and initially formless) and critical (or regimenting) faculties. And we beg to emphasize the word delicate before going on to note that we believe these faculties are mutually interdependent and must be developed together, where the precisians seem to hold rather the belief that they are discrete, separable, and may be independently developed. Excess in the function of either faculty leads to danger. To realize that without the critical faculty, with its invaluable qualities of control and order, art goes soggy or runs amok, we have only to accompany such an undisciplined writer as M Romain Rolland into the Cloudcuckooland of *Jean-Christophe,* where all is soppy and sloppy and soulful, or, taking a more serious example, to wander with M André Breton in the dated wilderness of Surréalisme, whence only the personal genius of certain of the group was able to extract anything of permanent artistic value. To realize that without the creative faculty, art becomes a tinkling cymbal, we need only glance, on the one hand, at the great body of bad minor poets who, unconscious of the lack, are perpetually engaged in saying, with great technical facility, nothing whatsoever; or, on the other, among those who are conscious, mere critics like — shall we dare say when he may a week from Thursday overturn us with a large-scale poem of unanswerable vigor and merit? — Mr Eliot himself. The inevitable conclusion, that both qualities must be present, needs no belaboring.

Taking, as we do for reasons which we shall hereinafter offer, criticism to be no art at all, but a relatively useful craft, taking, that is to say, the point of view of the artist (and even when we recall that it is the other side which has 'written all the books', it is still amazing how neglected that point of view is), we may leave out of consideration the type of artistic

mind which deliberately abandons creation for criticism, and confine ourselves to the artist qua artist. In his mind, between these two indispensable
faculties, of what nature is the relation? And in what way may they be
best developed? The precisians' answer is engaging and specious. Direction-
ally speaking, they tend to separate the two and to develop them independently, intellectually, and deliberately. How logical, the theory that
by the deepening of the unconscious creative faculty and the refinement of
the conscious critical faculty the artist gains, not only in both depth and
order separately, but also (here the non sequitur) in the brilliant cresis of
the two which is true art. Mr Eliot, for example, if we do not misunderstand him, holds that by separate development the artist may avoid con-
fusions of the two and be better in both. If only the living mind of a living
artist were as amenable to such ordering as are the materials of bibliographies,
how simple it would all be! But the likelihood is (again speaking direction-
ally) that these faculties must, even at the cost of occasional confusion of
their functions, have at all times a parallel development, an intimately related development, and a development as nearly as possible equal. For (perhaps unfortunately) the critical, as well as the creative, problems of the
artist are personal, and the attempt to apply to them a critical faculty which,
instead of being sharpened to an almost instinctive sense of fitness, is become
an impersonal and almost inimical critic, with a whole system of fixed
criteria, inevitably tends to sterility. And the equality of development is
important because letting the critical faculty get too far in advance of the
creative faculty leads equally to sterility by killing a certain quality of
which we shall have much to say in the last section of this paper. The theory
of separate development seems eminently logical; yet this separate development means divergence and opposite directions, and the result is predictably
scholarship or criticism — sterility.

We have, besides our primary thesis (that criticism as a fetish is like
calcium carbonate in the artistic blood of our young men), three main
faults to find with precisian criticism in its present pretensions: that it is
not an art at all, that it is a contradiction in terms, and that it is dead.

Criticism is, despite some claims, not an art at all, yet because it is readily
confused with art in that it deals with art with art's tools, it is dangerous
to the artist as likely to withdraw him from his proper sphere and to unfit
him for return thereto. Being no art, but a literary craft of minor use, it
is, in itself, all form and no matter, all means and no end. The critic is at
best a superior form of librarian, and at worst a superior form of lecturer
to women's cultural societies. The basal use of criticism seems to lie in organization, synthesis, and expatiation of givens; and the trouble with such
expatiation is that everybody[1] knows already. Except in the realm of scholarly

---

[1] Perhaps 'everybody' should be qualified. The alternative is 'vulgarization' (such
as to the societies mentioned above); I give criticism the benefit of the doubt in
using 'everybody' in a culturally limited sense.

research, it is not usually the discovery of anything new; it is merely the more or less skilful and novel marshaling of facts, elsewhere loosely apprehended, either into a formula, or, that being in all honesty unattainable, into an easily apprehensible synthesis of corporate fact. In the ultimate analysis, then, it is kicking a dead dog: it is parochial situation, it is cataloguing (both admirable enough, to be sure, better say than pseudophilosophizing or writing advertisements, but hardly the highest occupation to which the human mind can attain). And it would not surprise us if the taste for it formed one aspect (we expect at any moment now the lightning to strike our irreligious head) of the same Zeitgeist for predigestion that gives us, in other fields, patent breakfast cereals and Professor Durant's little uade mecum on philosophy.[2] If Mr Eliot wants to decline to the post of librarian or scholar-critic, none can prevent him; but the generation which gaped when the symbolic eagle left his pyre might note that Mr Eliot poet and Mr Eliot oracle are different things.

Precisian criticism is a contradiction in terms because all criticism, however precise, is, when not mere factual cataloguing, essentially æsthetic and 'impressionistic'. In offering reasons for withdrawing with polite distaste his critical mantle from such as Mr Symons (not that we hold any brief for Mr Symons except that he isn't even pretendng to be impartial), Mr Eliot, postulating a comparative impartiality which is not even *that* partially attainable, attempts to erect with the tenuous materials of pure reason[3] a precarious edifice of detached intellectual criticism. Now anything from 'I am' to 'This book is well written' is infinitely arguable[4], and of the ensuing

---

[2]In this concern I recommend a reading of Mr Eliot's Ezra Pound for Little Tots, Latecomers, the Illiterate, and the Feeble Minded, which serves as introduction to his selection from the work of that extraordinary poet. There is a lucid (and, be it gladly granted, intelligent) explanation for the layman of how these odd folk called poets work; there is technical predigestion on verse styles and traditions; and — but let Mr Eliot speak: 'I have omitted . . . *Homage to Propertius*. I was doubtful of its effect on the uninstructed reader, even with my instructions' — whenafter he goes on to intimate that almost nobody ever read Propertius, or that, if he could do so, is probably an ass who couldn't distinguish a 'persona' (in Mr Pound's technical use) from a trot. Now the point lies not so much in Mr Eliot's gratuitous assumption of the smallness of the number of his contemporaries whom the reading of Propertius has failed to stultify, nor in the rather unexpected conceit about his 'instructions,' as it does in the assumption of the pontifical manner, inevitably suggesting the popular aim. Mr Eliot, I think, would have to perform some brilliant mental gymnastics to demonstrate that the poem in question has not a considerable interest apart from a historical one. Mr Eliot's almost sacerdotal timidity lest the full significance be imperfectly apprehended, or the reader's mind be distracted by poems of lesser magnitude than those he has seen fit, in his paternal wisdom, to include, is a little funny, reminding one of the way his own less finished poems gradually drop and will drop out of successive collected editions. This touchstone was used to distinguish between Mr Pound as a major poet and Mr Eliot as a minor poet some years ago in an essay whose brilliance and sense makes me regret my inability to recall the name of the writer.
[3]Cf: in hac re *The Emperor's New Clothes*, by Hans Christian Andersen.
[4]Just as only he who is constantly catching himself in deceptions and self-deceptions can have any assurance that he is on the track of honesty, similarly only he who

opinions, all containing both truth and falsehood, none is likely to be exclusively true, or, indeed, anything more than a relatively tenable argumentative position. What a field this opens in which men may spend their lives nicely disputing in polite public 'notes'! Intellectual honesty may overcome the accidental of a touch of liver, and the maintenance of consistency through large scope may offer the specious effect of a divinity in judgment; but, no matter how far precisian criticism may struggle away from its origins, it is essentially personal and therefore essentially relative, æsthetic, and to some extent 'impressionistic', to wit, a human's 'impression' of this in relation to all the thats. The logical result of this constant desire for rightness and impersonality is the settling on some agreeable form of exterior authority. In Mr Eliot's case this seems to be 'royalism, classicism, and Anglicanism' — truly an imposing triad. But it is ipso facto a retrogression, a confession of failure to create any personal standards. Mr Eliot may aver (and we are certain the reasons he will offer in his three promised volumes, one on each of the triad, will be nothing if not plausible) that his decision marks an advance, that he has seen the celestial light; well, credat Iudæus Apella, but to us it looks rather more like capitulation to Mephisto. Faust wanted youth; Mr Eliot wants this imposing triptych soundingboard behind his already fairly resonant predicatory voice.

Precisian criticism is dead, not only because, to chance on one of Mr Eliot's pétards, it 'removes the remains of [a dead writer's] reputation to a last resting place in the dreary cemetery of literature', but because (whether intentionally or not) it tends to produce in the fluid[5] currents of literature and philosophy (so far as philosophy is personal to the artist) an artificial stasis. It thereby either relegates the invaluable qualities of ceaseless spiritual[6] and artistic doubt and search, always profound stimuli to the artist, to the level of a library speculation, or it reduces them to search for the paregorika (do not forget that Mr Eliot is these days essentially a weary man) of a false exterior background or architecture of an academic problem dissociated from our actual living and our actual problems. If one follows Mr Eliot step by step in his personal decline, there is a certain plausibility dependent solely upon the personal nature of his problems; but if one plunges in

knows how personal are his opinions can approach even relative truth by a conscious discounting of bias. There is perhaps nothing so opinionated as an 'unbiased opinion', and nothing so likely to keep one biased as a belief that one is not, for the very consciousness of right keeps it from being so. Cf: e: g: righteous indignation, religious intolerance, etc.

[5] While using this abused word, I decline to be assigned to Bergson, Herr Spengler, et al.

[6] Nor have I been basking in dilute Hindooisms. What the abused word spirit represents is an important artistic factor. V: Aragon, *Le Libertinage,* where we find the equivocal following: ' . . . de l'esprit. Qu'on me pardonne d'emprunter au langage de la philosophie . . . ce mot vague qui désigne avec précision une réalité si élémentaire que le premier damné charretier de ma connaissance . . . n'aura pas l'idée de la mettre en doute.'

medias res, it is difficult to conceive that our young Americans can illude themselves into the belief that *they* are the ones to whom 'the relation of Church and State is an actual and importunate problem', for example, as it well may be with Mr Eliot on his side of the Channel as with Une Action Française on the other. Mr Eliot's concerns are growing daily less catholic, more parochial, and of less genuine interest to Americans. If even certain Anglo-French circles in Paris which are in close touch with the English scene still consider the best joke of the past three years Mr Eliot's 'daring' in proclaiming himself a royalist in politics (and after all, for England, it *is* pretty funny), of how much less interest to our present generation in America are Mr Eliot's however sincere preoccupations with out-cocteauing M Cocteau in what is to American-born eyes the so much swankier English Church.

If we have left argument for ridicule, it is because, seen with fresh eyes, the thing is so essentially ridiculous; because it seems like some colossal and incredible joke to see young Americans solemnly reading *The Library of Anglo-Catholic Theology* and gravely disputing about the apostolic succession over their glasses of bootleg gin. Mr Eliot may personally believe that such a stable external prop is best for his own soul, but the Cunard Steamship Company, *Vanity Fair,* the Lipton Tea Company, the leagues for 'closer relations with the mother-country', and all the snobisme that followed Henry James contradicentibus notwithstanding, we cannot seriously believe that it is in that direction there lies salvation for a generation of Americans who are searching for something stable in a far too Heracleitan world.

We have little hesitation in terming the process of growing up a process of intelligent limitation, but Mr Eliot, in his personal idiosyncrasies, seems to have limited and refined himself into something that to these barbarian eyes looks pretty juiceless. And unless our young men of promise, turning their back on the American scene and the rest of the world, are all going to rush over in a body to England there to plunge themselves into the charming, scholarly, but essentially alien pursuits to which Mr Eliot seems to be permanently devoting himself, it is about time they got a new prophet.

Returning after this discursus to our statement that criticism is dead, we say that the false stasis which precisian criticism produces leads ultimately, on the philosophical side, as in this example, to the need for and choice of an equally artificial exterior bulwark, of something established to cling to. If Mr Eliot has sailed grandly into a haven with a gesture which only the exact brilliance of his mind keeps from looking pitiably resignatory, that is not a cause for us of other instincts and tastes to blindly direct our lesser barks in after him, and (of all things) to live on the lotuses of prose style and Anglican theology. On the artistic side, as intimated supra, this stasis, involving fixed criteria instead of a universally applicable artistic taste, tends to limit genuine development, not only of both matter and form, but of a thing more valuable and more intangible yet, artistic courage.

Criticism, as practised among us as a literary mode, is a too drastic remedy for a recognizable artistic disease. Surely none will deny that we are all thoroughly tired of watching or participating in the blind-staggers of an auto-intoxicated romanticism, but just as it is possible to cure an offending hand by less than the amputation of an arm, so is it possible to control a creative spirit sick of its licence by less desperate measures than the extermination of that spirit. Or, in another medical figure, we may say that criticism is, in a sense, the substitution of the medicine for the patient; whereas what we want is a cured patient, not a bottle of panacea.

III

Mr Eliot is corrupting the youth. But which part of it are his upas-like emanations killing? why? and how?

Not the Lefts, certainly: they cavort as before, noticing Mr Eliot only with a few cliché curses, usually beside the point. If we examine their most characteristic organ, the 'experimental' *transition,* we find the same situation as that noted supra about Surréalisme: the emergence of some remarkable talents from a welter of strange techniques and stranger theories.[1] And we look in vain for the influence of Mr Eliot. Except, perhaps, on the rebound.

It is not the Rights, who, in America, seem to be less the Tories, or the Catholic Wing, or anything comparable to anything non-American, than the Never-Had-Anythings-In-The-First-Place. One cannot consider as a serious modern literary force the spiritual descendants of William Dean Howells, Bronson Alcott, or Henry James. Perhaps the Historical Societies are the most characteristic manifestations of this wing; and of its principal organ, *The Atlantic Monthly,* the less said the kinder. Mr Eliot will undoubtedly have his effect on them, but only to provide them eventually with a new set of prejudices.

No, it is the great Centre which Mr Eliot dessicates. This centre has for its kernel chiefly the young men, of good cultural background, of catholic interests, usually undergraduates or graduates of good universities, young men who are earnest, sensitive, talented (and with the latency of greater things than talent alone). The loss of this group is, we believe, a genuine one. This we hold despite the fact that their committing artistic hari-kari on Mr Eliot's tomb might seem ipso facto to indicate their second-rateness.

---

[1] If *transition* contains a surprisingly large percentage of the best work that is being published in English we may credit that less to its theories than to its lack of theories, i: e: to the admirable broadness of its editorial policy — and to what is the basis of all art: individual ingenia.

But, driven by circumstances, they are explicable and excusable. Let us attempt to imagine how they came to this pass.

Either personally or vicariously, having taken licence for liberty, they were suffering from mental and spiritual indigestion. Such changes as we are now considering come in vague cycles, helically: it is difficult to assign definite causes or definite points of departure, and the theories of say either Henry Adams or Herr Spengler impress one more with their ingenuity than with their likelihood. These helical returns, which combine the essences of the pendulum and the inclined plane, have strangely diverse symptomatic manifestations: we saw simultaneously occurring such apparently unrelated things as the vulgarization of imagism, the rise of the neo-Zola Mencken school, the myriad imitations of the unique and serious Mr Joyce; but most especially we saw the failure of an unsure youth to bear up under the greater burden of artistic integrity which the breakdown of order and tradition, both technical and philosophical, laid upon it. These young men seemed to have neither the strength nor the daring to create their own canons, nor was it difficult to predict, seven or eight years ago, that, failing to create any new internal assurances, our youth would start looking for the exterior bulwark of some received tenets to keep up its confidence in itself, and, accompanying this, would engineer a swing back to classicism in one form or another. The symptoms of that swing, which was as violent as things American usually are, were sometimes amusing: the Loeb Classical Library of Text-Translation of Latin and Greek Authors sold like hotcakes; young men who up till then had apparently thought of Poe only as the author of *The Raven,* and Swinburne of *The Garden of Proserpine,* hastily rushed to purchase copies of their critical works; Aristotle suddenly became the dernier cri; after *The Criterion* began, the appearance of the proximate number was awaited as the revealments of Sinai; those of us who had been till then meditatively counting the nisi clauses in the *De Senectute* were politely elbowed aside by an onrush of well-dressed young men clamoring for scholia on Quintilian, and, armed wth Dr Santayana's essay and a hasty glance at Allen & Greenough, burning to plunge into the *De Rerum Natura;* and young men who had met one three years previous with pale manner and some query like 'And what is *your* art?' now, with furrowed brow, asked one's opinion on Chapman's use of cæsura. The looseness of poetry was stiffened with clapboards torn off all sorts of philosophies, tricked out with classical allusion (all in a glass of Gayley darkly); poor old Œdipus was rudely dragged from eternal bliss so that brilliant and despairing undergraduates might put out their spiritual eyes with more dignity; and the sententious couplet flourished among us. It was all hugely amusing and valuable and a good time was had by all and the young men managed to render their fashion of restrained desperation quite lyric and touching and many people thought it would probably do them a world of good to learn that the word dunce maligns Duns Scotus, that even Racine might be read with both benefit and pleasure, that Abélard exists apart from Heloïse, that by reading Seneca they might learn something about Shakespere, and that there was once a strange figure named Laurentius Valla. But the thing has gone beyond the proportions of a joke: it is — here is the rub — no longer a stimulant, but a depressant. The need to be right, which was healthy as a deterrent, has become a psychopathic mania; and the trend which began with much salubrious self-control is petering out in bibliographies, 'notes', and style. And if they are still unhappy, and the fashion of restrained desperation remains with only the change that it is more restrained than ever, we must conclude headaches follow constipation just as surely as they do drunkenness.

Of all people, it is the humorous Lowell whose words most neatly describe the present condition of one of this Centre,

'. . . who is so well aware of how things should be done,
That his own works displease him before they're begun, —
Who so well all that makes up good poetry knows,
That the best of his poems is written in prose;

* * * * * * * * * *

The ocean of song heaves and glitters before him,
The depth and the vastness and longing sweep o'er him,
He knows every breaker and shoal on the chart,
He has the Coast Pilot and so on by heart,
Yet he spends his whole life, like the man in the fable,
In learning to swim on his library-table.'

It is interesting also to note that this condition, this unexpectancy, this collapse of the sense of spiritual adventure, this mania for rightness, is almost invariably accompanied by snobisme in some of its funniest aspects, trifles of clothes, English spelling, accent, social standing, k:t:l:. Confer again Henry James and Mr Eliot. There is a feminine note about it, something very different from either homo- or heterosexual masculinity. The hypercritical attitude somehow implies communication and the social field; and an interesting study of the phenomena and noumena of this connection might well be undertaken by somebody whose specialty is sociology.

The probable explanation is this: snobisme, which is, of course, a form of timidity, is the social manifestation of the spiritual timidity that brings about the literary situation we are discovering. For it is one of the great advantages of both 'criticism' and what passes for classicism, that they never let you down. At the opposite extreme, say automatic writing, there is the danger that if the person is absurd, the production will be absurd; but in the field of pseudoclassicism and criticism, failure is only dulness — and dulness with a good deal of dignity about it. There can be little doubt that much of the charm of this type of work for our young men lies in the sense of dignity, rightness, safety, and solidity (not to mention solidarity) which they gain from meticulously dealing with Rhadamanthine impartiality in large and imposing generals. It takes a different (and may we be pardoned for adding healthier) sense of humor than that with which they are actually endowed to see this aloof pomposity as being just as ridiculous as the soulful regurgitations at which we have all been amused.

They were ripe for Mr Eliot, the prophet of their death. It is, if perhaps an indeterminable, at least an interesting speculation: whether Mr Eliot were consciously foretelling his own demise in such poems as *The Love Song of J. Alfred Prufrock, Gerontion,* and *The Hollow Men; The Waste Land* is certainly, in one stratum of its numerous significances, a less personal amplification of the same theme. Armed with undoubted genius, Mr Eliot became, as it were, the lyric spokesman of defeatism, the vox et praeterea nihil. Enabled by seniority and the emotional velocity of a sensitive nature to lead the van, he has, by his death and apotheosis, become an important oracle; and we shall do well to pay serious attention when the leaves of this English Dodona rustle. For however little faith one may have in it personally, the extent of this influence is likely to have a secondary effect on everyone.

There is a quality which is rarely mentioned by the precisians, a quality usually peculiar to youth, a very valuable quality. That is the quality of abundance. And it is that quality which their insistence on regarding the oracular utterances of the late lamented Thomas Stearns Eliot as divine truths is killing in the young men. It is with the greatest regret that we confess our inability to offer to our precisian contemporaries a nice definition of this invaluable quality. We *can* say that it is the offspring of the creative faculty and the diuinus afflatus; it is referable to William Blake's dictum (though he was speaking rather more generally), 'exuberance is beauty'; and, on its darker side, it is much the same thing as what Joseph Conrad called 'the obscure inner necessity'. It is that need and the gratification thereof without which any writing is mere literary exercise, or, like the present paper, a mere communication. To a genuine artist, this should be apodeictic. And we have a crescent suspicion, after a reading of Mr Eliot's *The Humanism of Irving Babbitt,* that this quality to which we hold may be identical with or similar to Professor Babbitt's 'enthusiasm'.[8] Mr Eliot

---

[8]Once this essay is finished, I shall take the opportunity to verify or correct this suspicion. To do so in medias res were confusing.

casually dismisses this by politely suggesting that 'it is not clear that Mr. Babbitt has any other enthusiasm to offer except the enthusiasm for being lifted out of one's merely rational self by some enthusiasm.'[9] And right there Mr Eliot gives himself away, admits his failure, and presents the usual spectacle of a man defending his own shortcomings by denying that the missing virtues are virtues at all. Let Mr. Eliot ask himself why he wrote *The Waste Land* instead of a thesis on sociology, if he would know what we mean. And let him ask himself (quite apart from whether he would care to) if he would dare publish a novel. The kernel of the matter is the very fact that abundance is logically inexplicable[10] (just as genius is logically inexplicable[11]), that it feeds on itself, and seems to derive from nothing exterior. Mr Eliot, whose weariness and defeatism cannot seem to conceive of anything not patently derivative or dependent, and whose timidity about mysticism will seem to permit him no credence in it except in a religious form, wholly misses this: evidently the theory of the *diuinus afflatus* itself is exceedingly out of fashion. Now abundance or enthusiasm alone can do nothing in art, except by the rarest of miracles (their only unique use is in the opposite field of action, where circumstances rather than artistic canons determine courses) : there must be specific talent. But that talent without enthusiasm, without abundance, is like a complicated printing-press running without paper: there is an admirable intricacy of operation, but there is no production. Again it is means without end. Genius cannot be learned ; talent cannot forever cloak emptiness. If the young men have, essentially, nothing to say, neither push nor facility will make them anything ; but if they *have,* and if they are, under a certain influence, deliberately muting that something in a way that ends in an inverted form of intellectual stultification, then is that influence a noxious one.

It well may be we overestimate the latent capabilities of these young men, and that greatness will out, come what may ; still, if we are to err at all, let it be on the side of kindness, attempting to counteract that pervasive defeatism which destroys the possibility of their achievement even before they have well begun. Against that defeatism, we postulate the enlargement

---

[9]Alas, that we cannot all, like Mr Eliot, be lifted out of our merely rational selves by such burning and immediate issues as the apostolic succession or the vernacular mass. Nor has everyone Mr Eliot's itch for feeling authoritative, especially if it is to be obtained only by the expedient of having 'a formed and visible Church behind him'.

[10]Though, for all I know, Professor Babbitt may offer an explanation of his quality of enthusiasm, which Mr. Eliot declines or fails to apprehend.

[11]That a man makes literature rather than sleeps is readily explicable by the much misunderstood inferiority complex ; but that a man makes literature rather than social reforms or mousetraps (aside from the false artists, whom Mr Wyndham Lewis has turned with such gusto on the spit in *The Art of Being Ruled*) is the mystery of genius. Genius may eventually be explained ; if it is, it will not be by the post hoc ergo propter hoc methods of criticism, but by a form of psychology that is more physiological than speculative.

of the quality of abundance, of enthusiasm; the turning from the dignified easy escape into second-rateness which Mr Eliot has taken in becoming a mere critic, to the higher attempt, perhaps doomed to failure, perhaps not, perhaps mad, but certainly, in a larger sense, braver, to persist in that essentially creative course where the ubiquitous critical faculty is to be, not exclusively nourished into an end in itself, but employed as a personal critical canon for the formation of genuine creation.

M Georges Hugnet in these pages recently noted that 'notre époque a plus que jamais soif de liberté'. The profundity of that remark, which its simplicity conceals (in these days when critical dicta can make little impression without much juggling in elaborate periods of terms like extraversion, solipsism, modalities, and apperceptions), may be more obvious if we gloss it with the note that liberty from licence is as clearly indicated as liberty from dogma: in fine, liberty from the very struggle either for or against anything regimentary, conversely or inversely. Liberty, that is to say, conceived as rigid personal intellectual autonomy; for movements of all sorts seem to be pretty well played out, and the time is ripe for a return to the only criteria that have any significance to the artist, his honest artistic canons. For example, contra, Mr R P Blackmur, in his essay on Herbert Read[12], remarks: 'If we employ the type of perfect art as criterion, and surely there is none other even relevant ...' Therein lie both the plausibility and the error. This attempt at synthesis, tried again and again since the beginnings of the world, has failed as often, the 'august ideal' an ignis fatuus to the systematizing[13] intelligence of man. From this limit the genuine genius always escapes. The critics make a readjustment to include him, and the critical edifice stands so until the next genius escapes from its stasis. There never has been, and there never will be, such a thing as perfect art; there are only innumerable comparative achievements of personal ideals of perfection. Perhaps the error of such synthesizers lies in their belief that art is a communication rather than an expression, an approximation to a single ideal rather than a realization of diverse ideals.

It is, if we recall aright, Mr Eliot himself who notes that inferior talents imitate, but genius frankly steals. If we enlarge this from lines to principles, the following of an abstract ideal of perfection, relatively exemplified by divers writers in divers traditions, is the most killing form of imitation. The artist knows previous literature, but the strange and devious ways in which it influences and enriches him we must leave to greater psychologists than either Mr Eliot or ourselves. He is rather more likely than not to derive stimulation and growth from odd sources that he, unless he is a

---

[12]In *larus*, vol. I, nos. 5-6-7.
[13]This instinct seems referable to man's constant desire to relegate as many of his reactions as possible to habit and reflexes. In essence, fixed exterior standards and compendia are simply trouble-savers.

naïf, cannot intellectually approve. And we doubt strongly that, in the unpredictable mind of genius, a lucid synthesis of the entire philosophical and literary significance of say Donne, will have anything like the valuable effect of a strange and tattered remembrance of a few of that same writer's lines, figures, and concepts, singing themselves over and over in fresh and stimulating relations to other unrelated remembrances in the uncharted depths of his mind. This is perhaps unfortunate: the opposite would be so much neater. But it is probable.

Genuine liberty, of the sort which we understand M Hugnet to mean, is a grave responsibility. In the ruleless field in which a truly free artist works, failure is a harsh, single, and undignified thing. Unsupported by a school, movement, or tradition, he succeeds magnificently or fails cruelly. His scope is not discounted in advance by the advantage of attempting purely second-rate goals. But that, the acceptance of the responsibilities, not the licence, of liberty (strange that such ancient saws need belaboring), the single determination to be true to the severest personal canons, to the artistic truth as one sees it — that, rather than either an ungenuine neo-classicism or a weak collapse into the passive critical attitude, is the true route whereby we may climb out of the morass of dogma, licence, or the wasteful battle of dogma and antidogma, in which we have been bogged.

Mr Eliot was a great poet; he is an ingenious, charming, and stimulating scholar. His apparent death as a creative artist we deeply deplore. He remains, since his apotheosis, in his oracles, a brilliant intelligence, though, as far as the artist is concerned,[14] it is bad medicine insofar as it is all directed to the justification of failure, the praise of death. It is because he *is* so intelligent that he attracts all the young men. And that, in the ultimate analysis, is perhaps what is the matter with criticism.[15]

If there is, after all these suggestions, a summary, it is this, so simply stated that it may seem beneath notice to these young men who are now absorbed in playing with the building-blocks of nice large philosophical words: that it would predictably be better for literature in general, American letters in particular, and in person these young Americans of promise over whom we have (perhaps needlessly) been worrying, if they would desist from attempting, in disregard of their individual problems, to follow Mr Eliot into whatever penumbrous and lifeless places his personal failure may be logically leading him, and, continuing to avoid the Sirens of licence under cover of artistic liberty, take a long deep breath, stop being afraid of themselves, and make something. 'Poieîte ti.'

---

[14]As intimated above, Mr Eliot's real appeal, similarly to but on a higher plane than, Mr Durant's or Mr Wells's, is a popular one. It is 'vulgarization littéraire'. But we are concerned with the maker, not the observer, of art.

[15]Query, whether, on the rebound from disordered emotionality, the function of intellect has not got equally out of hand. The subject is dynamite, with which anyone is quite welcome to blow himself up.

NEW MEXICO

Norman MacLeod

I

AFTER FOUR CENTURIES

Children after four centuries
darker with Navajo
and touch of the earth
come to a knowledge unmanifest
in an understanding of kindred spirits,
country impregnant
and toil.
Their hands speak of labor and sun,
and their eyes
of generations.

II

TATTER SONG

mission bells are only curfews pueblo
brats cast stones upon to hear
resounding ring skatterdetallions
of sound. it seems to them
so much more frolicsome than handsome corn
in a weather of turquoise revelry
and heavy incantations.

III

PAST: FROM ZACATECAS

A cigarette in the taste of cedars,
pinion smoke like faint disturbing incense
mantles the town
and even the Mexican girls
three generations removed
send letters back before time.

IV

NIGHT SONG AT JEMEZ

Caverns of space hovering
above a multitude of stars,
and airplanes moving in the sky
like nightshot comets,
and only a soundlessness
of rapid memories like water
in a current of refrain.

THE STILL AFTERNOON
Janet Lewis

Even at high noon the streets were hazy in November. The elm trees dropped their grey-brown leaves on the wet lawns, and the pavements were littered with fallen twigs. Here and there shallow puddles gleamed from last night's rain. The grammar schools were letting children loose all over town. They ran out in a crowd on the graveled playgrounds, and spread by twos and threes down the side-streets.

Hillary was in sixth grade this year. She sat down on the curbing to fasten on her skates, drawing the strap tight over the instep of her buttoned shoes. She skated down Ontario Street, making little jumps over fallen twigs and small branches. The air was fresh on her cheeks after the staleness of the schoolroom.

At the corner of her own street she met the old Bohemian grandmother who lived next door. She was walking up and down, her hands wrapped in her apron, watching for her grandchildren. She said to Hillary, "Is dere anybody sick at your house?"

"Oh, no," said Hillary.

"Well I see de doctor driving up quick two times dis morning. I t'ought dere was maybe somebody real sick."

"Oh, no," said Hillary, "we're all of us all right."

She took off her skates by the front steps, and dropped them crossed, so they wouldn't roll away. Enough sun came through the haze to make a scattered shadow on the porch from the big elm tree. She rang the doorbell and waited, whistling softly. There were still some straws sticking out of the birdhouse that Babs had fastened to the branch above his window. Their Irish Margaret opened the door. She had been crying.

"What's the matter, Maggie?" said Hillary.

"Hush, now," said Maggie, and began to weep again. The tears rolled out of the corners of her eyes, and she wiped them away with her apron.

"Is that Hillary?" said her mother's voice. "Tell her to come up here."

Hillary ran upstairs, her feet clattering on the uncarpeted wood. Her mother's room was long, the width of the house, having windows that looked out to north and south. You crossed it to reach Hillary's room or her father's study. The walls were covered with faded yellow poppies, and it seemed sunny when there was no sun. The furniture was old-fashioned. There was a sofa covered with brown plush by the south window, and a little sewing-table near it. The mirror was a tall one, with candlesticks on each side fastened to the mahogany frame. The big fourposter bed had once had a canopy and a flight of steps by which to climb into it.

Grandma lay in the bed with a white cloth tied under her chin and over the top of her head, like a mump rag. She did not turn her head when Hillary came into the room. Aunt Sadie was sitting beside the bed, holding Grandma's hand and patting it. At first Hillary did not notice that she was crying too.

Hillary said in a loud young voice, "What's the matter with Grandma?"

"Hush, darling," said her mother, "Grandma's dead." She threw her arms around Hillary and held her so close it hurt. Hillary went into her own room and lay down on the bed and cried. She was afraid of her grandmother's body lying there in her mother's room, on her mother's bed, and wished she did not have to go through that room again. When her mother called her to come downstairs for lunch she went quickly, without looking.

Her Aunt Sadie, who looked like her mother without being pretty, sat opposite and cried as she ate, wiping her eyes with the back of her hand. Her cheeks were wrinkled and wet. Hillary's mother was not crying. She was trying to act as if it were any day. Hillary watched her spread a piece of bread with butter and bite it carefully, and lay it down and forget it. She drank her tea slowly and carefully. She moved things about on her plate, but she did not eat much.

Hillary ate all her lunch and sat very still. They looked as if they had forgotten her. The quiet of the house made her feel strange. She loved her grandmother and she was full of her own grief, but the grief of these older people was something she did not understand. It hung far above her, like the branches of trees, far, far above. Her mother said, "You needn't go back to school this afternoon, Hillary."

She stood behind the big pane of glass in the dining-room window and watched the red-haired Nelson boy going by. When he got to the corner of Elm Street the bell would ring, and he would begin to run and be late just the same, just as he almost always was. In a few minutes she would be late to school herself. The hands of the clock on her mother's desk moved down, jerking. It was quarter after one and school had begun, and she was still at home.

She wandered about the house. Everyone was busy, and no one noticed her. She did not think she ought to go outside.

By and by her mother called her and they sat down together on the little worn green sofa in the library. Her mother put her arm about her. She said, "Father and I are going east, to take Grandma home. Aunt Sadie is going with us. You are going to stay with Aunt Caroline."

"When are you going?" said Hillary.

"Tomorrow night. Then we'll be back in a week."

"I can't go to school at Aunt Caroline's. It's too far," said Hillary.

"You can do your lessons at home," said her mother. She looked as if she might smile, but she didn't. "Will you miss me?"

"Yes," said Hillary, "I ought to go to school and get my books, because tomorrow's Saturday."

Her mother nodded. "Maybe you'd better go now."

The streets were empty. There were no children, only a few grown people. It was not like Saturday or Sunday. It was rather like the church across the street. They had crept in, one week-day afternoon, led by the janitor's little boy, through a side door to the basement and up into the empty auditorium. The pews were empty, and the pulpit and the choir-loft.

She met a little boy who was too small to go to school.

She said, "I'll give you my old paint-box if you'll walk down to Cuyler Avenue with me."

He said, "I can't go off the block."

He walked with her to the corner. She talked to him as if he were as old as she. When she left him at the corner she said, "Wait here and I can walk back with you in a little while."

She went on into the schoolhouse, and up the wooden stairs to the second floor. She heard the soft drone of voices behind the closed doors. She stood outside the door to the Sixth Grade, very unhappy and a little frightened. She did not know if it was because she should have been seated quietly at her desk inside the room, or if it was because her grandmother was dead.

THREE POEMS
R P Blackmur

WATER-RUINED

Take, from these waters, Lord, their slowing,
Ah, take away, for me, their growing
Into a silence, their sheathing me.
In such stillness I can hardly be
More than a memory flowing
(Water-ruined) interminably.

FLOWER AND WEED

Lacking another thought
Take rosemary I said
of the salt marsh kind
to bring those shortly dead
back from the damp lot
and cramp them in your mind:
and take the fireweed then I cried
that flames where a house once burned
for all those thoughts that never earned
by dignity of sense a peaceful death
and so have never died —
let them discomfort you and slack your breath.

This flower and this weed
shall sum us till we're dead indeed.

OF A MUCHNESS

Sweet the cold sea-moss, the old
tide-sounds and sea-change, the folding
of the waters on the earth — sweet
the sea pools and enchanted

these to the salt verge of youth
the breaking of life upon the shore

and here the tree
that other sweetness
— look where the two thieves
their bright harsh eyes embrace
with all the slow variety
of Noah's Ark
male and female, each in kind.
Sweet are we
hanging taut on the like tree
of the great dark

— what mercy of this world
what roman spear
could sweeten so
the new year

May 1st. /30

Dear Johns :

It has not been lack of desire to do so which has
kept me from writing to you of the second Pagany but the same
shameful lack of time which keeps us all - save those who
have more intelligence and courage than the rest of us - isolated
and dulled in wit . Instead of having more time for the things
which are important to me this winter I've had less .

It's awfully hard to know what to say to you . You've
a hell of a hard row to hoe . People like Parker Tyler and the
Blues people generally seem to have a legitimate kick when
they see you presenting an unorganized front to the world . They
would want you to be extreme-left or nothing . And they are
right - from their viewpoint . Tyler wrote me a hot letter last
week asking me if I was the one responsible for the acceptance
of so much bad stuff by Pagany . I replied, in self defence,
that I had nothing whatever to do with the issue in question
save that I had previously passed on a few of the things which
were included . I agreed with him that several bits were
especially poor, the Evelyn Scott poem for instance but that I
could not agree with him that you are "a faker".

What further I said to him is what I say to you now :
that Pagany is and must be a miscellany, a true , even a
realistic picture of the rather shabby spectacle America still
makes from the writers viewpoint . At least you are not "decent"
even tho' you are not organized - as perhaps you should be .

It's a time just now - as you know - of Symposiums,
of Hound & Horn meticulousness and of a searching generally for
an intelligent viewpoint in those things which concern us . The
successes in this quest have been slight . Pagany seems not
to be taking any stand at all . Well, it is better than some of
the stands that have been taken .

All I can say is , it's up to you . I like much that
you have printed but somehow or other the punk stuff must be
kept out . No doubt I've be of little help to you .

By the way, though, your Paris Letter has been a
great success . I like the Sherry Mangan. , I think it an important
contribution to the general mess over humanism , etc. Norman
MacLeod, not so good . Vogel, only moderately good this time ,
but always interesting . As you know I highly prize whatever
Louis Zukofsky does I think his poem the best in the issue if
not the best - oh well .

And if you do my poems next time , won't you do both
of them ?

More later . Must rush off .   Yours

William

DURING THE EARLY SPRING of 1930 William Carlos Williams and Johns discussed at great length potential plans for publishing Williams' first attempt at pure fiction, the novel *White Mule*. Though *A Voyage to Pagany* had fictional form, this was primarily used as a skeletal frame to support a kaleidoscopic appreciation of European culture and scene. Now Williams had a full set of family figures to be placed in an early American setting. Williams talked enthusiastically about what he wanted this novel to be, a running biography of a girl from birth to maturity. He was always frank in stating that it would develop out of what he knew of his wife Florence's early childhood and her family life.

127

It was a good feeling for Johns to know that he had been instrumental in getting Williams to assemble out of the attic all the stirs and starts he had jotted down over the past few years. So, when Johns read the reworked first chapter, he wanted to print it immediately, letting the balance develop as it might even though he knew how Williams could be taken by procrastination. But if this novel were ever to be finished, some sort of editorial deadline would be necessary.

Williams promised that he would delegate first attention to literary matters, so that there would be consecutive chapters for each future issue. Anxious for others to read this vivid and exciting first chapter, Johns sent proof copy to Mangan, who commented:

> This, so far as it goes, is excellent, and I certainly recommend it strongly. But—
>
> Except in a periodical like *transition,* which so preoccupies itself with style, or in the case of authors like Joyce, who are working on only one thing and are closely followed, I begin to wonder about the value of the publication of hunks of "Work in Progress."
>
> In the present instance, where we have a chapter which is vivid, stimulating, and accurate, one feels very much the lack of a sequel —a lack which prevents the work from having any particular significance.
>
> It seems to me that, though in special cases the "Work in Prog-

ress" mechanism may be used, if a work is of sufficient value the whole thing should be published serially. I think this shows especially clearly in the present instance, where the sense of incompletion and of lack of any significance other than vivid aliveness is extraordinary and disappointing. Have you seen any of the rest of this?

By itself, if you don't agree with me on the matter of complete publication, I should certainly recommend publishing it; certainly it is excellent.

After carefully considering Mangan's comments, Johns still wanted to run further chapters sight unseen. He believed that Williams would produce a superior novel with the same degree of intensity and interest that he showed in the first chapter. And so the baby White Mule kicked her way into literature in the third issue of *Pagany*.

138-143

The reaction to this first chapter was widely divided between acclamation and recrimination. One newspaper commented:

> Speaking in terms of likes and dislikes I think that William Carlos Williams' story "White Mule" in the current number of Pagany is a most disgusting tale. Williams is a physician and in literature a man of taste, but you won't believe either when you read this story of a newborn baby and its behavior . . .
>
> *New York World,* June 12, 1930

After the first chapter appeared, Williams became mentally blocked, temporarily unable to recapture the energy and enthusiasm necessary for continuing the novel. Totally discounting this setback in terms of *Pagany*'s loss, but realizing that completion of the work would represent a major literary accomplishment for Williams, Johns felt that a little friendly persuasion was in order. Although its second chapter did not appear until the first issue of 1931, *White Mule* began taking shape again in Williams' mind after a few long conversations with Johns. Future chapters appeared uninterrupted throughout the two year balance of the magazine's life and they contained the same lively, exciting exposition that had appeared in the first chapter.

Johns was as pleased with the quality of Albert Halper's "From Down South," in the third issue of *Pagany* as he was with *White*

June 5, 1930

Dear Johns :

"Extraordinary and incomplete" : yes, I'll accept that as the perfect description (in brief) of a proper first chpater . There are two others written, or blocked out, and I will finish the novel for you as fast as you care to print it . I have it all in my mind from beginning to end . You have greatly excouraged me to go on with the thing - after a seven years' interval .

McAlmon is a tough nut to crack . I should not like to see you rpint the thing he sent you and which you sent me to read over . He has forwarded me another bit which I haven't read yet; as soon as I do I'll #########. let you have it with my opinion .

Carnevali will be delighted .

I'm already looking forward eagerly to the appearance of No. 3 . And it is enheartening to me to have you speak as ## you intended to go on with Pagany after·
tho'
this# year . I nearly took it for granted that the first four numbers would be the the progressive strokes announcing the end of another good venture . You have my heartiest good wishes for continued success which I feel you uniquely deserve .

Louis Zukofsky has a swell essay on the American phase of the modernists in poetry, what they have said and done . It is rather predjudiced in my favor but it is good . Why not write asking him to let you see it ₤

Here's to White Mule , may she have as healthy a kick in the writing as she has (believe me) in the living of her life .

Yours

W. C. Williams

Mule. He felt that as *Pagany* continued he would be printing more stories by Halper which were certain to expand and develop in depth.

What had come in from abroad for this issue was printed with mixed feelings. The scintillating style of Mary Butts brought "Heartbreak House" fitfully alive. But Gertrude Stein's "Advertisement" was included only because that imperious lady wished it to be; and who, after all, was Johns to refuse her? Besides, she had sent him small samples of a very free translation of a lengthy poem in French by George Hugnet which might be available before too long and this Johns knew he wanted, so "Advertisement" was printed.

Certainly the most interesting writing sent in from Europe was Emanuel Carnevali's "The Girls in Italy," which was submitted by Ezra Pound from his retreat in Rapallo. Johns had never met Carnevali while he was living in America, but Williams had known him well and found the man an erratic genius. Having earlier forsworn this country, he was now living in poverty in Italian slums. His poems were soft, delicate expressions of emotion and a peculiar sense of loneliness; warm and passionate yet gentle, they reflected his own tortured life in both America and Italy. Johns considered Carnevali's *A Hurried Man* one of the most extraordinary books he had ever read and was glad to hear that other writings would be available.

Anything Yvor Winters could spare Johns was sure to want to print, and "Snow-Ghost" pleased him immensely. Solon R. Barber, who only recently had suspended publication of his own little magazine *Janus,* contributed the popular "At the Cabaret Infierno." Johns was also delighted to print the brittle but crackling lines of William Ailshie's "Portraits of Two English Ladies, Both Bitches, but Much Maligned." Ailshie had an unusual profession for a poet. He was in the American diplomatic service and Johns had frequently enjoyed listening to him over lunch humorously expatiating upon his chosen profession.

145

146-147

132
148-149

GERTRUDE STEIN
27 RUE DE FLEURUS
PARIS

My dear John,

May I change my mind and ask you
to print the advertisement the way you
intended and will you add in the note that
the Novel it to be printed in July by the Plain Edition, an
edition of my first Editions address, 7 rue du Chalet, Boulogne
sur-Seine. Seine. It would be very nice indeed
for me if you would. I will send you the
little leaflet about it as soon as it is

out, and I am pleased that you are printing Hulbell's poem, I liked it a lot, he sent it to me some time ago and we had a little correspondence and I liked him. And I also like you and Pagany, so there we are. Later on I will send you a little thing when it gets done, a play in which only contemporaries appear, it will amuse you, and Virgil may later do music for it, anyway we are all active, and pleasant,

Always

Gtde Stein.

Dearest Bill:

I wonder if you could arrange it with Pagany
so that they will send me the payment for my poems with
out waiting for the time of publication. I am in much
need right now, and should appreciatex tremendously
even if that meant a breach of their habits.

Also I wish you could try for me to get me as much
as possible for them . I saw in an ad appea ig in trans
ition that I am in very good company. If one Bill Williams were alone on the list that would suffice for good
best company.

I shake likehell and I cannot write more
And besides I want this to arrive soon.

Please send me the photo you promised.

Emanuel

JANUS

A Quarterly Review of Letters Thought, and the New Mythology

Solon R. BARBER, Editor
T. Swann HARDING, Dissenting Editor
Harry Francis CAMPBELL, Art Director
Barbs FARRELL, Contributing Editor

EDITORIAL OFFICE
Apartment 2, 800 Eighteenth Street, N.W.
WASHINGTON, D. C.

January 26, 1930.

MR RICHARD JOHNS
Editor of Pagany
Boston, Massachusetts

Dear Johns,

Yes, JANUS (as JANUS) is dead. The Dissenting Editor is so exceedingly busy with his own writings--- he has a book of humor accepted by Lincoln MacVeagh, 2 others in prospect--- and decided he did not want to go on with the magazine. His interests, I found, are mainly personal. He cares nothing essentially for the work of others and it was obvious that he would grow cold sooner or later. He grew cold sooner than I expected.

And that brings me to a matter that might interest you. Would you be at all interested in a merger that would make me an associate editor of PAGANY, to work out of Washington? I have many excellent contacts here and in other parts of this country and in Europe. I have on hand a deal of excellent copy that I think might interest you as editor of PAGANY: work by William Carlos Williams, Nelson Antrim Crawford, Maynard Shipley, Harding, Joseph Vogel, Paul Bowles, Wolfe Kaufman, Cha. Henri Ford, Parker Tyler, S. Lubin, Richard Thoma, etc. I would undertake to swing this work your way. I would also undertake to divert the interests of our subscribers (we have about 30) to you, paying the money still in (for 3 numbers of JANUS at 35¢ the copy) to PAGANY.

If this interests you, let me know and explain upon what terms you would consider such a merger. I have other details in mind, but shall wait until I hear from you.

I am glad you are using "At the Cabaret Infierno".

Sincerely yours,

Solon R. Barber

1108 east grand
albuquerque

dear dick,

just had word about FRONT: it is to
continue after 4 and starting with 5 in same
format quarterly instead of bimonthly with
same publisher and organization priced at
2 bucks a year, but its policy will be
different. Instead of the "complex countenance
of a generation" it will be entirely left.
Of course that will limit our interests and
will circumscribe the types of material that can
be used. Do you think you could scrape up
some work that could be called proletarian or
left or revolutionary? i know you don't go
in for that sort of thing but would like to
use some of your work if you could possibly
do some work of that order.

FOSP of Russia is going to help us and we
are going to try to have every article, poem or
story above proletarian reproach.

I am glad that the sheet can contine: our
subscriptions from Japan have almost flooded
us and that is one of the main reasons we
can continue.

Let me hear from you when you have time.

fraternally,

Norman
macleod

NUMBER 3 *July–September*

CONTENTS

PAGANY

148-149

WHITE MULE — A NOVEL
CHAPTER I

William Carlos Williams

She entered, as Venus from the sea, dripping. The air enclosed her, she felt it all over her, touching, waking her. If Venus did not cry aloud after release from the pressures of that sea-womb, feeling the new and lighter flood springing in her chest, flinging out her arms — this one did. Screwing up her tiny smeared face, she let out three convulsive yells — and lay still.

Stop that crying, said Mrs. D., you should be glad to get outa that hole.

It's a girl. What? A girl. But I wanted a boy. Look again. It's a girl, Mam. No! Take it away. I don't want it. All this trouble for another girl.

What is it? said Joe, at the door. A little girl. That's too bad. Is it all right? Yes, a bit small though. That's all right then. Don't you think you'd better cover it up so it won't catch cold? Ah, you go on out of here now and let me manage, said Mrs. D. This appealed to him as proper so he went. Are you all right, Mama? Oh leave me alone, what kind of a man are you? As he didn't exactly know what she meant he thought it better to close the door. So he did.

In prehistoric ooze it lay while Mrs. D. wound the white twine about its pale blue stem with kindly clumsy knuckles and blunt fingers with black nails and with the wiped-off scissors from the cord at her waist, cut it— while it was twisting and flinging up its toes and fingers into the way — free.

Alone it lay upon its back on the bed, sagging down in the middle, by the smeared triple mountain of its mother's disgusted thighs and toppled belly.

The clotted rags were gathered. Struggling blindly against the squeezing touches of the puffing Mrs. D., it was lifted into a nice woolen blanket and covered. It sucked its under lip and then let out two more yells.

Ah, the poor little thing, look! it's sucking its fingers. Laaaaaaa! it whimpered, its whole lower jaw shaking with cold; its lips were blue, its feet were blue.

Ah the little love. Hear it, Mam, it's trying to talk.

La, la, la, la, la la! it said with its tongue — in the black softness of the new pressures and jerking up its hand, shoved its right thumb into its eye, starting with surprise and pain and yelling and rolling in its new agony. But finding the thumb again at random it sobbingly subsided into stillness.

Mrs. D. lifted the cover and looked at it. It lay still. Her heart stopped. It's dead! She shook the —

With a violent start the little arms and legs flew up into a tightened knot, the face convulsed again — then as the nurse sighed, slowly the tautened limbs relaxed. It did not seem to breathe.

And now if you're all right I'll wash the baby. All right, said the new mother drowsily.

In that two ridged lap with wind cut off at the bend of the neck it lay, half dropping, regrasped — it was rubbed with warm oil that rested in a saucer on the stove while Mrs. D. with her feet on the step of the oven rubbed and looked it all over, from the top of its little head to the shiny soles of its little feet.

About five pounds is my guess. You poor little mite, to come into a world like this one; roll over here and stop wriggling or you'll be on the floor. Open your legs now till I rub some of this oil in there. You'll open them glad enough one of these days — if you're not sorry for it. So, in all of them creases. How it sticks. It's like lard. I wonder what they have that on them for. It's a hard thing to be born a girl. There you are now. Soon you'll be in your little bed and I wish I was the same this minute.

So she rubbed the oil under the arm pits and carefully round the scrawny folds of its little neck pushing the wobbly head back and front. In behind the ears there was still that white grease of pre-birth. The matted hair, as if larded to the head, on the brow it lay buttered heavily while the whole back was caked with it, a yellow-white curd.

In the folds of the groin, the crotch where the genitals all bulging and angry red seemed presages of some future growth — she rubbed the warm oil, carefully — for she was a good woman — and thoroughly — cleaning her fingers on her apron. She parted the little parts looking and wondering at their smallness and perfection and shaking her head forebodingly.

The baby lay back at ease with closed eyes — lolling about as it was, lifted by a leg, an arm and turned.

Mrs. D. looked at the toes, counted them, admired the little perfect nails — and then taking each little hand, clenched tight at her approach, she smoothed it out and carefully anointed its small folds.

Into the little sleeping face she stared. The nose was flattened and askew, the mouth was still, the slits of the eyes were swollen closed — it seemed.

— You're a homely little runt, God pardon you, she said — rubbing the oil again about the ears, and under the chin, but carefully avoiding the soft spot in the top of the head. Better to leave that — I've heard you'd kill them if you pressed on that too hard. They say a bad nurse will stop a baby crying by pressing there — a cruel thing to do.

She looked again where further back upon the head a soft round lump was sticking up like a jocky cap askew. That'll all go down, she said to herself wisely because it was not the first baby Mrs. D. had tended, nor the fifth nor the tenth nor the twentieth even.

She got out the wash boiler and put warm water in it. In that she carefully laid the new-born child. It half floated, half asleep — opening its eyes a moment then closing them and resting on Mrs. D.'s left hand — spread out behind its neck.

She soaped it thoroughly. The father came into the kitchen where they were and asked her if she thought he could have a cup of coffee before he left for work — or should he go and get it at the corner. He shouldn't have asked her — suddenly it flashed upon his mind. It's getting close to six o'clock, he said, How is it? Is it all right?

He leaned to look. The little thing opened its eyes, blinked and closed them in the flare of the kerosene oil lamp close by in the gilded bracket on the wall. Then it smiled, a crooked little smile — or so it seemed to him.

It's the light that hurts its eyes, he thought, and taking a dish towel he hung it on the cord that ran across the kitchen so as to cast a shadow on the baby's face.

Hold it, said Mrs. D. getting up to fill the kettle.

He held it gingerly in his two hands, looking curiously, shyly at that ancient little face of a baby. He sat down, resting it on his knees, and covered its still wet body. That little female body. The baby rested. Squirming in the tender grip of his guarding hands it sighed and opened its eyes wide.

He stared. The left eye was rolled deep in toward the nose; the other seemed to look straight at his own. There seemed to be a spot of blood upon it. He looked and a cold dread started through his arms. Cross eyed! maybe blind. But as he looked — the eyes seemed straight. He was glad when Mrs. D. relieved him — but he kept his peace. Somehow this bit of moving, unwelcome life had won him to itself forever. It was so ugly and so lost.

The pains he had seemed to feel in his own body the while the child was being born, now relieved — it seemed almost as if it had been he that was the mother. It was his baby girl. That's a funny feeling, he thought.

He merely shook his head.

Coffee was cooking on the back of the stove — the room was too hot — he went into the front room. He looked through the crack of the door into their bed-room where she lay. Then he sat on the edge of the disheveled sofa where, in a blanket, he had slept that night — and waited. He was a good waiter. Almost time to go to work.

Mrs. D. got the corn-starch from a box in the pantry. She had to hunt for it among a disarray of pots and cooking things and made a mental note to put some order into the place before she left. Ah, these women with good husbands, they have no sense at all. They should thank God and get to work.

Now she took the baby once more on her lap, unwrapped it where it lay and powdered the shrivelling, gummy two-inch stem of the gummy cord, fished a roll of Canton flannel from the basket at her feet and putting one end upon the little pad of cotton on the baby's middle — wrapped the binder round it tightly, round and round, pinning the end in place across the back. The child was hard there as a board now — but did not wake.

She looked and saw a red spot grow upon the fabric. Tie it again. Once more she unwrapped the belly band. Out she took the stump of the cord and this time she wound it twenty times about with twine while the tiny creature heaved and vermiculated with joy at its relief from the too tight belly band.

Wrapping an end of cotton rag about her little finger Mrs. D. forced that in between the little lips and scrubbed those tender gums. The baby made a grimace and drew back from this assault, working its whole body to draw back.

Hold still, said Mrs. D., bruising the tiny mouth with sedulous care — until the mite began to cough and strain to vomit. She stopped at last.

Dried, diapered and dressed in elephantine clothes that hid it crinkily; stockinged, booted and capped, tied under the chin — now Mrs. D. walked with her new creation from the sweaty kitchen into the double light of dawn and lamps, through the hallway to the front room where the father sat, to show him.

Where are you going? For a walk? he said.

Look at it in its first clothes, she answered him.

Yes, he said, it looks fine — but he wondered why they put the cap and shoes on it.

Turning back again, Mrs. D. held the baby in her left arm and with her right hand turned the knob and came once more into the smells of the birth chamber. There it was dark and the lamp burned low. The mother was asleep.

She put out the lamp, opened the inner shutters. There was a dim light in the room.

Waking with a start — What is it? the mother said. Where am I? Is it over? Is the baby here?

It is, said Mrs. D., and dressed and ready to be sucked. Are you flooding any?

Is it a boy? said the mother.

It's a girl, I told you before. You're half asleep.

Another girl. Agh. I don't want girls. Take it away and let me rest. God pardon you for saying that. Where is it? Let me see it, said the mother, sitting up so that her great breasts hung outside her undershirt. Lay down, said Mrs. D. I'm all right, I could get up and do a washing. Where is it?

She took the little thing and turned it around to look at it. Where is its face? Take off that cap. What are these shoes on for? She took them off with a jerk. You miserable scrawny little brat, she thought, and disgust and anger fought inside her chest, she was not one to cry — except in a fury.

The baby lay still, its mouth stinging from its scrub, its belly half strangled, its legs forced apart by the great diaper — and slept, grunting now and then.

Take it away and let me sleep. Look at your breasts, said Mrs. D. And with that they began to put the baby to the breast. It wouldn't wake.

The poor miserable thing, repeated the mother. This will fix it. It's its own mother's milk it needs to make a fine baby of it, said Mrs. D. Maybe it does, said the mother, but I don't believe it. You'll see, said Mrs. D.

As they forced the great nipple into its little mouth, the baby yawned. They waited. It slept again. They tried again. It squirmed its head away. Hold your breast back from its nose. They did.

Mrs. D. squeezed the baby's cheeks together between her thumb and index finger. It drew back, opened its jaws and in they shoved the dripping nipple. The baby drew back. Then for a moment it sucked.

There she goes, said Mrs. D., and straightened up with a sigh, pressing her two hands against her hips and leaning back to ease the pain in her loins.

The mother stroked the silky hair, looked at the gently pulsing fontanelle, and holding her breast with the left hand to bring it to a point, straightened back upon the pillows and frowned.

The baby ceased to suck, squirming and twisting. The nipple lay idle in its mouth. It slept. Looking down, the mother noticed what had happened. It won't nurse, Mrs. D. Take it away. Mrs. D., come here at once and take this thing, I'm in a dripping perspiration.

Mrs. D. came. She insisted it should nurse. They tried. The baby waked with a start, gagging on the huge nipple. It pushed with its tongue. Mrs.

D. had it by the back of the neck pushing. She flattened out the nipple and pushed it in the mouth. Milk ran down the little throat, a watery kind of milk. The baby gagged purple and vomited.

Take it. Take it away. What's the matter with it? You're too rough with it.

If you'd hold it up properly, facing you and not away off at an angle as if — Mrs. D.'s professional pride was hurt. They tried again, earnestly, tense, uncomfortable, one cramped over where she sat with knees spread out, the other half kneeling, half on her elbows — till anger against the little rebellious spitting imp — anger and fatigue overcame them.

Take it away, that's all, said the mother finally.

Reluctantly, red in the face, Mrs. D. had no choice but to do what she was told. I'd like to spank it, she said, flicking its fingers with her own.

What! said the mother in such menacing tones that Mrs. D. caught a fright and realized whom she was dealing with. She said no more.

But now, the baby began to rebel. First its face got red, its whole head suffused, it caught its breath and yelled in sobs and long shrill waves. It sobbed and forced its piercing little voice so small yet so disturbing in its penetrating puniness, mastering its whole surroundings till it seemed to madden them. It caught its breath and yelled in sobs and long shrill waves. It sobbed and squeezed its yell into their ears.

That's awful, said the mother, I can't have it in this room. I don't think it's any good. And she lay down upon her back exhausted.

Mrs. D. with two red spots in her two cheeks and serious jaw and a headache took the yelling brat into the kitchen. Dose it up. What else?

She got the rancid castor oil and gave the baby some. It fought and spit. Letting it catch its breath, she fetched the fennel tea, already made upon the range and sweetening it poured a portion into a bottle, sat down and rather roughly told the mite to take a drink. There, drat you. Sweet to unsweeten that unhappy belly. The baby sucked the fermentative warm stuff and liked it — and wet its diaper after.

Feeling the wet through her skirt and petticoat and drawers right on her thighs, Mrs. D. leaped up and holding the thing out at arm's length got fresh cloths and changed it.

Feeling the nice fresh diaper, cool and enticing, now the baby grew red all over. Its face swelled, suffused with color. Gripping its tiny strength together, it tightened its belly band even more.

The little devil, said Mrs. D., to wait till it's a new diaper on.

And with this final effort, the blessed little thing freed itself as best it could — and it did very well — of a half pound of tarrish, prenatal slime — some of which ran down one leg and got upon its stocking.

That's right, said Mrs. D.

(To be continued)

FOR A THING BY BACH

Louis Zukofsky

Our God, immortal, such Life as is Our God,
Our God, apportion us thy rest,
So those of ours we live to love
            vaunt not against us,
But are merged, together our blood. Our wish:
For their selves, for our selves!

Our God, immortal, such Life as is Our God,
Our God, share with us under thy vault of strength,
So it lies on all thy beloved that they pass
            underneath like the stars
On further pilgrimage. Hope nor force wasted, our wish:
For their selves, for our selves!

Our God, immortal, such Life as is Our God,
Our God, if this cannot be,
We accept your lives, thy will, give us at least
            such portion of rest
As allows us to pass under lone, but not futile, stars. Our wish:
Impeding none, our selves alone!

Our God, immortal, such Life as is Our God,
Our God, if like to errant stars we flutter
In our passage ever, of thy source —
            (as to the immortelle,
Form, color, long after the gathering, is given) — give. Our wish:
Give measureless your urge that is our strength still increate.

THE PLAIN EDITION
27 RUE DE FLEURUS (VI)
PARIS

AN EDITION OF FIRST EDITIONS
OF ALL THE WORK NOT YET PRINTED

OF

GERTRUDE STEIN

EACH EDITION TO BE LIMITED TO ONE THOUSAND COPIES

NOW READY

LUCY CHURCH AMIABLY

A NOVEL OF ROMANTIC BEAUTY AND NATURE
AND WHICH LOOKS LIKE AN ENGRAVING

ONE VOLUME   THREE DOLLARS

TO BE FOLLOWED BY

HOW TO WRITE SERIES   TWO VOLUMES

TREATS OF GRAMMAR PARAGRAPHS SENTENCES AND VOCABULARY

TO DETACH AND SEND TO PLAIN EDITION 27 RUE DE FLEURUS PARIS (VI)

I SUBSCRIBE TO   COPIES OF

LUCY CHURCH AMIABLY . . .   DOLLARS

NAME

ADDRESS

SIGNATURE

THE GIRLS IN ITALY
Emanuel Carnevali

BOLOGNA

The women of Bologna are peppery:
Most conspicuous among them are the grisettes:
and it is of the grisettes I wish to speak.
The grisettes, too, wear hats so that it is hard
to know whether they are ladies or simple girls.
Smallness is theirs, a pretty smallness.
Wrapped around by the eyes of the young fellows
who seek preliminary love in the open air,
they walk quickly with little steps
as though they were running away.
What do you run away from if it isn't
the love of young fellows who follow you in the streets;
if it isn't to cool off with the
rustling of your skirts
the warmth of young fellows?
They have fine eyes but no shame is in them, no modesty.
Often it happens thus:
One year the tailor-shops gather them
and the next is the turn of the brothel.

BAZZANO

Like powerful mares the girls of Bazzano
seem to gallop triumphantly.
Their breasts are big and mighty.
Love is a war to them and they fight valorously.
No pretty faces, no well rounded legs.
They answer roughly and violently
when one approaches them
with love-talk.
They fling an easy insult
to him who would
pursue them.
And they walk about
like powerful mares.

VENEZIA

As supple as the supplest in the world
are the Veneziane:
secretly and wonderfully elegant
under their stupendous shawls.
Blondes they are for the most part,
and the sun kindles their hair so that
they seem haloed.
Their blood is lukewarm
and they are slaves of a bland sort of love.
They walk so lightly
that in the city where one hears
only the steps of passers-by
their steps are not heard.

MILANO

In Milano the girls haven't time
enough to be pretty.
They have pale faces and they hold them up
in sheer and beautiful defiance.
When one is kind to them (poor forsaken things)
they thank exaggeratedly.
For in the city no kindness is recognized by the spirit of the people,
and all walk around alone and lonely:
of a loneliness that is felt only in the big cities.

NAPOLI

In Naples the girls wear broken shoes.
They are black-eyed and black-haired,
Black as night and black as dirt.
Abundant girls,
singers and objects of serenades.
They live without an effort.

AT THE CABARET INFIERNO

Solon R. Barber

Gindrunk, she took my arm, reeling, "come," she said, "have a drink
with me this music thismusic." The music was working hard. The fat
black buck smoked a cigar, pounded the drums and grinned and smoked
a cigar. The pianoplayer was a ghost from Baudelaire — the sad boy with
the sax out of Rimbaud who despised mankind. "Come," she said, and took
my arm, "more gin, baby, more gin, baby, more gin. The room is dancing
on its toes, baby, and they have turned the devil at the frontdoor loose.
Hello, Flora," she said, "les have a drink, Flora, leshavadrinkbabycomeflora,
les have a drink — "

"LET'S HAVE A DRINK," I said.

We went to the barroom.

"I'm an Americano, baby," she said. We stood at the bar, I took bacardi,
she took gin, Flora was talking to a fat man. "I'm an Americano and these
spigs don't like me because I'm an Americano are you an Americano, baby?"
"I'm an Americano," I said. "What will you drink?" she said. "I will have
bacardi, what will you have?" "I will have gin," and the barman poured
four fingers into the small glass. She stood up on the rail and leaned over
the bar. The barman grinned at me. "WHAT THE HELL ARE YOU
GRINNING AT?" I said, "THIS GIRL'S ALL RIGHT." He turned
back to his rows of bottles and started mixing a ginfizz. "For me, baby?" she
said, "for me? Have a drink — what makes you so sad?" I told her I was
not sad. She sat on the bar and her dress slipped above her knee. "Have I
pretty knees, baby?" she said, "or what makes you so sad?" "You have a
pretty knee, Americano," I said, "will you have a drink?" "I will have a
drink of gin, baby," she said — "let's sit at a table."

And so I took the drinks to a table and sat with the Spaniards. The
Spaniards were busy talking about the bullfights and they did not look at
us. We drank the gin and I began to feel that life was very beautiful. "Life,"
I said, "is very beautiful and exciting." "Life is beautiful, baby," she said,
"do you like me?" She stood up and danced a few little steps very carefully. The music was playing. The music was playing something Spanish,
something very beautiful, and I knew that a Spanish girl was dancing
alone on the floor. It was that kind of music and it was 3 o'clock in the
morning, time for the girl to dance something Spanish alone on the floor
and then soon the comedians would come out. She leaned very close to me
over the table and tapped my hand with her fingers and her hair was the

color of paper ash and she was very American and very drunk. "Do you like me, baby?" she said, "do you think I have beautiful hair?" "YOU HAVE VERY CHARMING HAIR," I said, "I LIKE THE COLOR." By this time life seemed gay and full of a beautiful color. She got up from the table and held the glass to my lips. "Drink some of this," she said, "and then you will not feel so sad. Drink some of this and then we will go and ride along the *avenida.*" I ordered more of the gin and bacardi at the bar and carried the liquor carefully to the table. She was poking little holes in a pattern in the soft wood of the table with a pin. She took the gin and drank it. "It is good," she said, "it is very good I needed this I need this now it is a thing I always need now baby and I like you but why are you so sad shall we go for a ride along the avenue?"

The music was bursting into American jazz and I heard the gay talk and laughter as the patrons got up and scraped their chairs on the tiles and then filed to the floor. "HE WILL BE SMOKING HIS CORONA," I said, "AND BEATING OUT DRUNKEN PATTERNS ON THE DRUMS.... HE WILL GO MAD WITH SAXOPHONIA," I said, "AND THE PIANO IS WHIMPERING IN THE DARK."

"What did you say, baby?" she said, "what did you say about whispering in the dark?"

The Spaniards were now still. They sat and looked at us seriously, they did not smile. A slim boy with a yellow face and eyes like tiny purple plums came to me and said, "Amigo, the lady is a poet, eh?" "She is only drunk," I said, "SHE IS DRUNK ON GIN AND I AM DRUNK ON BACARDI WE ARE GODS MY FRIEND AND WE SHALL NOT KILL ANYONE NOR KISS STRANGE BARTENDERS."

The dark boy smiled gravely and shook hands with me. Then the spigs talked again about the bullfights.

Mount Vernon, Maine
July 12th 1930.

Dear Johns: Williams gives me an inelegant puke with his White Mule
but he's got <u>something</u>(God knows I don't know what it is)that nobody
else has ever had. He's as creative as a bull jumping a fence but
I don't like the windward smell.   It's a hell of a sight better
though than the "sweetness and light" the monthlies turn out.---No 3
has some fine stuff---very fine. The stories are better than ever,
one or two or more. Personally, I like anything that has the utmost
in vitality, no matter the style, subject or point of view. ---God,
as long as you don't grind any axes or let some scented paper drive
you off your wheels, I'm with you. ---I hope you don't change your
mind about having done with pieces-about-pieces. Criticism wears
out the best of creative work, after a time. ---I still have fifty
pages more to read yet, and I might have something else to say
afterward.---I'm sending the final draft of Hours Before Eternity.
I think it is better than the other one and I'm ready to let it
stand. It will go in the book as it is now. The end is worked up
to a finer point, I believe, and should be more effective.

                          Hastily,
                          Erskine Caldwell

July 24 1930

Editor
Pagany

Dear Sir:

A week or so ago I recd a copy of Pagany
which was forwarded from my old address-- 321 West
19th Street, but as yet have not recd a check for
the story.

Thinking that the delay might be due to
oversight or that perhaps the letter might have been
sent to the old address where possibly it has been
snowed in, I am taking the liberty of dropping you
~~this note.~~

And I want to tell you that the summer issue
is a swell number, free of the freak stuff of Transition
and also the pretentious scholarly note of a magazine
called Hound and ᴴorn. It seems to me that you have
struck a fine balance between extreme experimentalism
and the rather rigid Dial standard. If you can keep
the home fires burning it goes without saying that Pagany
will be considered the new trail blazer.

sincerely

Albert Halper

302 East 135th st
New York City.

Alamos Sonora. Mexico Aug. 7, 1930

Dear Bill:

Your lecture letter arrived and I ain't heard it more like
it since I left college. I had one like it from Kirstein, in
which he thinks I turn the searchlight on people and a situation
and let it go. All I can answer is I don't think you people read
or like Chekhov, Balzac, (in his short stories) De Maupassant,
etc. I do.   Of course, about the poem, if you re-read the letter
I sent, it was draft. Written on hot afternoons when I couldn't
sieata, and couldn't work. The form it'will take, I feel and
have felt for a month, is a longish prose book where I get into
the town and its characters, limpidly, tranquilly, lazily, and
let whatever satire or sardonic quality there is reveal itself
simply. Moreover, I only one-tenth knew the town then. Now I
am a real town character; do a cabaret turn on the plaza, sing
for them, get drunk with them, and had eight of the town's young
bloods staying up till two one night, not drinking, because they
liked me, thought me loco and drunk, and didn't want me to get in
jail. I was only cutting up, and didn't get that they were staying
with me to be loyal. Also I've discovered the Indian hut where
late nights we eat menuda, tripe and all of the rest of the
cows insides in a soup, **of** brains, cabeza, I think it's called.
That I have not not arisen to.   Anyway, your comments on that
poem are out of order, as I sent it only for a quality I had
then felt of this town, and knew it was notation only.

Sure, what Johns and Pagany prints is mainly bunk, but he
has a smaller percentage of bunk than the Criterion, Hound and
Horn, etc. The last transition is puerile with its deification
of a mere weak rich boy and pretender like Crosby. His suicide

doesn't make him important, and his poetry is tripe; and why
the death of the King's English at this late date. Mencken 15
years ago wrote about the American language. Any half bright
person knows that battle can remain to history for the little
importance it has. Pagany in the three issues has had more
good short stories than magazines that have been going longer
and with more chance to get good material, one would assume.
Jolas never took a stand. Every number of transition was
a conglomeration of miscellany which pagany hasn't equalled .
Neither Jolas nor Bob Sage are intelligent or detached enough
or ironic enough to publish silly sentimental stories for a
gaga sophisticated public. Jolas likes mysticism, tears, and
sentimentality, actually. Joyce and Stein both confuse him.
Pagany on the other hand has had some good things of Mary Butts,
who balmy and rotten as she can be, has distinction. Mangan
has a mind, Erskine Caldwell, and some of the others have
turned out good short stories, that were not arty, 'modern',
etc. They were just good stories, not great, but there they
were. In the nearly 400 odd pages of the last transition, a
farewell number that Jolas might have waited to bring out and
make a corker, there is not 20 pages of writing which a
bright college class could not excell, for craft, wit,
authenticity. Jolas is anti-progress, romantic, mystic,
---- where does he get the idea that this age is pragmatic?
Science now is headed towards becoming a religion and almost
religious in its attempt to synthetize metaphysics, and
elemental realities.

   All this doesn't mean I don't get what you say; but
you can't use Jolas as an example of anything; and you can't
call Pagany when all other publications publish such tripe,
while pretending to have standards, or taste. I think most of
my late work has manner and is in the ffame. However, if

I'm off, that's that. But the draft poem is no point of attack. Incidentally what you say about it will apply to your last things in transition and Pagany. They are notations.

I'm getting restless, having done so much work, and being where I can't get magazines, and hear nobody speak English, or American, and talk of nothing that has made up my world. That's good, but it leaves a hunger in me. I may head to Hollywood, and return here. Write me next time to my mother's address. I have a hunch I depart from here in about three days, when I finish a short story that I haven't been able to finish for a week. I know the end. I just can't look at the tpewriter keys. My address is

859 North Mansfield,

Hollywood, California,

Yours,

Bob

JOHNS SPENT THE SUMMER of 1930 by the ocean at East Gloucester on the North Shore of Massachusetts. When not reading contributions for the fourth issue of *Pagany,* he attended the various summer stock productions of the small theaters clustered in and around Cape Ann.

Cape Ann had many interesting summer residents—artist, Stuart Davis; Danish interpreter of songs, Povla Frisch; writer and editor of *1924; a magazine of the arts,* Edwin Seaver. But unquestionably, the most important news during that summer was that just after Labor Day, William Carlos Williams and his family would drive in from Rutherford for a week at the ocean with Johns.

During that week, Williams became a warm and mature friend to Johns. He also had a disciplinary effect upon the young editor, induced by the realization that an honored and established writer was truly concerned not only with the success of *Pagany* but with Johns' own personal development as a writer.

Back in Boston, a tanned and somewhat wiser editor put the finishing touches on the final issue of *Pagany*'s first volume. There were many new names on the cover of that fourth issue. Eugene Jolas had ceased publishing *transition* with its Summer issue, and Pierre Loving, who had been personally connected with the launching of this international little magazine, wrote an article on its demise. "Experiment and Expression" seemed to Johns both timely and skillfully handled. Late in 1930, however, Johns received an angry letter from Eugene Jolas. Much disturbed with Loving's article, Jolas demanded that Johns return his pieces, which would otherwise have appeared in a later issue of *Pagany*.

199-204

Johns saw no reason to apologize for printing what still seemed to him an unbiased account of Loving's connection with *transition,* so he informed Loving of Jolas' reaction. Loving replied, in agreement with Johns, that any impartial reader would regard the article as a just appreciation of *transition*. But there was one more violent objector besides Jolas: Kay Boyle. With great admiration for Kay

156-157

158-159

116 Waverly Place,
New York City

January 28, 1931

Dear Johns:

    I shall be glad to see you when you return to town.

    Some people cannot avoid acting as if they belonged to a
tight cabal; hence the flood of " damning letters". I have recieved
one or two commending me--that's all . But I put no special significance
on praise or blame .

    Mr. Jolas who is by nature cabalistic is not above urging his
friends to protest to you; and I venture to say I can name two people at
least who have sent in their protest. In any case, the letters would amuse
me if you felt you could show them to me without violating a confidence .

              Sincerely yours,

              Pierre Loving

Why not consider publishing the letters in a future issue?

It may interest you to know that I wrote Jolas that I was contemplating a reply this bulletin containing the word in which I would set down my disagreement with his theory. I would so far as to offer to debate with him in the pages of transition — but I received, as you may imagine, no encouragement. I am, in this, merely interested in ideas. My friends lean toward the tactics of the chapel, I am afraid. P.L.

116 Waverly Place,
New York City

January 2d

Dear Richard Johns:

Your story, I think, can be improved by dramatising certain
vivid incidents which you touch on briefly--that is building them up as
scenes for your reader. You can also add more moral (in the sense of
Stendhal , Proust and Gide) reflection upon the acts of the characters .
This can be witty, paradoxical, philosophical or what you will. Forgive me
for being literal . The best example of this sort of writing, lately, is
Eva , and Interrupted Journal by Jacques Chardonne (Simon and Chuster),
which I think you will find suggestive. I am happy to find you working
in this fine tradition and I wish you all good luck.

Please get in touch with me when you return to New York.

Jolas has a habit of attributing the bile in his own
heart to others . He has been terribly hurt by things, and I am willing
to overlook his animosity to me for the sake of a fundamental generosity
in his nature which I recognize and appreciate . Although he has, I believe,
deliberately sought to wound me, I have never retaliated. My article has
been, as I feel and as I have every reason to believe any impartial reader
will feel, a just appreciation of transition and of the contribution of
Jolas himself.

I am looking forward to seeing the next issue of Pagany.

With all good wishes

Sincerely yours,

Pierre Loving

                              Villa Coustille,
                              Moyenne Corniche,
                              Col-de-Villefranche,
                              Nice, A. M.

                              Jan. 9, I93I.

Mr. Richard Johns,
I09 Charles Street,
Boston, Mass.

Dear Sir:

               "The rage for living is over me, while
                  the dogs in the far-off villages
                Begin their lunar bark, and the owls cry
                          in the ivy."

          A copy of your magazine "Pagany" was sent me re-
cently by Dr. Williams. It was, incidentally, the first
number that I had seen. May I congratulate you upon the
contributions of Emanuel Carnevali and Robert McAlmon, and
may I add that, as far as I personally am concerned, your
magazine can never be anything but a disgrace to its editor
because of the inclusion of Mr. Pierre Loving's article on
"Experiment and Expression" ?

          I have no inclination to consider, point by point,
Mr. Loving's genial and complacent statements, nor to dwell
upon his measured equity. Mr. Loving is an old man, and I
respect his years. An old man ? Simply because it takes the
blood of the young to respond to what Mr. Eugene Jolas has
done. "'transition' gave encouragement to young writers'"?
It gave the heart, the faith, the speech, and years from the
life of its editor to a spirit he loved and revered. Just
what this spirit is eludes Mr. Loving's practical grasp. He
has forgotten, for it lives in every young man's heart. But
there is not, I daresay, a man amongst you, not one. There is
not a young man amongst you all who has the grace to stand up
and say that Eugene Jolas, IN HIS OWN WAY, brought the poetry
and prose of America withinX the past four years to flower upon
European soil.

          The publication of this article seems to me further
evidence of how greatly in America is lacking the dignity of
knowledge. For Mr. Loving's own ignorance, I can find no ex-

-2-

cuse. Mr. Loving, at least, can read both French and
German, and if he has read and digested the written opinion
of both the French and German press upon the subject of Mr.
Eugene Jolas and "transition", upon the creative works in
the two tongues of which Mr. Jolas is the author, if he for
one moment understood the place and importance of Mr. Jolas
in international letters today, then he most willfully kept
all such knowledge apart from his article in your magazine.
Mr. Loving was content to cite Mr. Wyndham Lewis' insular
attack upon Mr. Jolas as an indication of the general attitude towards "transition" 's editorial policy. Such a mis-
representation of facts succeeded in reducing Mr. Loving's
critique to an exposition of personal spite, and I take it
that Mr. Loving was acting as spokesman for a small and vir-
ulent group of literary gentlemen.

The consistency of purpose which Mr. Loving seeks
in "transition" and cannot find is, nevertheless, there. It
resides in the simplicity of a few words that he has spoken
to the people he has published: "I believe in you."

Yours faithfully,

Kay Boyle

richard johns:-

       your story in the last pagany was swell.

       I do not see how you dare to publish loving
on transition. when a publication like pagany prints an
article on the publication that was transition giving it an
all around hell for its enormous strength and incongruity
and concluding with a benevolent bestowal of a certain number
merits there is something funny.

       there is something very funny.

       although your story was grand.

       jon cheever

Boyle's writing, Johns was disturbed that a wholly inoffensive piece of opinion had enraged her to such a degree, but when other comments came in praising the article he accepted her reaction as a personal one, probably generated by her own personal spite against Pierre Loving. It is ironic, however, that Kay Boyle should enter *Pagany*'s archives in quite this way.

To Johns, the most rewarding piece of work in this issue was Kenneth Burke's "Tenth Declamation." Burke's volume of short stories, *White Oxen*, was a book Johns cherished, for he felt that the stylized context of those superb stories expressed the pains and pleasures of love in the heightening complexity of this difficult age. "Tenth Declamation," though continuing the tone set in earlier pieces in *The Dial* and *Hound and Horn*, accepted the devious characteristics of modern men and women and commented acutely on the mysteries of love and death. Burke's words held for Johns the full meaning of a sophisticated point of view.

178-182

Albert Halper's "Two Sisters" demonstrated the tight economy he had now achieved in his writing. Life was especially rough for this young writer during the depression, and Johns understood Halper's telling him that he did his best writing when closed away in the small solitude of one cubicle of a New York City rooming house, without the physical affections of a woman. "Two Sisters" seemed the sort of work a man might do with clarity and simplicity during his own sought-out short discipline of celibacy.

On the other hand, Erskine Caldwell's "Inspiration for Greatness" was an entirely different product of a similarly enforced retirement to Manhattan and a rooming house, where he wrote much and lived on very little. While Halper was essentially urban, Caldwell was an overgrown country boy; and his particular experiences gave an immediacy to the words written from his self-imposed city cage. Johns was deeply impressed with the same stark, barren imagery that he had earlier read in *The Bastard*. He knew "Inspiration for Greatness" would be unique among the continuing spate of Caldwell's anecdotal and earthy stories.

170-177

Johns was pleased with his own story, "Solstice." He felt that now he was beginning to add texture to a constantly changing and improving style. Just as Caldwell owed much of the quality of "Inspira-

186-197

tion for Greatness" to his reading of Sherwood Anderson, "Solstice" was fashioned after the style of Mary Butts. As Caldwell had used Anderson to arrive at his own individuality, Johns felt that he had successfully made use of Butts' intricacies of style to give his story the glossy overlay he had to discover outside of himself.

"Solstice" also created a small incident which showed that the reading and writing world of the little magazine was actually as provincial in its interests as any rural party line with its grapevine of gossip and conjecture. The story portrayed the impact of an amoral expatriate society on a young college intellectual. The first hint that someone had decided that this story was a cruel portrait of another little magazine editor came to Johns in a letter from Sherry Mangan on November 13, 1930, which said in part:

> Liked the story very much. I was on a false track about L.K., since it might have been another, but not very dissimilar.

Johns, who at this time had met Lincoln Kirstein only twice, was both surprised and chagrined that a fictional character had been so mistakenly personalized. However, in future meetings between Kirstein and Johns, this gossip was never mentioned, Johns wishing to avoid any discussion of an obvious coincidence, Kirstein silenced perhaps by both pride and embarrassment.

Johns had hoped that John Herrmann, husband to novelist Josephine Herbst, would have some prose to contribute before the issue was closed. Earlier, Herrmann had indicated that he had nothing suitable for publication but he surprised Johns by sending in "Fast Under," which Johns insisted the printer squeeze into the issue.

In lieu of the second chapter of *White Mule,* William Carlos Williams submitted two short poems, "Flowers by the Sea" and "Sea-Trout and Butterfish." Ezra Pound sent in another Carnevali poem, "Italian Farmer," clear proof that the poet was finding a fresh outlook in his chosen exile. From Charles Reznikoff, whose novel *By the Waters of Manhattan* had just been reprinted in Paper Books by A. C. Boni, came "The English in Virginia, April 1607," a poem styled directly from *The Works of Captain John Smith,* edited by Edward Arber.

198

Oct. 17/30
109 Nahant Street
Lynn, Massachusetts

Dear Bill:

Up to the neck is right. The printer decided after printing the first three Paganies to read the fourth and has raised a disgusting stench about much of the material, calling in a lawyer and acting in a generally odious manner. At last things are settled and the magazine appears as I originally intended except that I have had to leave out one whole piece of work I thought particularly fine. Its appearance is merely put off until January. The Fall number will reach you within the week, and at about the same time my New York address. I was there for two weeks directly after leaving Gloucester and feel it more than wise to spend a while there this autumn.

Glad you liked Gloucester. If in this country next summer I shall be there and right here ask you and yours to visit me for as long as you will. My best to your Lady and to Billy and Paul. I look forward to the attic room.

Yours,
Dick

Oct. 20, 1930

Dear Dick :

Come out when you can, sorry it wasn't this time .

Practice has been light so that I have had time to
write . My attic room, too, has had something to do with it .
But what the underlying cause of my choice of form has been
I do not know . I'm even curious about it to a degree that is
funny . I've had a crazy bug on .   It's been short stories,
quite short ones . Suddenly for no reason at all I've found
myself interested and as a consequence I've written six of them.
as fast as I can write . God knows what they're like . But
it's been fun . Lord, I could write a hundred - if anyone would
read them . Maybe I've been doing it to amuse you or Eleanor.
It wouldn't be a bad reason . I know Ezra would pass out if
he could see some of them . Most are ten pages long , a sort
of self determined classic . One is very brief, two pages.
and one is seven pages . These with five or six others which
I sketched out last year and partially completed would make a
rather fair sized book . Hell, I wish I had a stenographer to
boss around . My own who does work for me in odd moments is
sick and anyway I don't ever dare hurry her since she works for
love and not money .

This letter seems to be a fair sample of my recently
found style . Anyhow I've had fun, as I said .

It's been really amusing to me to watch myself . At first

I was slaving away on that damned Old Doc Rivers thing which
nearly killed me . I can't work that way . It nev r got to be
a unit , just wandered around trying to cover a big piece of
ground . (Scribner's turned it down, thank God)   Then I
did another short story very carefully . Then I did one, a
funny one about a red headed woman , that tickled me pink .
And then I got a perfect diarrhoea . I wrote so fast I couldN8t
see straight . Now the drunk is over and I'm back on White
Mule .

That is all ready for you , almost as much as you could
print in one issue . It is ready for you any time you need it
so count on it absolutely . I'm enjoying that too . And think
you will also .

Got to rush off now . I love to write when it drips off my
fingers the way it has recently . I hope I don't get roasted
for what has occured . I'll send the whole batch of stuff as
soon as it is ready (the short stories I mean) just for you
to see .

It's fine news that Pagany is selling .

                        Yours

                        Bill

Send the recent copy of Pagany to :

        Kay Boyle
        c/o Laurence Vail
        21 avenue du Maine
        Paris

NUMBER 4 *October–December*

CONTENTS

PAGANY

INSPIRATION FOR GREATNESS

Erskine Caldwell

I

In the daytime I wanted to be alone so I could feel the growing of myself
and at night I wanted to lie awake in the darkness and know that I would
soon be a man. Nobody ever knew what was happening inside of me but
I could feel something there all the time.

II

Sunday evenings I went early to the room where I lived and sat by the
window and watched a man put a girl to bed. She stood like a piece of un-

finished sculpture in the center of the room while he took off her clothes and folded them carefully on a chair. Even after he had laid her between the sheets she was without motion of life but when he reached up to switch off the light she began to giggle and kick and reach for him with her fingers.

III

There were men who were always saying things that sounded vulgar but I could never make myself laugh like they did.

IV

A woman fell to the street from eleven stories up. When we ran and lifted her in the ambulance her body felt like a wheat sack half full of rotten potatoes.

V

I lived four months in the construction camp where we were building a new railroad. Saturday nights after supper a woman came and climbed into a gravel car. One night near the end of summer somebody crushed her head with a spike-hammer and took all her money.

VI

When snow began to fall I went to a town and worked in a restaurant all night. In the spring when I was ready to leave I went to the station and the girl who sold the tickets opened the iron grilled window and put her arms around my neck and kissed me. A man behind me said angrily hurry up you damn fools I want a ticket to Saginaw. I said one way to Chicago. The girl gave me a round trip ticket and said you will come back won't you. Ever since then I have wished I had used the last half of it before it was too late and now it is almost worn out.

VII

It took me a long time to walk all the way from Chicago to New Orleans and my feet were sore and all my clothes wore out.

VIII

I lived for a while in a room with two girls. Neither of them could speak English nor understand it and I never knew what they were talking about.

IX

Down on the levee one night somebody shot a negro until he died and two other negroes began to fight over his pocket-knife. The yellow man was the bigger but the black one put his hand in the other one's mouth and tore out his tongue and threw it in the muddy river water.

X

A woman in a saloon told me where I could get a job from a man she knew. She said just tell him I sent you and I walked thirty miles or more but when I got there he said tell that bitch to feed her own pups because I am through with her and I had to walk all the way back again and I could not find anything to eat anywhere. I looked for the woman but I could never find her again.

XI

Once the sun was so hot a bird came down and walked beside me in my shadow.

XII

In a city I saw the loveliest girl I had ever seen and she made me feel lonesome all the time. I followed her for a week or more. One night I ran to her and begged please let me smell you. She took off her hat and bent her head toward me and the scent of her hair has been somewhere near me all these years.

XIII

An old man was riding a white mule bareback along a dusty road. He fell to the ground dead with age and the mule turned around and came back and stepped on the old man's chest.

XIV

Early one afternoon a negro at the sawmill had one of his feet mashed under a big cyprus log. We all went down to the creek and watched the foreman amputate the negro's foot. The man got up and wrapped the foot in a newspaper and took it home to show his wife.

XV

In a cane field behind the levee some men tied a woman to a tree and cut off her clothes with a cane-knife. Her breasts swung in the wind like ripe gourds and when the wind blew hard I could hear the rattling of the seed inside.

XVI

I never heard a pickaninny cry after the sun had gone down.

XVII

In summer a black storm came up the river almost every day and the rain made deep red gullies in the soft earth.

XVIII

There were lots of women who would lie down for a little while when it was night but I could never find a girl who would lie a long time with me when it was day and the sun was shining brightly.

XIX

When I went away I worked on a farm for a man with short black whiskers. In the fall at butchering time I had to sit on the hogs' backs and stick a long sharp knife into their throats. Sometimes the hogs would squeal and run so fast I could not get on them. The man gave me an axe and told me to knock them in the head. After they were killed and butchered we took the blood and everything else that was left over and poured it into trenches in the cornfield. In the spring when his wife's two babies were born dead I helped him carry them and three buckets of afterbirth to the cornfield. We dug some new trenches and put everything into them. After a while we plowed the field and planted white corn there.

XX

I loved my mother and father and I wanted to be with them but I could not stop living with myself.

XXI

In a store at the crossroad I saw a man hang a dozen or more dead rabbits on a wire and sell them for fifteen cents apiece. The rabbits' eyes were always looking at something nobody else could see.

XXII

The birds seemed to sing more on Sunday than they did on any other day.

XXIII

There was an old negro who was almost a hundred years old. When he worked in his cotton patch the buzzards walked behind him all day and clawed the red earth with their feet and pecked at it with their beaks and at night they roosted on the top of his house and flapped their wings until the sun rose.

XXIV

I saw a man and a woman with flowers in her hair lying together in the woods. After a while the man said come on and let's go back to town but the woman said she wanted to stay there for ever.

XXV

In the fall after all the crops had been gathered some men lynched a negro boy. When they were ready to go home they cut off his ears and fingers and toes and put them in their pockets. One man wanted to take both of his arms but they were too hard to cut off.

XXVI

I was walking through the swamp and I found the skeleton of a man leaning against a tree. When I tapped the skull with a stick some lizards came out and forked their scarlet tongues at me and ran back inside. When I tapped the ribs a chipmunk heard the vibration and began to sing overhead.

XXVII

I always liked to go down to the pasture early in the morning and smell the horses after they had been eating grass all night. Whenever I stood close to them and put my hands under their manes and closed my eyes I wished I had been a girl so I could kiss them.

XXVIII

Two men were standing on the bridge over the creek talking to each other. One of them said I am going to sell a bale of cotton tomorrow and buy my little boy a tricycle. The other man said I wish to God me and my wife could have some children.

XXIX

I ran across the fields and through the woods and rode a hundred miles or more to a city and tried to find a job. A man took me by the arm and we went down into a poolroom under the street. When we got there he said the police are looking for you and if I was you I would get out of town right away. I said I never did anything wrong but they found me and locked me in the jail and I stayed there a long time anyway.

XXX

I saw a girl and she was clean and she wore an orange colored ribbon around her head. I touched her hand with my fingers and I said I want to touch you for a long time but she cried as loudly as she could and ran away. I wanted to run after her and catch her and keep her but I was afraid.

XXXI

At night after everybody had gone home the dry dusty wind blew through the hot streets and choked me and I had to run as fast as I could before I could breathe again.

XXXII

Sometimes I picked up old pieces of bread near the back doors of restaurants if the dogs did not find them before I could.

XXXIII

Late one night when it was raining I found a girl crying in a doorway and she took me home and put her arm under my head and I dreamed I would always sleep with my face held close to her face. The next night when it was not raining she came home late and she was drunk and the odor of whiskey on her breath when she kissed me made me cry so much I could never go to sleep again. She came home drunk every night when it was not raining and I waited a long time for it to rain again but it never did.

XXXIV

Here where I lived the sun was always hot and the heat of it scorched my eyes when I wanted to see and it seared my tongue when I tried to speak.

XXXV

A man walked into a restaurant through the front door and ate all he wanted to eat.

XXXVI

In a house of many women the oldest one was always laughing but the youngest girl never smiled.

XXXVII

Once the sun suddenly burst through the darkness overhead at midnight but there was nobody awake to see it.

XXXVIII

In a yard where roses bloomed a dog went every day and smelled the ones that he could reach but the people who lived in the house never knew that there were flowers there.

XXXIX

There was a man who caught snakes in a bucket and built a fire under them. He held them in the flame until their feet burst through their bodies and they rolled out of the fire and walked away as quickly as they could.

XL

I walked through the South from one city to the next and every night I felt lonesome. I lay under a pine tree and cried all night. Sometimes I cried because I was afraid my mother would die before I could see her again and sometimes I cried because I could not find a girl who would let me love her like I wanted so much to love someone.

XLI

I was always a long way from home and it seemed as if I could never get there.

XLII

A man was driving his automobile along the road when it turned over and killed him. He lay face upward on the hot concrete road and his blood ran down the hill like an overturned bucket of red paint. Other men stood talking for a long time about the price of cotton but nobody spoke to the man who had just died.

XLIII

Each day I was a little nearer home and each day I walked a little faster. The farther I went the less there was beside the road to see. Once I was sure I saw the town and the house and my mother and father standing beside it but when I ran toward them all day everything at last faded away with the sun and I could not see anything there.

XLIV

In this hot country almost all the girls I saw were beautiful and on the hottest days they were even more beautiful than before. I never heard a girl whose face and body and eyes were lovely say anything but lovely words. When I did see an ugly girl she always said some ugly words that I could hear but I never saw a girl like that when the sun was shining.

XLV

They who were mulattoes never laughed as long as the negroes did.

XLVI

When now I met a man walking along the road he never spoke to me because he did not see me. When I spoke to him he stopped and looked around him and even overhead but at last he laughed to himself and went his way while I went mine.

XLVII

The men who gathered the corn and the women who picked the cotton laughed a lot among themselves but none of them ever looked up in the sky.

XLVIII

I knew that when I got home my mother and father would scold me and pretend to be angry because I had stayed away almost two years but still I knew she would take a long time to put clean sheets on my bed and that he would take me out into the backyard and show me everything that had happened there while I was away.

XLIX

I stopped beside the road to rest one day and a man walked past me through the dust. I asked him where he was going and he said I am going toward the west and live on the land where the sun goes down and sleeps beneath the trees at night. I jumped up to go with him but he ran away and left me.

L

When at last I reached the town where I had lived there were strange people walking along the streets and when I spoke to them nobody spoke to me. The streets were the same and most of the houses too but the people who lived there were not the ones I had known.

LI

Some boys threw rocks at me and a girl standing in a doorway laughed and went into the house.

LII

I ran into the house where I had always lived and cried as loudly as I could for my mother and father. A strange man came to the door and pushed me out into the street and told me to go away. He said I bought this house and the people who owned it have moved away to another town and then he shut the door. I sat down in the street and did not know what to do. It was getting dark and everybody shut the doors of the houses and lighted the lamps. I saw the baseball I left lying under the doorstep of our house and I wanted to get it and put it in my pocket and keep it always but I was afraid to go near the house again.

LIII

I got up and walked in the street and everything was dark with night and I was hungry. I began walking toward the town where my mother and father had moved but there were so many towns in all the world I did not know which one to find them in. All night I walked and waited for the sun to rise but it never did and I thought it would always be night.

LIV

In a dream someone told me I would never see the sons and daughters that I had made and when I begged at least to know their names he shook his head and laughed and went away.

LV

I opened my eyes in the morning where everything was strange to me and I saw a girl running through the country and she tried to hide from me because she was naked. Once when she stopped and looked at me I could see that her breast was bursting like a blossom in the warm sunshine and I ran all through the South trying to catch her so I could bury my face in the unfolding bloom and know the fragrance of it. Then when I reached her all the petals fell from her breast and they were blown away in the wind and I could not see her any more and I never knew where she went but the seed that were scattered that day are the flowers that are blooming there now.

TENTH DECLAMATION

Kenneth Burke

In an age of tumult, we might best command attention by speaking in whispers. In this age of tumult note how I, gratified, raise my voice. Let this be a song, the learning-burdened lyric of one who, without hope, was relieved of illness. Gleaning, he came upon an object of value. Or like some characters of legend, he fled from one country to another solely to mitigate his state of danger and in the second country became a sovereign. If, living in the city and awaking at night, one were to arise, dress himself, and go into another section of the city; if he, as though guided, were to stop at some destined house hitherto unknown to him, were to mount the stairs, and choose a door among many, knocking for admittance and saying to those that opened it, "I am here"; if he should never return to his former bed, but were henceforth dedicated to another life, with other people, and were to enjoy this greatly — or if he were to watch himself performing accustomed acts with astonishment, finding his usual habits made miraculous, he would be doing in his way what I have done in mine.

There are sickly louts who peer into the love-making of others and are deviously satisfied by observing exaltation on strange faces or catching the syllables of half-articulate endearment. Confused by this corrupt pleasure, they may even destroy or mutilate, though had their vocabulary been roundly developed they could as readily have blessed. Surely I am among this contemned number, and in this my era of privilege feel as though I were spying upon my own alien felicity. I learn, Anthony, that I was not greatly unhappy in seeing you with Florence — and thus the present, in becoming kindly, has placed even my past difficulties in a kindlier light. If there are some processes in the body whereby the memory of sorrow is imprinted in blood, nerves, and pigment, if there is an observable and measurable parallel in my tissues so that, with the proper instruments, we could test for prior gloom by a histologer's analysis, then I believe we should find these symptoms suddenly reversed — ducts, formerly dry, must now be flowing, to fill me with some biologic unction, and others must have fallen into desuetude which were once dangerously profuse.

I do not neglect the fact that this is error. I do not maintain that, were human living fitly managed, this exaltation would be necessary, or even possible. I say only that mankind has added sums for many centuries, that a grave miscalculation is lost somewhere among its reams of figures, and that accordingly one more mistake is needed if we are to arrive at the proper total. I say that, given conditions as they are, precisely this illumination was required. And I see no good reason why I should not somewhat discourage those who still are as I was — while among my former enemies I believe I could now find cronies.

Do not think, Anthony, that what you cast aside I have salvaged. These are new shores, previously known but to lizards. This woman is, only by the records of birth and citizenship, the woman you once knew. It is virgin soil that I have opened up, though you might say that I have come upon a settlement. You might say I follow in your footsteps. How — is that not grossness? If one seeks new metaphors, will he not also find new women? I am not tricked when she confides that she preferred me always, though it is useful to our happiness that she should believe this slogan and feel her months with you as little more than an apprenticeship. Nor have I openly called it a deception, choosing to keep such accuracy to myself and not to stickle if she express a present fact as a past one. I shall respect the peculiarities of her mind, and permit her to invent whatever fiction she chooses for bolstering up this momentous reality. In love, Anthony, I believe we were like elephants.

People may slay themselves through sheer lack of want — not in despair, but in gently letting their rich blood. We should distrust the tenacious of living, for they are unappeased. Death, luxuriously managed, has but this one thing against it — that unlike love, it does not well up anew. Yet we must watch, under prospering conditions, lest we be without the guidance and good taste of fear. He who commands a large salary thinks little of boring his neighbours. And if we have spent the best of our years in repairing our defences, we may find ourselves wholly unequipped for times of peace. So I am not unmindful that my good fortune may but cancel past proclivities and leave me at zero. I am already to this extent grown shrewd, and like a pawnbroker before lending on a pledge, I hold up our affection to the light, hem, shake the head in doubt, and stroke the chin. I would not willingly choose to live in a dungeon, but if I have lived in one too long, I may find growing upon me a mental pallor in living elsewhere. Should such prove to be the case, we are forced to seek misery as better fitted to our talents.

Who is so denuded of character as not to be at least two selves, one desiring to be bound and the other without encumbrances? And now that Florence is with me, must not the recalcitrant fellow be heard occasionally? Must we not admit that were we living in a whole pigeonry of contentment, there would be times when it rained, and as it grew dark we should slip out to walk slowly back and forth along a deserted road?

But hold. In the midst of my paean — and I sought to sing paeans cautiously — I have become disloyal. I shall return to Florence, with doubled attentiveness. I shall return in apprehension, lest she has been equally subversive. Thus can one's distrust of another grow from defects in his own reliability. Yet he may be trained to such bargainings, may reach out in his speculations without recourse to overt act, as I am sure that she cannot. And were she, during my absence, to have gone so far as I in tentatives, then I am back with the damned wisdom of my damned dungeon.

To you I shall not catalogue the excellencies of Florence, since you would but misread the privilege of your priority with her, and whatever aspects of her I discovered, you would think yourself remembering. I shall only mention that she is not avid of admiration, for she has not lacked it. Yet despite many hours devoted to frankness, I have retained so much of policy that I contrive to compliment her as a peer, revealing nothing of my awe, and even abjection. Though I have not bluntly questioned her as to her life since leaving you, she has given me to understand its profitableness. For reasons which she has not yet made clear to me, she is travelling with these trivial but entertaining actors, whom she loves with amusement and belittlement enough to make them resentful if they knew of it, though I need not be affected as one outside their group. A woman less capable might feel obliged to offer some defensive account of her presence among these motheaten fellows, to explain away appearances — but her unquestioning delight in them, her obvious pleasure in observing their irregularities, places upon me the burden of guilt. I recognize the uncontested steadiness of her position, her confidence maintained without effort. A wellbeing which I had not dared hope for, she accepts as her due.

Well, am I not in a motley army? We throng the beaches, we make the noise of frogs, we acknowledge our kind vaguely, and smile partially in passing. We go about the roads at night, we are seen talking at corner tables, many of us must feel the half-neglected seasons as obscured by the metropolis, considering spring, not as it lies broadly on a remote meadow, but as seen from an office window. There was a man of seventy who had got for himself a girl scarcely nubile. Some wag named him Goethe, though the discrepancy in the lovers' ages marked his only claim to the title. And I knew an unripe druggist who, in drunkenness, would boast of his exceptional sweetheart and then of a sudden grow pale despite the flush of his liquor, fearing that he had made his happiness seem too desirable and might tempt his listeners to follow after him, whereas in reality they were but waiting for him to finish that they might burst forth reciting glories of their own. I might further recall a couple, no more accurately described than as Walrus and Doll. They remained playful, inseparable, and enwrapped until the day of their joint death in an accident. These are among my band, as is the young woman who, though living in dissolute company and herself somewhat dissolute, persisted in chastity. Many ribald and recondite explanations were offered for her conduct, but I felt that she rightly saw in virtue her one distinction. Her closest friend was in great contrast. If a man but made some outstanding name for himself, in an exploration, a work of science, or a potato race, she could not rest until she had shared his couch with him. For the bearers of medals she had the attentive eyes of a dog lying on the hearth of his master. But the uncrowned she forgot like doormen. I should include these very dissimilar women in my band — and the wife of an ambitious lawyer, who cared for her husband assiduously, until he was prosperous enough to leave her and support her handsomely in an asylum after her collapse. And the student, joined in an irregular union with a shopgirl. The relationship being such as it was, he could not summon to his aid the usual precepts of fidelity, and he could think of no others. I should include the young author who wrote an article in caricature of love, and confided to me that he found love generally on the wane following its publication.

Two people of my band I thought generally abhorrent, owing to the amorphousness of their bodies, the bluntness of their movements, and their sluggishness of mind. On first acquaintance I assumed that they had come together as companions in degradation, but later I understood that they had sought each other out and were delighted with their find. And high among this group of my fellow-thinkers were two cultured but slightly morbid men, intimate since childhood. Both married, they conceived a dismal plan for testing the fidelity of wives. Each, it was agreed, should attempt the cuckolding of the other, afterwards making a frank report of his experience. One, it seems, was successful, but gave assurance of the wife's great rectitude, whereas the second, who failed, announced success with a show of great reluctance.

Dare I go further into this uneven lot? I go no further, except to mention briefly a beautiful, and even picturesque woman, loved by two men. Through letters, telegrams, sudden visits, and the intervention of relatives, she carried her drama tumultuously across many states. With her arms about Joseph, she would cry out that she loved Josephus and thereupon, misled by too literal a symmetry, would cross the room to embrace Josephus and protest her love of Joseph. For such was her nature that to be alone with one of them was far greater impoverishment than to be with neither, and whichever she lived with, she thought herself conscience-stricken for leaving the other, though in reality suffering most from a diminution in the vivacity of her situation. She wept in contentment, insisting that she was degraded — and friends, stopping to rebuke her for her inconstancy, would become her suitors. On one occasion I drank a toast to her elopement, using for the purpose glasses given prematurely as a present for her prospective marriage to the groom now temporarily abandoned though on hand to bid her and his rival farewell — and I left in complex cordiality, loving her, her two men, her dog, and the darkening inhospitable sky which matched my lonesomeness.

In these multifarious ways they prepare themselves for oblivion, utilizing as best they can their few clear years out of vagueness. But all, all are like the receivers of a legacy, who would keep their good fortune to themselves while sharing with others their delight in it. It were better that they be destroyed at the peak of their intensity, as boys stamp out insects in conjunction — or like the man struck down by an unanticipated bullet as he was smiling to himself, so that he passed without gradation from delight to nothingness, and was dead before the signs of pleasure died on his lips.

EXTRACT

Paul Frederic Bowles

On the far pampas the hurricane withers the gourd.
The mockingbird shrivels in the hedge and reeds no longer
    sprout by morass.
At the border of the alkali lake the sassafras droops.
Tiny tornadoes of dust pattern the land and the acid air is a
    concavity.
The locusts have broken their oboes and under the arch where the
    cataract hurried it is still.
Plantain stems are snapped by the wind and the mudflats near the
    bay crackle.
The odor of limetrees becomes an axiom.
A red star flames above the mountainrange and the trestle shakes
    with the weight of its light.
In the pumice cave where the fungus forms a carpet the serpent
    eggs ripen
and the wind dips into the canal.
Dynamite blasts the quarry and the foxes listen from the moor.
Strike, bell in the tower, and we shall see the rings of metal
    light that scatter outward.
The centipede runs along the ditch and the eagles wheel above
    the plum-orchard.
The afternoon is wind-driven across the desert and the cathedral
    drops into the dusk.

THE ENGLISH IN VIRGINIA[1]

APRIL 1607

Charles Reznikoff

They landed and could
   see nothing but
   meadows and tall
   trees —
Cypress, nearly three
   fathoms about at the
   roots,
Rising straight for
   sixty or eighty feet
   without a branch.
In the woods were
   cedars, oaks, and
   walnut trees;
Some beech, some elm,
   black walnut, ash,
   and sassafras; mul-
   berry trees in
   groves;
Honey-suckle and
   other vines hanging
   in clusters on
   many trees.
They stepped on
   violets and other
   sweet flowers,
Many kinds in many
   colors; straw-
   berries and rasp-
   berries were on
   the ground.
Blackbirds with red
   shoulders were
   flying about

[1](Works of Captain John Smith, edited by Edward Arber.)

And many small birds,
    some red, some blue;
The woods were full
    of deer;
And running
    everywhere
    fresh water —
    brooks, rundles,
    springs and creeks.
In the twilight,
    through the thickets
    and tall grass,
Creeping upon all
    fours — the
    savages, their
    bows in their
    mouths.

SOLSTICE —

Richard Johns

So he was going at last to Europe, he, himself; no one with him but John, his friend. The pier swung back, and in the blare of horns he let the shell of himself break brittly into sound. "Good-bye," he called, calling to no one. The break of water between ship and dock seemed for the moment something quite too much to bear. He walked forward to the very front of the boat, into the V at the bow. Here he wedged his body, his eyes strained forward, focussing past all islands in the harbor.

Came the crossing and the merry din of plates, the solemn wash of sea against an alien monster, spewing the refuse of man's living upon an unguent surface. Suns rose and set, and moons; while in the floating gulch, bound by steel and rivets, life hid and revealed her motives and compulsions. There was a suicide, two deliveries and many conscious plays at love. The third night out a man entered a woman with a prayer, she received him with unwondered yielding, but it was shy and secret.

Hoffmann, in the bar, upon the dance floor, in his cabin, was little aware of life about him. Life to him was the property of a sunset, a conscious painting or a poem. Acquaintance with happy lusting was not his; he was on a search and thought flesh an incidental. Once, oh, long ago, he had thought there was love within him, but the twitching of sensation in his bowels, too quickly slackened, he put aside as an empty, rather dirty urge.

So then, to wake a talent, to have something for Boston drawing-rooms to honor. Yet never, in a drawing-room admission, prostituting his candor, his attempt to touch a Cambridge, rich with erudite humanism. There was room for two desires, the acceptance of lank clumsiness, an El Greco face, in Copley-hung chambers, the sharing of metaphysical conjectures with those precise, elegant young men who worshipped so carefully their dry imperial-minded idol. And was it he would meet him? He wondered, stretching his long and slender legs in anticipation.

What misfortune in that stretching. What sad misfortune for an aspirant to the Avenue, to the intellectual comradeship of Buzzell. A beautiful mind, Buzzell's; in a tiny body made smaller by a booming little voice. Oh the pride of going to the theatre with Buzzell, Buzzell who stood between the acts of *The Cherry Orchard* and calmly killed Nazimova with words. Why had he, Robert Hoffmann, been moved by her hands, her silly gestures? Everyone listened to Buzzell as he killed her in the lobby. "The Last of The Red-Hot Mummers" he'd called her. "M-u-m-m-e-r-s, you know — " Hoffmann always spelled in telling of the evening. He stretched a second time, and misfortune walked. Lady Mary Oates came over and sat down.

So then this vital woman came over and sat down. Her chair had faced his, and in his reverie he had not seen the careful study of her eye. Sitting and thinking so tranquilly of what to be, to do and say, he did not know his body to have been handled by an all too human woman's wiseness.

Oates, oh, Oates was wise; a Cybele for young men to learn from. Her careful glance for detail had noted his face, dark under short, soft hair, the Semitic sensitivity in a head that gathered into eyes as soft. She saw the book, read the title and the author. With a smile slightly curled for the book, her eyes lowered, still on him, below the book. This was new to her, this sort of boy, a bit too much the gentleman, reading a careful dust. But she was wise, oh very wise; the hair, the eyes, the things about him which seemed vital centered in untroubled thighs. How unique, an untroubled boy, untroubled as she knew the word. And then he stretched and they were both undone, not quickly but surely. He arched as he stretched, and her expert imagination removed the stretch-tightened cloth. He thoughtfully surveyed the slowly slipping sea, she studied him closer with acute attention. The second stretch and she put down her book, walked over.

It was a casual beginning. The book he read led her to talk of other books, and Hoffmann was amused, intrigued. And so they sat, and in a while it was he who did the talking, while she observed his restless hands, patting, smoothing tie and hair and set of trousers. She watched, and thought of uses for a nervous fine-drawn hand like his. He, when she left, remembered a lady, surely a lady with such pearls and such a voice. They would talk in the evening and he would learn her name, he smiled at himself for once, her friends in Boston.

Robert dressed for dinner, carefully and elegantly, masking his studied asceticism with conventional evening clothes, dinner clothes that even in a man suggest after-dinner frailties. John looked at him and wondered at his care. Robert had been aloof from life aboard the ship ever since the voyage began. He, John, eager to make connections for his next year's teaching in Boston, had been a gallant mixer, rushing with his squeaky little whisper from group to group, binding chance acquaintances into a sense of friendship.

"Rob, where will you want to go when we land, — to Paris?"

Robert turned, swivelling his close-cropped head away from the mirror. He spoke concisely.

"Why, John, I thought it was decided that we go directly to London. I may want the whole summer there.'"

John stirred. This might be awkward.

"The Dennetts have asked me to visit them in Paris. They'd like you, too, if you'd come."

Robert was displeased. He said so and they quarrelled mildly.

"London will be better later," John stated. "And Mary Oates is in our party."

Robert veered.

"Mary Oates? *The* Mary Oates?"

"Of course, *the* Mary Oates. You seemed quite friendly this afternoon."

Robert hid his fluster.

"Why yes," he said. "I like her very much."

And was it Oates had sat beside him, was it Oates who talked so charmingly? Could he not go to London later and say, with subtle hint "Oh yes, she is my friend"? Oates was a lady surely; Oates with her title, her hard, glittering books, her notorious protegées, and her set of friends. London disapproved and loved her; she who most of modern ladies proved the heat of English blood. Even the idol had liquefied his "frein vital" and painted a bold picture of the legendary woman and her tomes, slightly garrulous in his interest to point out the living models of her perverse characters. Merely to see, to build a stream of conversation for his meeting with the critic, more to carry than the praise of an enchanted undergraduate Cambridge, whose writings were such mimicked host given back to the god. The Avenue had relished gossip always, and would delight in stories casually whispered, never doubting but what Robert Hoffmann had been but a delighted and amused spectator at the Paris circus.

He filed his nails in silence. John looked at him, amused. Robert glanced up, and diffidently colored. He smiled at John, trying to look knowledged.

"I had not known she would be in Paris." He widened his smile. "We must see the Dennetts after dinner. I think I'd like to go."

* * * * * * * * * *

Paris was very warm, the Dennetts' very crowded. Mary Oates was delighted with Robert. Inside of two days she had a book all planned. She called it in her mind *Francis Talmund* and Robert would be Francis. Another two days and she had planned to spirit him to the shore, had sharpened many pencils in anticipation. She saw what he thought of her, guessed that he was studying her, daring to dream to create her on paper. It was all very amusing. She recalled still the fine stretching he had done. That would come later; now she wanted him quite what he was, unawakened, potential, sad and querulous.

Luck brought a note from George Benton, the painter, hiding in a little spa to the south, asking her to come down and bring a bit of interest with her. She knew George of old, had been amused under his love some years ago, had shared him with another woman and two men. He was a grand person, as unconscious of sin as a dog, quite as unmoral. She remembered expostulating with such a bull-in-the-bed lover that he should carry on with men like any Paris joy-boy. He had been most polite, not at all ashamed, assuring her it was quite different in his case, pointing out the ways of quite normal animals of the same sex when left a long time alone together. "It got to be a habit," he said. "I see no reason to break a pleasant habit. You know damned well there's nothing bitchy about me." It would be nice to see him, the place was wonderful. She would have the chance to dig out Robert, casually but surely, writing a tight little book about him.

She told the two boys about the invitation, saying nothing about George which didn't praise him. Both of them knew his work and were anxious to meet him. They shortened their stay at the Dennetts' and went south at the end of a hot, gregarious week.

* * * * * * * * * *

Mitou was a jewel of a town, swept on one side by a pure white beach. At low tide a great reef filled the harbor, comfortably near the beach itself. Within sight of the Casino, it was a pleasant swim for sunning.

There were delightful people in town. Natalie Stevens was there, very much engrossed with George, merely having heard vague rumors of his bisexual pranks, believing them not at all, quite under the spell of his strong brown body, eternally at the beach, waving magnificent arms over the brilliant scene he loved, pointing out sailors most properly, apparently interested only in the color of their jackets, the swaying of their unsteady land-gait.

They fitted in well, both boys thought George wonderful. The first two days they were constantly together, and under the ripe spell of the body-conscious artist began to thaw. Then Robert, frightened at himself, bewildered that he should be feeling as he did about George, turned with full attention to Oates. Greedily she took him over, the book began to shape itself. John, freed from fears and self-distrust because of his admiration for the artist and his careless lightness, let go as he had never dared in Boston, postured his bodily fragility before Robert who scarcely noticed, unhappily engaged with Oates, keeping one eye secretly on George.

And Oates, did she see or guess what went on before her? Surprisingly she didn't. George swam with John, they came at times to interrupt her diligence in probing Robert's lack of living. She was intrigued, quite sexlessly for the time, hearing the sad recital of adolescence, gathering not at all the reason for the boy's openness about his wealthy Jewish magnate father, who did not understand, no, not at all, his son. Grand figure this, the parent; cigar in mouth, departments of a mighty business in either hand, surrounded with strings of horses and a wife who moved from residence to residence, always a bit behind the season.

And Robert, wretched, thinking "What would Father think, what would he do?" He saw his careful life endangered by emotion, he saw a minded pattern shattered. Frightened, he held closer to the woman, unreeling his life for her, slowly, thinking it over himself. He guessed at last there was a book in progress, he changed his story slightly, told as truth what he would wish his family to be, relating entrées which could never be.

Two weeks were preparation, preparation for dismay and sorrow. So sure the lady, so unhappily unsure the boy. Frail trees above the sea reviewed their coming, the flutter of their words and hands seeking some point of contact for their thoughts. The boy had lost his haven of pose, his thought to be studying a famous woman. She took him in, included his every motion and moment. To sit upon the beach was torture for him, to watch John and George turn from him with her and, after polite words, go down the shrieking pebbles to the sea, darting in swift strokes to the reef, sunning and talking in loud, merry voices. And beside him, endlessly, in jewelled gesture, bleeding him for her book, was Oates. Strange that he could not bring himself to break away, could not let her end her writing with a bitter barb of sorry truth. To cajole her with his shyness, to be a nice person in her witty wording was all he saw to do. Because of silly letters sent too quickly, every one he cared about would know the Francis of her book to be himself, and he could not, would not let misfortune make ludicrous the Hoffmann pride. So, weaving out her pattern, she drained him, made him waspish with boredom and sharp thrusting impatience.

And then, one night, so simply; Oates sleeping, having written all night and day before; he, walking along the Plage in moonlight, lifted his eyes from the harbor to the candid gaze of Natalie, strolling with John and George.

"Come," she said, simply. "Walk with us a way."

Robert let his glancing, shy and furtive, creep to George, who, amused at last, a little overbearing in high-set mirth, smiled at him drily.

"May I speak a moment, Natalie, to George?"

Keen eyes looked jealousy a moment then crinkled to dancing, and the pleasant softness of her voice said "Surely, child, little lost Robert. Why not?" A hand, unjewelled, youthful, swept a scarf across rich brown shoulders and patted the ripe nate of hair stirring in the salt-tanged air. "We'll see you at Le Noir in a while."

John looked at George, a little hatred in his glance, a smile for Robert who did not care to be smiled at so.

Strolling silently, high on rocks, the boy and the man found the moon and a path of light on shadowed water. They sat down on a craggy promontory, gleaming with mica. Robert saw the smile of George, felt it an insult to his sadness, and whispered sharply, "Suggest something. What do I do? What should I say?"

George, enclosed in virile solitude, feeling richly alone and satisfied, let solicitude for Robert touch his heart.

"Why, break away from her, from her probing of your littleness. She has pickled many a better man than yourself. Be Hoffmann, a talented Hoffmann, who, himself, turns to portraiture and puts an honest piece of charcoal to *her* features. She has been Melisanded long enough in far too many books. As she draws, you take from her, nail it down in sharp print, against her picture, sure to be horrid, of yourself. Can't you do this?"

Robert picked a spray of mimosa, strangely growing out of rock. "Like this, you see, are you. But I, manured, nurtured, trimmed and plucked, have nothing to give which is myself. Give me a subject and a lot of thoughts to study and connotate my words and I can review a book, a philosophy or any art of seven. Hand me life, a feeling or an action, and I can but regret a catalogued erudition."

George stirred, drawing deep breath into cavernous lungs, a bit too healthily to please Robert's mood.

"I'm glad at last you see it. Be alive yourself. You don't know me, I don't know you. I can tell you baldly I am bad, am criminal, not a nice person to know, as your friends would have it. But; important for a bit of happiness, a little moment even, I am alive. I love myself, my body. I give it to the waves, to the sun, to the mirror, and, if so inclined, to this one or that one; — but then, not that for you. You don't know what I mean just now, no reason why you should." He turned under the moon, slid ruddy fingers down Robert's arm, turned back, caught knees to chin, went on. "But come alive, find something to do other than tea-table it with groups from here to there, emasculates, with heads like dusty granaries, pigeon-holed with dead systems to be weighed and measured, forcing the new ism into a teapot tempest for a time. You, Semitic, blood and bone, hot drowsiness, why are you half-born, indulging the 'higher criticism' or whatever you call it? Where is wit, intuition, sensibility, a proper reflex? I am a painter, thank God; I know little your sad defeated friends. I see them, sorry creatures; some, of course, are meant for nothing else, they will spend lives without ability to react or observe or reflex properly, digging and delving in a scholar's library, daring to believe that they may understand and properly interpret the life that we are busy living."

He threw his head back suddenly and roared with laughter.

"Have you listened, child? Remember it then as self-amusement. Recall the story 'Je m'amuse' and laugh at a bawdy painter gone literary. Forget it, it is silly. True for me is not true for you."

Robert stood up. "You are alive," he said. "And I so strangely dead. I will be alive, it shall be fun and music, lights and wine, I shall be happy, let the past sleep."

George looked at him, afraid of such a lusty birth, such Rabelaisian conception. "Is it my own? Is this my work, oh Lord?" Then sharply. "Don't say anything more now; come on."

Robert felt fine, he felt fresh. He wished the philosophic systems, the routines of living, in Hell, and forgot them quite. He let his eye follow the suave lines of George's body, preceding him. He did not blink or peer, he took his fill of looking. He felt heady and happy.

They reached the night-club arm in arm, George feeling like a god but much more powerful. For the first time Rob thought the place vivid, delightful. He waltzed with Natalie and she looked up at him surprised.

"What have you done? What has George done to change you so in so short a time? Tell me, you little live one."

Her eyes were curious, and curiously grey with fear. Robert tossed his head back, coltish, lightly smiling.

"We only talked," he said. "He only said something."

The music reached him and he relaxed to rhythm, feeling it quite as it should be felt. A first and second drink warmed him kindly, and when Oates sailed in to find him, tossing her fan with possession to the table before him, he leaned back and laughed, laughed happily before them all and cried: "Well, Mary, have you drawn the picture farther, have you caught a new light, a new approach?"

Oates turned, impatient, stiff. "You've been drinking, Robert. It is not good for you, I'm sure."

John looked at Robert, quizzical, puzzled and pleasantly interested. "Youngster, you've come to life. Is it a dream I dream?"

Robert raised his glass. "Let us all know ourselves dreams within dreams; let us sit outside with sharpened pencils and sketch our antics, the ponderous movements of our dance."

Oates stirred, felt changes in the atmosphere, held a questioning finger to the wind and whispered: "Rob, I must speak to you."

Dark eyes, cruel for an instant, veered from sea-green flashing in a face of enamel to stirring questions in the limpid brown beside him. "Natalie, let's dance."

She rose, and he whirled her away. Majestically, Oates raised her fan, swung it in wide arcs through tobaccoed air. Her chin was high.

* * * * * * * * *

So, a new Robert, a different Oates; an Oates who, finding a more difficult side to her Francis, decided to finish him up in the story. Brilliantly she did it, smiling at her pad of paper, gazing out thoughtfully over pelagic flux dancing under boats with tinted sails. She paused at times to watch Robert leaping and swimming with John and George. He graced the reef with lithe movement, with a sinuous awareness of his body which stirred her. She recalled the dry book, the slow arch of his body in stretching, the gliding sea mirrored in cool eyes. That such a change could be, that she herself had not been the play to mould the actor, the stage, the lights, the whole of his creation, irked her. She smiled ruefully, thinking she at least had been tormentor.

She spent an hour one day before the mirror, dreaming lines upon her face, brushing the mad mop of hair which was her signal and her sign. She wondered if it were the end of a period for her, if the glamorous woman she had been known to be was to become a lesser figure. Was her fan-play, her pearl-play, the flash of sea-touched eyes, to become less a success, a futile burlesque of a firmer grace? Resolutely she turned from the glass, raised a smart parasol and walked slowly to the beach.

Robert, high on the reef, watched George swimming in clear aquamarine, watched the muscled play of his bronzed body turning leisurely between each wave. John, behind Robert, watched him, curiously wondering if George were responsible, George with his casual acceptance of pleasure, with no unhappy bondage to any ethical regimen. Robert rose slimly, stretched, facing the sun, climbed the rock and dived into blue translucence. John, turning to bury his face in his arms, saw Oates foray upon the strand, grinned wickedly and hailed her. She called clearly, suggesting tea. Robert, who had reached George's side, swore softly.

"You better go," said George. "I'll see you before dinner. We might drive over to Le Trayas to eat."

Robert ducked him, swam away in leisurely fashion toward shore. As he came from the water Oates picked up his beach-robe and started up the strand. John, with her, turned back and waited for Robert. Robert, lightened, relaxed after a day in the sun, allowed the hand across his shoulder, the dark little head confidingly close to his own. Amused, he imagined John back in Boston, wondered what he would do with the winter, if he would find his teaching slightly empty after such a summer. For a moment he thought of himself, how he had changed, and in so short a time. He wouldn't plan for a little while yet. It all depended on what would happen or not happen in the next few days. George intended going to Vienna for the rest of the month; Robert wondered was he going alone.

"Come along, come along," called Oates from the Casino, impatiently tapping her foot. "The music is almost over." As Robert reached the ramp she ran down with the robe, holding it for him to get into. "How wonderfully you have filled out in the last week," she stated. She moved John from his arm to her own, threw the emeralded other arm along Robert's back. "Come on now, boys." She smiled from one to the other. "You've been friends for years, haven't you?"

Tea was what it had come to be in a week, a ritual, a re-acting of earlier polite gayety. Oates peered from one to the other, stressing the long friendship between them, seeing in Robert's eyes, looking always toward the beach, the first hint of what had escaped her. A panic seized her; she could never let such come to pass; she had never been cruel, never been responsible for hurt or pain. Was this another proof of fading? She pulled herself together, gave herself a sexy air, and feeling time was short and need most pressing, lavished a battery of charms to capture Robert.

Effect: quite simple. She seemed a bitch in heat, a great white bitch, drooling sorrily. She would capture him for a moment as she swayed her body with odd abandon to a waltz, rustling her dress beneath the table near his feet. Then eyes, in a frightened coyness which leered, would chill. He saw her panic finally, guessed it to be selfish and could not imagine lessening it. John caught the air, swished himself about, then feeling everything quite too hot for afternoon, moved away.

Oates grasped Rob's hand, hers seemed a talon to him, a hot dry grasp of need. It loosened, he felt George behind his chair, felt hands upon his shoulders, pressing, warm, indolent, caressing. Oates looked sharply into eyes, hating their owner. He made them quizzical, gazing at her wrist. She rose. The boy rose. George spoke.

"We're going to Le Trayas for dinner." A gesture, silencing. "Just Rob and myself." He paused. "Remember the terrace, Mary? There'll be stars tonight, too." He smiled at her wickedly. "Remember the stars, Mary?"

Oates remembered, sat quiet, waved as they waved from up the hill.

* * * * * * * * * *

High on a terrace they sat, and it was darkening. Two cigarettes played fireflies as arms gesticulated conversation. They finished talking and the pause was charged.

"You're alive now, Rob. There is nothing in your way. You, at last, have found your body beautiful, and" — full moment — "I would know it so."

Hoffmann leaned back, blood surged within him, built him into passion. He looked at George, held eyes across the table, turned, inwardly, from Boston, drew the scene before him in, harbor, lights, sailors, the handsome forward push of thighs.

Whitman on his father's table! *Calamus* at the bedside, unread of course, a library-set. What if he did read it? What if he heard that his son — ? What if he knew? What did people do, people at home, when such things entered their own household? "I'm going dead," he thought. "I shall return dead to Boston, with a memory only of what might have been. I shall hear sad music and stew in regret." He found his voice.

"You mean it, then?"

A brown hand caught his own and held it, a body drew closer, wooed elegance into abandon, toward a strange delight unguessed at. Two cigarettes burning to ash were no more fireflies but small lights fading to darkness, dying on a little private terrace, high above the sea.

* * * * * * * * * *

The morning broke brilliantly, fresh and sparkling with sun. Robert, rising from a dream, awoke to his own room, to cool air touching his forehead, soothing. In a moment he remembered, turned his head to the sea, the pillow in his arms. He could not speak, he could not think of what had happened. Life seemed quite the same this morning, but in some unreal way sharper, more reasonable. He felt at peace, realizing for the first time, fully, how far from peaceful he had been. Oates and John seemed sad puppets in a string-jerked play. He felt sorrow for them as he rose and shaved. In the glass his eyes looked as always, brighter perhaps, certainly happier. He thought of the late ride home, the swift race of car along the cliffs above a thundering sea. What was his place in this bitter-sweet unreality, this dream?

He went downstairs, guessing that they all knew, feeling, despite his wonder how they felt, rather proud. Suddenly, surprised, he sought out shame but could not find it. He was glad of that, he had been afraid to know it.

Oates looked up as he came in. His mood was startled to read pity on her face. John he saw strolling toward the beach.

Oates' voice was very soft.

"Good morning, Rob. Another lovely day."

He answered casually, caring not at all to talk. His eyes turned from the corner of the room to the hall, looking for the coat George had drawn about him on the ride home. He remembered it being thrown carelessly over a chair. It wasn't in sight. Robert was disturbed for the day was very warm.

"Where is George?" he asked sharply. "Has he gone walking so early?"

Oates was fussed. For the first time in years she was completely at a loss, knowing neither what to do or say.

"Where is he? Where is he?" cried Robert, frantic.

The woman stared out the window. She felt very wretched, and blamed herself. There might have been something said, a hint dropped casually. This little one was needing love, not a strange vagabond passion. And her he could never trust again, she had spoiled herself for him the afternoon before. She turned as silence lengthened. A face of chalk was before her.

"He didn't go to Vienna?"

She nodded slowly, and looked away as from an animal in pain. She heard the chair scrape back, heard feet cross the parquet to the terrace, turn toward the sea.

She did not need a mirror. She knew her last scene played and was glad to call the curtain down. It would be England now, Paris perhaps at times, but no more manipulation of other lives, no more setting of stages for drama. A hand plucked out a hair, held it to the light.

"I'll let it grey," she mused, twisting it around her fingers.

Upstairs she took out her manuscript, gave it a grimace and tore it quite in two.

"It is the least," she thought. "That I can do."

Robert spent the day on the beach, face downward. Toward evening he came back to the house. John and Oates were reading.

"Well, that's that," he said. His mouth twisted to a sorry smile. A hand touched Mary's hair, and settled. "I trust the book was finished, Lady."

She caught his hand; happy, thinking he understood.

"Quite finished, and quite forgotten."

"Thank you," he said. "And I am still alive. I've come alive and can't be sorry. I'm glad of everything, and thankful, too."

Oates saw he meant it, saw he would be glad to live, guessed sympathy and love to be his possessions.

"I've come to love the world, to see clearly, look fully. There's no person can ever take it from me." He paused, his hand squeezed hers. "I've found it here, have you to thank."

Oates watched his eyes turn to the beach, drift along the road to Le Trayas. She felt chilled and old, a useless thing.

FAST UNDER

John Herrmann

From the west flat lands of Jersey and the flat wide bumps of the road underneath and the sun in streams

Faster past buggy riders edge past Packards Cadillacs Fords trucks of Mack.

Down hill breaks circle turn right into and under.

Hurry hurry

Some roar kid

Fifty cents comes back with a pink from a dollar and in second to cop to high and slammo

Down into the guts of it trucks on the right with some noise baby **faster** hold it easy.

Lights above and white tile already growing grey and air millions of it pumped in with gasoline hurry.

Straight ahead between the line to left of center faster seventyfive feet apart and uphill thirty **go slow closer edging up to light** above three lanes slower out in air slower easier and **quiet now. Quiet now** like the middle of a great swamp New York.

EXPERIMENT AND EXPRESSION
Pierre Loving

With the current summer issue *transition,* the experimental review published in Paris, bids farewell to its readers. Those who have closely followed
its stormy career know in a general way what it stood for, although I doubt
whether anybody, gazing back impartially over its two-year existence, can
clearly isolate its aims, save that it was against the machined type of story
or poem, and that it welcomed to its pages all manner of experimental writing. The first issue was like a breath of fresh clean air, not because of its
editorial pronouncements but rather because the experimentalism was fully
visible in the kind of stories, articles and verse *transition* actually printed.
As the second and third issue came out, it was obvious that the new magazine was a most hospitable organ to young writers who chafed under the
standardized restrictions of the American literary scene, and although not
all that was published was good or even passable, some new young writers
did get their chance, and were later taken up by reputable publishing houses
in New York and London. This much must certainly be set down to the
credit side of the ledger, when we come to assess the contribution of *transition.*

Being open as "all out of doors" the magazine naturally lacked unity, and
even some kind of coherent policy, although the editors persistently claimed
a method in their expansive madness, which they sought to express by the
two recurrent watchwords: Mythos and Dream. If you will pick up almost
any issue of *transition* you will be surprised, or convinced, that the review

as an organ for experiment hitches very meagerly, if at all, onto the eloquent attitudes or principles adopted by its editors, and chiefly by Mr. Eugene Jolas, its founder and chief animator. This incongruity, in view of the undeniable good which the magazine has done, would be quite negligible were it not for the fact that the editor continued to hurl his manifestoes and policy at the reader in every fresh number. These statements were usually couched in a rather thick Carlylese; and logically and stylistically they lacked precision. This lack of precision enabled Mr. Wyndham Lewis to attack the magazine at its most vulnerable point, namely, its apparent alliance with *Surrealisme;* it does not much signify now that Mr. Jolas disclaimed any such alliance, for it was obviously a sign of editorial weakness if Mr. Jolas, chiefly by reason of his manifestoes and pronouncements, gave the reader this impression. And, as a matter of fact, the differences of policy between Mr. Jolas and M. André Breton, the spokesman for the Surrealistes, is so small as to be almost invisible. Mr. Lewis's error lay in the assumption that the magazine was coordinated intellectually, and consequently that every contributor, whether American or European, subscribed to the dogmas of Mr. Jolas.

If we examine the magazine in retrospect, we grow amazed at Mr. Lewis's error, at the egregiousness of his assumptions, for it is plain that Mr. Jolas disagreed with his sub-editors and they with him. Moreover, such contributors as Mr. Stuart Gilbert and Mr. Church, in their apologies for Mr. Joyce and Miss Stein, went contrary to the often-reiterated theory of the editor summed up by the words: Mythos and Dream. Thus we see that it is no easy matter to disengage what *transition,* for all its protestations, was really driving at. In the last analysis of course it may not greatly matter; but since questions of a general nature have an odd way of cropping up unexpectedly (as was apparent in the recent discussions of Humanism), especially when creativeness in literature is at a low ebb, it may not be amiss to consider the platform and manifestoes of *transition* apart from the creative writing which the review published. I say "apart"; but what I mean is that, granted the importance and superiority of a good deal of the writing, that every statement of the editor has a right to be tested by every other statement he has made. These statements are often highly contradictory. To resolve the dilemma we may then refer to the creative matter published in the pages of *transition* for verification or enlightenment.

It is advisable, I think, to start with Mr. Jolas' valedictory in the last number.

"For three years (he says) *transition* almost alone of all movements today, set its face against the pragmatism of the age. Almost alone it fought for the vision of a new humanity. Its arrival coincided with a crisis of the imagination. In the chaos of the post-war period a confusion of values set in. In an epoch that was interested primarily in reducing all creative expression to a mere auxiliary and conductor of a collectivistic program of living, *transition* sought to present an ideology that would combine the primitive instinctive mythology with a modern consciousness. We therefore fought the realistic idea of poetic values."

From the above we may conclude that *transition* arrogated to itself the dignity of a ripe literary movement which, among other things, combated pragmatism, fought "the realistic idea of poetic values," presumably with the weapons of "instinctive mythology," and endeavored to fuse this myth-making impulse with a "modern consciousness." Whatever a "modern consciousness" may be aside from a strict definition of the term, I do not know; and as for the other claims — stirrup-cups or calls to arms — they leave us a bit chill and indifferent after all; and if we are unpersuaded it is because, behind the thrum-thrum of the earnest confession of faith, we detect a species of futile quixoticism in the void. What is more, if *transition* was, as is nominated in the elegy, at odds with realism, then it was not made plain in its pages save by the mere assertion; for realism both in the prose and poetry crop up again and again, to bedevil its own exalted ballyhoo. Also, if its policy was at any time levelled at pragmatism, this is nowise apparent from the photographic reproductions of machinery; and the campaign against the realistic notion of poetic values — assuming the realistic idea and the campaign to have ever existed — was carried on by *transition* in a queer, a most paradoxical fashion: that is, within the scaffold of the poems themselves, as may be attested by referring to the lyrical contributions of the editor himself.

When next we come to Mr. Jolas' vision of a new humanity we find that we can fix in our minds, hard as we may try, no coherent idea or image of what it is. Editorial comment in *transition* was frequently couched in humanitarian epithet it is true; it was pontifical about the Promethean role of the imagination as the genuine redeemer of life and art; but, according to the valedictory cited above, the imagination is condemned to operate on a non-pragmatic plane (saints have achieved it, says Mr. Jolas); and thus before long we are brought up short before a faith in the after-life, a cradling in the lap of Mythos and Dream, a fond belief in some form of millennial bliss, a future haven reared by the thirsty imaginations of men doomed to leave their impress on spirit and never on lowly matter.

The editorials in *transition,* whether written by the editor or others, have been at times most unpardonably vitriolic and vindictive in tone. If we are to take them at their choleric word, such persons as H. L. Mencken, Burton Rascoe, Edmund Wilson and Sislly Huddleston—to name a few only —are sappers of the new vision of humanity and on the payroll of Belial, the arch-pragmatist. Opposed to these no doubt, and opposed to the whole low crew of "anecdote" writers, hack poets and bourgeois critics, is the demiurge of "primitive, instinctive mythology," than which, it goes without saying, there is no other god. What then is the connection, if any, with Mr. Joyce whose Work in Progress has been serialized in *transition?* The question is inevitable; and in reply Mr. Jolas offers us the following explanation:

"By publishing and defending *Work in Progress . . . transition* established a basis for a literary insurrection that included a radically new conception of language."

Apropos of Miss Gertrude Stein, who is supposed to have stamped her influence on the styles of Mr. Sherwod Anderson and Mr. Ernest Hemingway *transition,* we are told, published her work in the belief that her "psychological experiments with language have made a profound inroad into the conventional ideas of philology."

From these two statements, and some others of a like nature, we may take it that in Mr. Jolas' opinion Mr. Joyce is laying a contribution at the door of literary revolution and Miss Stein at the door of philology. To these claims we can offer no valid objection, I think; but I do not quite see how Mr. Jolas reconciles them with his pet theory that literature is expression and not communication, unless he is willing to allow that both these writers are engaged in the field of philology rather than literature. This, of course, Mr. Jolas will not grant; and in the Revolution of the Word manifesto, it is quite clear that he and his fellow-signatories were thinking of literature. Elsewhere I have already suggested in refutation of this manifesto that all artists, whether they are conscious of it or not, aim at some kind of public and that writing as literature has always been an act of communication. Mr. Joyce himself deals with language on the implicit theory that it is an act of communication. However, it may not be amiss to add here, in further elucidation of this point, that expression as *transition* conceives it is also a vital incident in the language process. Language, as we know quite well, and as Mr. C. K. Ogden has re-emphasized for us in his excellent *Meaning of Meaning* frequently quoted by *transition,* has two distinct functions: words are symbolic of reality i. e. communicative, and they are also emotuve signs. Philology is thus unexorcisably opposed to Mr. Jolas' view; but the manifesto goes on to frame some other equally vulnerable assertions such as: Pure poetry is a lyrical absolute. The imagination is autonomous. Narrative is the projection of the metamorphosis of reality.

Precisely because we do not know what "reality" is, the imagination is not "autonomous," not free and unconfined as light, a theory solemnly held by the Romanticists which Mr. Jolas appears to swallow with all its absurdities. Words are like Einstein's new concept of space: bounded yet infinite; and they are subject to all kinds of auras and essences. This means that they neither communicate nor express just one thing—unless, to be sure, we arbitrarily subtract all other possible meanings and implications. The two functions of words, besides, may act simultaneously; and the imagination, when it is not fulfilling itself through the ritual of images, does so through words, which are ipso facto limited to their functions and uses. The imagination is indeed lamentably gyved to words and their emotive histories; and this is why the cheap fictioneer can evoke a lot of mawkish sentiment in his reader by the repeated use of certain catchpenny phrases, debased by long usage, which allure by their sound and color and yet bear no profound link with life. What the *transition* manifesto calls "the hallucination of the word" comes from the auras and essences that have accreted around human speech and its evolutionary fusion or break-up.

Expression is primary like the cries of animals and therefore undifferentiated; it is indeed the least important factor in literature or art. And it is this fact, namely, that literature is communication, that in a sense gives color to the interesting experiments of Mr. Joyce who is not at all concerned, so far as I can make out, with lyrical absolutes. Indeed Mr. Joyce is so far traitor to Mr. Jolas' manifesto that he chooses to deal with combinations of syllables, vocables and rhythms — jabberwock couplings as Mr. J. C. Furnas has pointed out in a recent issue of The New Freeman — that depend for the success of their *communication,* their felicity, on emotional and associational values. This is a sound experiment with language, the outcome of which we cannot as yet foresee; but the point I wish to make here is that Mr. Jolas, judging at least from his editorials and manifestoes, is blissfully unconscious of what his headline contributor is heroically attempting to do.

As a movement then, standing for something concrete and realizable, *transition* missed fire; as an organ of experiment on the other hand it succeeded far beyond the dreams of its well-wishers. The self-contradictory character of its program may have been due, after all, to the non-cooperation of the age, which is opposed to Romanticism of the Schwärmerei sort. Another sort of Romanticism, the Romanticism of the picturesque buccaneer of letters, originated by Mr. Mencken and Ambrose Bierce, was responsible for the flagitious tone of the editorials. Concepts long dead were trumped up as emanations of the "modern consciousness"; but it is clear that the sails of doctrine were bellied by a jejune wind.

Yet, as I have said, the magazine did vindicate itself. The explanation is not far to seek: A review that goes in for creative literature should have no policy. In spite of its pretensions *transition* had no policy. It requires no policy to publish the work of William Carlos Williams, James Joyce, Gertrude Stein, Hart Crane and Kay Boyle between the same covers. In his introduction to Transatlantic Stories Mr. Ford Madox Ford has humorously shown that an Anglo-Saxon review in Paris has an odd trick of editing itself. *Transition* in a way edited itself. Its contributors took hold of the magazine and ran it, ignoring the grandiose principles of the editor. Which is as it should be.

That it gave encouragement to young writers is one of its greatest claims to our gratitude. I shall record only a few names: Kay Boyle, Hart Crane, Yvor Winters, Virgil Geddes, R. Ellsworth Larrsen, Walter Lowenfels, Lawrence Vail, Emily Holmes Coleman, etc. It mixed French, German, English, Americans and Balkans, so that at times it resembled an international ragbag. But what of it? It always gave proof of a good deal of healthy ferment, and sometimes it had its weak joke, as when it pretended to discover a young Balkan poet who was really the editor himself. In most ways it was superior to Mr. Pound's Exile. The whole enterprise, in short, was worth while, and it remains a fine tribute to the zeal of Mr. Jolas and his disinterested passion for good literature.

BOSTON'S BEACON HILL IN 1930 was the scene of a diverse community ranging from the luxurious private homes of Louisburg Square and Chestnut Street to the Barn Theatre complex on Joy Street where experimental groups were putting on such plays as Eugene O'Neill's *The Great God Brown* and Virgil Geddes' stark *Native Ground.*

Johns, living on Charles Street, was not a part of "literary Boston," and Boston's bohemianism seemed to him contained and provincial. He enjoyed going to Ethel Sussman's and Lou Trafton's Venture Inn on the Hill, a meeting place for many artists and writers who were not a part of the more traditional Boston milieu. These two girls served excellent home-cooked meals and sold five dollar meal tickets which could be punched out as they were used, with a great saving for the holders. It was here that Lincoln Kirstein came, clad in his immaculate riding togs, to meet and talk with Johns and that William Carlos Williams first met Johns in person.

On Joy Court lived Norman Fitts, busy with his writing after the demise of his little magazine *S4N,* which he had published in Northampton, Massachusetts, in 1925 and 1926. Johns had great admiration for Fitts' editorial judgment as well as for his board of editors, which included Gorham B. Munson, e. e. cummings, Thornton Wilder, Jean Toomer, and Stephen Vincent Benét. It was in *S4N* that Johns first admired the critical minds of Kenneth Burke, Waldo Frank, John Peale Bishop, and others. He was delighted by the anecdote of the naming of the magazine: when the first issue was made up and ready for the printer with the exception of the cover, Fitts had written S4N as abbreviation for "Space for Name" and then let it remain as the final title for the magazine.

Early in the Fall of 1930 Witter Bynner, while lecturing in Boston, took Johns to an evening at the home of Mrs. James Perberton Hutchinson, who wrote poetry under the name Amory Hare. Here on Mt. Vernon Place were gathered notable professors from Harvard and M.I.T. as well as artists and writers native to Boston or in town for engagements. It was a genteel and charming affair and many important contacts were being made, but to Johns the entire atmosphere appeared constrained and academic. He missed the freshness of individual expression and straight-from-the-shoulder talk and disliked the empty phrasing molded and formed primarily from drawing-room adulation.

After that evening Johns seriously began to consider moving both himself and *Pagany* to New York City where, though the elements would be the same, he believed he would feel less sense of constriction. There would be more people, many of whom he wanted to know, outside the limits of candle-lit barns and carefully controlled proper intellectualism.

Late in the Fall Johns decided to move all *Pagany* operations except its printing to New York City. By December 1930, Johns was installed in his new office-apartment, at 9 Gramercy Park.

In Boston there had been a one-room apartment at 109 Charles Street; in New York City he had two rooms plus an elevator, but floor space was less. Gramercy Park, at the base of Lexington Avenue and only a few blocks north of Union Square down University Place, was a different world from Charles Street at the bottom of Beacon Hill close to the Charles River Basin. The Players Club was just a few doors away, and *The New Masses* was published in the next block downtown.

There were many more contributors available in this neighborhood of New York than there had ever been in Boston. *Pagany; a native quarterly* was one year old. Her growing pains had been many but now they were over and her adult years were beginning. Johns, more enthusiastic and eager than ever but now free from the stuffy Brahminism and cloying traditionalism of literary Boston, could continue with a renewed vigor.

October 5, 1930.

Dear Mr. Johns:-

Thanks a good deal for the attention and consideration you are giving my Ms. I've run into that kind of pussyfooting business myself and am thoroughly in sympathy with your desire to get away from Boston so that you can edit your magazine as you see fit and not as printers and purity squadrons would like to have it done. My own book, "Bottom Dogs" has never appeared in its original form, not even in the first limited English edition(limited to five hundred de luxe copies, at fifteen and six. It has been through a fourth impression since, and no one is more amazed than I). And in its American form it was highly bowdlerized; so that I hardly know what I'll do with my next book, Flushing to Calvary, when I am done with it. I don't like underground or sub rosa circulation.

Since you have had to somewhat change your plans for the date of my extract, I wonder if I could still send you the completed chapter. If you still can't manage it, of, course, go ahead with your own plans. But I do think it is much more finished now.

Anyway, all good wishes for "Pagany."

Sincerely,

3934-46th Street,   *Edward Dahlberg*
Long Island City, New York

Dec. 13, 1930.

Dear Johns:-

Spoke to Gregory about Joe Gould's Ms. As I suggested, he will check the things in the various composition books
that he thinks will interest you. Then you can make your own
selections. By the way, on a friday evening, either this coming
one or the following, a few of us expect to get together at
Harold Clurman's of The Theater Guild. Aaron Copland will be
there too. And Gregory is going to read some of his translations
from Catullus. There you, Gregory and I could talk over the
Joe Gould Ms. Would you like to come?

Instead of making corrections on a separate
sheet I have indicated them on the proofs you have given meanI
believe you will find this simpler. I notice my name on the
galley has been omitted altogether- this just to remind you
that I am holding no brief for anonymity. Not now anyway. There
are other things: a repetition on the first page; have run my
pen through it.

Will write Dos Passos right off.

Cordially,

Edward Dahlberg

Jewish Community Center,
Belmont and Bergen Avenues,
Jersey City, New Jersey.

2. Ring Around Grammercy Park

VOLUME II–1931

WHEN 9 Gramercy Park became known as *Pagany*'s new address, there seemed no limit to the cast of characters who thought Johns was going to provide them with a new home away from McDougall Street in Greenwich Village. This procession of thrill-seeking, hungry drifters ended quickly when Johns made it clear that he had neither money nor inclination to play bountiful host to gypsy fun and games. These scroungers made a way of life out of being decorative and decadent amusement for out-of-towners with money who drank the prohibition sneaky-pete wine from coffee cups in side-alley New York speakeasies, or swigged Canadian-made gin from hip flasks while attending the seven-day bicycle races at Madison Square Garden.

The first issue of Volume II began *Pagany*'s New York period. What Johns wanted was a detailed criticism of *Pagany*. Quite rightly, however, he felt it more sensible that this criticism be written from a distance, far removed from the pettiness of day-to-day squabbles, feuds, and other adjustments. And so it was Ezra Pound, looking out over the blue Adriatic from his mountainside sanctuary in Rapallo, Italy, who at Johns' request wrote a highly *212-213* personal evaluation not only of *Pagany* but of the entire little magazine scene.

Pound's "The First Year of *Pagany* and the Possibility of Criteria" was refreshingly different from the usual conventionalized *232-239* criticism which fit into the warring editorial policies of other little magazines. Certainly it was diffuse and as erratic as the unrelated thoughts and feelings of its author, but it was alive and highly readable, too, a definite challenge to all academic opinions. Although the piece did not study each issue in the first volume, it certainly held to the spirit and sense of variety for which *Pagany* was already noted.

During that first January in New York, Johns found he was not at a loss for free opinion and criticism regarding the way he ran

EZRA POUND

RAPALLO
VIA MARSALA, 12 INT. 5

3 Nov.

Dear Johns

I have in the enc. confined myself to the
critical attitude of Pagany (as shown mainly in Mangan)
and hope you may find the crit. useful.

On the whole I suppose you have printed as
much dead matter as H & H (and yr. letter seems to show
that you think so). The only useful crit. of the narratives
and verse wd. consist in finding something better. In
that effort I am ready to help you when I can.

I dont want to scold at younger writers or
even to indicate what or which I find DEAD. Only
justificable cause of older writer smacking younger is
when he sees the younger edefinitely sabbotaging something
better than the stuff the younger produces.

///

You will see that I have tried to keep off abstract
discussion and what wd. be mere yatter about past
error. Have simply tried to throw in material that
will prevent future waste. Mangan seems to me a good
chap to have round. Am writing him direct (in yr. care)
Have used one or two harsh expressions ; but that is for
sake of brevity and to keep things as lively as poss.

///

Yr: french correspondent seems to me rather unreadable. Heavy
style   but has the virtue of picking the right subjects
to write about.

(I dont know quite how much intelligence that
implies. A number of people in the quarter wd. also know.
However : VERY difficult to get anyone who WILL write a

EZRA POUND   RAPALLO

VIA MARSALA, 12 INT. 5

chronicle.

Dont you think you wd. locate the rest of yr. contents
more lucidly IF you had a couple of pages of brief
notes , simply news of what had appeared during the three
months pervious? There is very little worth recording
and that record does NOT need the puffed rice review
of 1500 words per book. At the same time ~~if~~ the subscriber
to a review wants to ~~~~ hear what has happened.
If you save him the sweat of ploughing thru a dull
weekly you earn his gratitude and your keep.

Nov. 5

OH Hell. There is a lot more to say . BUT this is certainly
enough for one swat. I have cut the cackle and tried
to keep to a few essentials.

I meant to ~~swat~~ swat that chap who wrote about Brish artists. But ,
shucks , no use going back of transitory error. I take
it we are both more interested in Pagany's 2nd. year than
its first.

Pagany. Gone was the genteel and cloistered atmosphere of "literary Boston." In its place was a harsh reality of voices, some of praise and encouragement; others, like that of Parker Tyler, expressing scorn, resentment, and perhaps even jealousy.

Parker Tyler had been Associate Editor of *Blues* in New York while Charles Henri Ford printed and mailed it from his native Mississippi. But now that Ford had brought *Blues* to New York and since it was located so close to Tyler's home at The Marlton on Eighth Street, Tyler's influence began to show. One might even say that he and Ford edited the magazine in tandem, each taking turns at the lead position.

Early in January Ford and Tyler came to 9 Gramercy Park for an unexpected visit. As soon as they stepped out of the elevator it was quite obvious to Johns who was who. The quiet, sensitive man with big, wide eyes, seeming the epitome of certain young Southern writers, was Charles Henri Ford. The taller of the two, with mincing gestures and a high staccato voice, was Parker Tyler. His appearance was astonishing. His white silk shirt lay open down to the navel, and his tight trousers were molded over the rest of him.

It became obvious to both Johns and Ford that Tyler had come girded for attack. With head cocked to one side, he first wondered what an undistinguished young man, apparently a Wall Street type, was doing trying to edit his own magazine. Then he roasted most of the contributors to the first year's volume. Finally, with a wide gesture of dismissal for all the rest, he launched into his major complaint: why, if Johns had planned to write a story about a "Harvard Jew-boy" riding an uneasy saddle through the fields of sexual amorality had he not come to an experienced master who knew such characters intimately. Perhaps now that Johns was in New York he might learn a thing or two. Or didn't he want to be in the know?

At this point it was time for them to leave. After Tyler swept toward the back of the elevator Ford whispered, "I'm sorry," through the closing door. This was the only time Johns ever met Tyler and he found it quite enough. But if Tyler's scorn for Johns and *Pagany* bordered on the theatrical, it was not lacking in depth, as his letters and comments after this meeting clearly indicate.

Johns did see Ford again when the editor invited both him and William Carlos Williams to a small party one evening when Tyler was out of town. Williams came in from Rutherford, and after a pleasant dinner at The Lafayette with Johns, both men went to Ford's apartment. Neither Johns nor Williams ever mentioned that evening to each other again. They were the only two men present who did not dance with their host.[1]

In addition to Ezra Pound's critical assessment of the little magazine scene, the first issue of 1931 included other controversial writing plus graphic and poetic innovations. Through Julien Levy, one of 57th Street's top art dealers, Johns received a few of the newly rediscovered photographs of Paris taken by Eugene Atget in the earlier days of the century when he peddled his photographs on the street. Also included was a watercolor reproduction of Beacon Hill roofs painted from a back window on the Hill by Margaret Laighton, artist wife of Harvard professor Edward Forbes. Of particular interest was the simple wash drawing of composer Virgil Thomson by his intimate friend, Maurice Grosser. Grosser had originally entered Harvard as a student of mathematics, but soon transferred to the department of fine arts. He later won a traveling fellowship and continued his studies in Europe.

Unquestionably the most ambitious undertaking in this issue was the printing of Georges Hugnet's poem in French, "Enfances." Opposite the French text, which was printed on the left hand page, carefully spaced to be directly across from the original, was Gertrude Stein's very free English translation entitled, "Poem Pritten on Pfances of Georges Hugnet." Technically it was a difficult job for both Johns and the printer, but finally it was set as close to parallel as possible. Meantime a literary storm was building up in France, with Hugnet telling Miss Stein that she had made a most pedestrian translation of his poem. She, in turn, replied that from the disorder of his words she had conceived one of her most original compositions.

---

[1] For a graphic description of the private lives surrounding *Blues* and its contributors one may read *The Young and Evil*, co-authored by Charles Henri Ford and Parker Tyler, of which Gertrude Stein commented, "it creates its generation." Originally published in 1931 it has recently been reissued.

Let two short examples of the French text alongside Miss Stein's translation suffice:

21

Au hasard des edredons rouges j'use mon corps et ma vie mon enfance absente a la canicule.

He likes that felt is made of beaver and cotton made of trees and feathers made of birds and red as well. He likes it.

22

J'aime t'avoir comme une mauvaise habitude quand nous sommes coucher dans ta chambre.

He likes to be with her so he says does he like to be with her so he says.

Johns came to feel that he had printed a poem in French by Georges Hugnet and a completely original piece in English by Gertrude Stein, rather than a translation. To top off this situation, a belated cablegram arrived from Miss Stein after the issue was on the presses. The text simply stated:

FORM 2TW   12-29-200M

FRENCH TELEGRAPH CABLE COMPANY

NEW YORK

EXECUTIVE OFFICES: 60 BROAD STREET

60 BROAD ST. (ALWAYS OPEN) **7934 HANOVER**
PRODUCE EXCHANGE · · · · 1371 BOWLING GREEN
COTTON EXCHANGE · · · · 1289 BOWLING GREEN
153 DUANE STREET · · · · · · 9696 WHITEHALL
65 FIFTH AVENUE · · · · · · · 1135 ALGONQUIN
2 WEST 31ST STREET · · · · 2310 LACKAWANNA
545 FIFTH AVE. (2 EAST 45TH STREET) 0588 VANDERBILT
5 COLUMBUS CIRCLE · · · · · · 0684 COLUMBUS

PARIS

MAIN OFFICE: 53 RUE VIVIENNE

LONDON

MAIN OFFICE: 24 ROYAL EXCHANGE, E. C. 3

OTHER OFFICES

0815 LIVERPOOL — HAVRE — BREST
ST. PIERRE, MIQUELON—ANTWERP
FRENCH WEST INDIES

FA7 PARIS 20   DEC 22 '30

     LCD RICHARD JOHNS 109 CHARLES ST BO

TITLE MY PEM IS POEM PRITTEN ON PFANCES OF GEORGES

HUGNET IMPERATIVE

       STEIN

QUERY 3RD PEN 6TH WRITTEN

TRY 9 GRAMERCY AND REPORT.

DELIVERED FROM

65 FIFTH AVENUE

FOR REPLY PHONE

ALGONQUIN 1135

Johns shrugged, and filed the cablegram as a souvenir.

Also included in this issue was the story "Tender Advice" by 250-253 Romer Wilson, who had died the previous winter. The piece was submitted to *Pagany* by her husband, editor and critic Edward J. O'Brien. Johns was very much impressed with this brilliant first-person *tour de force,* portraying a son's college experiences as seen through the eyes of an uneducated father.

Strangely enough it was this delicately handled monologue which had the word "cock" in it that finally cost Johns the services of his 251 Boston printer, C. H. Simonds and Company. He had his first inkling of trouble when on a trip back to Boston he heard that Miss Corinne Loomis, Boston's leading insurance executive and prominent bluestocking, had announced before several guests in her Louisburg Square apartment that *Pagany* was an obscenity to her sight. In decisive gestures she had ripped the current issue to shreds and fed it to the flames in her fireplace.

Johns could not understand what made *Pagany* such an obscenity. Nevertheless, he was called to Simonds' office and told that he would have to seek the services of another printer. Simonds suggested that since Johns had moved his editorial office to New York it would be much more sensible to have *Pagany* printed there. Johns sensed that Simonds himself was in no way personally shocked with any of the quarterly's content. He better understood the printer's dilemma when Simonds confided to him that he had been receiving a number of anonymous telephone complaints with threats of bringing *Pagany* to the attention of the Watch and Ward Society. As printer of the magazine, Simonds realized he would lose a good deal of local business if any sort of public exposure were made. Johns recognized that despite Simonds' personal feelings about the situation, business was business.

Perhaps Edward Dahlberg's "Graphophone Nickelodeon Days" 240-249 was also not quite suitable for patrons of The Old Corner Bookstore, but it was indeed rich and ripe, worthy of the author of *Bottom Dogs.* Johns was honored to print this extract from Dahlberg's coming novel, *From Flushing to Calvary.*

The second section of Williams' *White Mule* fulfilled the promise of the initial chapter. The novel was on its way to completion.

March 6, 1931.

Dear Johns:-

Thanks for your letter and check. I am glad that you are
pleased with Graphophone Nickelodeon Days in print. Had intended to
answer you sooner but thought I would wait and send this Ms. along wih
a note. By the way, have you sent the Paganys on to Dos Passos. He is
in Mexico City now, and if you want me to, I'll write him and see if
he won't send some of hisstuff to you. Have you made a selection from
Joe Gould's material. Very shortly, Horace Gregory's article on Gould
is to appear in The New Republic. I think you might be very intereste
ed in using some of Gregory's translations of Catullus. He has done
them in unrhymed verse, in the american idiom, and with distinction.
The marriage hymn from Gregory's Catullus is quite fine, I think. I
am going to review it in the New Republic and relate the invective,
the brutal Roman patois, to our own contemporary scene. Another thing
why don't you get something from Hart Crane? He's out in Chagrin Fall
Falls'now(what a name, eh), and since there's nothing to do in Chagri
rin Falls(I don't see what anybody could do in Chagrin Falls) but
write, it is quite possible that he has done something very unique.
He lives at Crane's Canary Cottage, but he feels so chagrined about
his address that he uses a post office box instead. His father has
a well-known inn there.

Am sending you my Coney Island chapter. It is still
unfinished. The last part has not yet been completely tied up. But I
have reworked it so many times that it has gone stale under my hand.
I can hardly look at it now. Wilson wanted to print some of these
parts but he said they were 'too improper' for the New Republic.

As soon as the New Republic prints my Bensonhurst piece
I will gladly send you a copy. As a matter of fact, I think and so
does Edmund Wilson, that the Coney Island part is far better. Anyway, will see how you take to it.
    Good luck.
        Cordially,

        Edward Dahlberg

Jewish Community Center,
Bergen and Belmont Avenues,
Jersey City, New Jersey.

From now on, a sizable part of it would be printed in each issue. Also Erskine Caldwell's "Hours Before Eternity" continued the prose of "Inspiration for Greatness," which had appeared in the last issue of 1930. Johns was able to print these works only because they had been flatly refused by the editors of *Hound and Horn,* who voiced the dictum that they would not publish any further contributions by Caldwell. These two sections, preceded by one already printed, comprised the third part of Caldwell's first book of short stories, *American Earth,* published by Scribner's in 1931. In 1936, The Southworth-Anthoensen Press published this third section separately as *The Sacrilege of Alan Kent.*

At this time Caldwell was living in New York, closeted with his typewriter in a small hall-room on the second floor of a West Side brownstone in the Sixties, halfway between Central Park and Broadway. He was bound and determined to stay there, without diversion, until he finished his novel *Tobacco Road.* Caldwell remained in his self-imposed imprisonment, although once or twice Johns was able to induce him into a ride through the neighboring countryside of Westchester County or Connecticut.

Caldwell did not usually like to discuss his writing but he showed Johns the first chapter of *Tobacco Road.* He felt a tremendous uplift when Johns offered to print it as an entity in itself. But with Williams' *White Mule* now in motion, Johns felt it impractical to start another serial work in *Pagany.* One serialized novel at a time seemed sufficient; with more, the quarterly would assume restrictive overtones and lose the spontaneity now captured in each issue.

Well into the novel by this time, Caldwell did not want one chapter cut out, reshaped, and presented as a whole, although if it had been printed, current opinions concerning the style and subject matter of the work might have made Scribner's less hesitant about accepting it. Johns did not pressure Caldwell about releasing this chapter. He admired the completeness of each of Caldwell's short stories printed in *Pagany* and could not understand why *Hound and Horn* had refused both "Inspiration for Greatness" and "Hours Before Eternity."

Also in this first issue of the new year Johns included his own story "Sorry Lady" which later made the Roll of Honor in Edward

J. O'Brien's poll for 1931. Johns was as stunned by Sherry Mangan's erroneous assertion that the character of Wendell Palmer was a portrait of himself as he had been earlier by the coincidental and spontaneous recognition of Robert Hoffman in "Solstice" as editor Lincoln Kirstein.

During the middle of February Johns' good friend Eleanor Herbert sent him a letter she had received from William Carlos Williams, in which he gave a straightforward personal reaction to "Sorry Lady."

> . . . a psychological tension—a maddish, modern twist that does not quite yet run clearly . . . I like the story. It hurts, it is good use of the scalpel but his style hasn't yet the delicacy to swing the situation.

Johns accepted Williams' searching analysis of his story. He recognized the persistent immaturities of style and worked to rid his writing of archaic emphasis. The part of Williams' assessment of the story which pleased Johns the most was:

> It recognizes niceties of moral and mental distress that need recognition and which in the "proletarian spirit" which now seems to be bursting the egg—may be lost.

The incoming contributions were increasingly inclined toward the proletarian spirit and somehow, as the commitment of now-forgotten Marxist poets and writers deepened, the literary quality of their works seemed less and less controlled. It was not experimental because it did not amplify or expand the meaning of words in any particular progression; furthermore, the work was careless and often downright sloppy.

The depression was tightening bank accounts as well as belts. Much of the writing that was sent in was wholly unformed, almost an extemporaneous dirge accompanying the depression. It was colorless despair, devoid of the cries of anger, pride, and resolution to make things better. However, such was the work produced by the best proletarian spokesmen of the period, from the writing of Joseph Vogel, Harry Roskolenkier, and Jack Conroy to the graphics and paintings of such native and foreign artists as Art Young, John Sloan, George Grosz, Diego Rivera, and José Clemente Orozco.

221-225

Mount Vernon, M aine
April 12th 1931.

Dear Johns:

Sorry as I can be that I couldn't see you in New York.
Called once when you had not got back from Boston, and was unable
to raise anyone with the bell twice. Did you find the note I left?

Would it be possible(bluntly)to send me a payment for
the story in Winter no.? I wouldn't ask but I'm down on the
bottom and can't see anything coming my way.

And will you do this, too: change Helen Caldwell's
subscription address from Ga. to here? If the new issue has already been put in the mail, will you send us a copy here, sub-
tracting the cost from that check above? I'd appreciate it; I
want to see something worth reading for a change. I want to see
something worth reading , written by some one who has something
to say, for a change. Me, I have finished the book I've been
doing these long, sometimes hungry, most of the time painful
months. Ten of them. I got to page The End by working for 22 days,
from 12 m. to 12 a.m. That last month was hard, but the other 9
were unbearable. Now that it's over, except another month to revise it for the last time in manuscript, I feel confident that
Scribner's will want to publish it. It's not sensational, experimental, nor important; it is just human. Maybe it's not so
good; but I have a sympathy for the people in it, and I have
become attatched to it. Enough.

Let me hear from you when you have a chance to write.
I want to know what you are doing.

Sincerely,
Erskine Caldwell

361 Gable St.
Houston, Texas

My dear Mr. Johns:

Glad to come out in Pagany. Do you mind
making the following changes? In "Out of the Egg" cut out
the whole windy title, please, and merely call the poem
"SALONS". I am sending you new versions of News(now called
WE), Sylvia(with the rest of the title out), and Revue.
I hope, for god's sake, you use them in place of the old.
In fact, don't show the old ones to anyone! Revue is
Much improved.

Now for some beggarly effrontery. It's
this way. I have a $200 bridge and inlay job I have to have
done on my teeth. I can't have the work begun until I have
some assurance the money is coming from somewhere. "Poetry"
is going to help. Can you give me some idea of what I can
expect for the poems in Pagany? A rough estimate. Understand
I am not trying to hurry you or cajole. But I'd like to
know how far I can let that damned carpenter work on my
grinders. Forgive me for approaching you so in a first
letterm or in any letter.

I have never seen Pagany. Can you send
me a copy Collect?

Do you have Margery Latimer's address?

Yours,

Callman Rawley
(Carl Rakosi)

Please address me as Rawley

My dear sweet Bill:

Could you ask Mr. Johns if he wuld like to see
the beginning ofa novel that I am writing, with the
intention, if it please him, to print itin instal,
ments. I should not claim more than ten dollars
a month, and I wuld send him fifteen pages a months,
or more if he expects more. It is of my autbbiography
I am seaking of.

I am sure it will comeout as being better than that
awful mess, TROUBADOUR by the late Alfred Kreymborg.
I say the latebecause by many signs he is dead.

Kreymborg of Mushrooms I shall always revere and
respett and also the Kreymborg of the first Playlets.

I am writing a poem about you, but it is a hard
taks. I am always afraid offalling   into adulation.

But you, I am sure, I sweat, I never adulated.

No since you deserve more praise than I can give
you.

Thank you for the check and for the words you said
about theallwanceyou send me.

        Yours till the beer grows stale (a saying
ofErnestWalsh)

        Emanuel

Feb. 4 – '31

Dear Johns —

Enclosed find "Meat" which
I like (speaking of the story) a
helluva lot.

Also "The Dope" which I
wish you'd use, since it contains
humor, and it wouldn't do any
harm to sprinkle a little of it,
in broad line's, into Pagany.
In fact, if I may offer a bit
of editorial advice, our "small"
literary magazines have frightfully
neglected American humor, and
as a result sometimes suffer
from over-seriousness. These
words are practically quoted from
the editors of the Amer. Caravan,

the first issue of which was
criticized for its lack of a laugh.

———————

As soon as I get some
extra cash I'm going to put
out at my own expense (since no
publisher would risk it) a
small book containing a story
done along Rabelaisian lines,
said story to concern itself
with the tragedy in the life
of a man whose new mode
of life and environment Suddenly
prevented him from farting
in the morning.

Your humble excuses,
Joe Vogel

227

The staff of *The New Masses,* the best known of all contemporary proletarian little magazines, was becoming more revolutionary in its editorial attitudes, while at the same time growing more strident in its demands for funds from those Party sympathizers who had money to contribute.

Johns was no "parlor pink." He had too much respect for men like Joseph Vogel whose energies and attentions were devoted to finding odd and part-time jobs in order to make enough money to subsist on while he continued his writing. Vogel was a Contributing Editor to *The New Masses* and had just had an article appear in the first issue of *The Left: A Quarterly Review of Radical and Experimental Art* published by George Redfield and Jay du Von out of Davenport, Iowa. A hard working writer, Vogel had no time for trying to milk money out of the "pinks" in order to support the message of the Party.

But others did. Johns walked around the corner to *The New Masses* office on 19th Street one day to pick up copy for the magazine's advertising exchange with *Pagany* and was surprised to run into Dorothy Parker hurrying out of the building. Although she stopped to say hello and exchange news of mutual friends, she seemed startled by the meeting, as if embarrassed to be found so far away from the dining room of The Algonquin. With a glance back at the elevator she left, apologizing for being in such a rush.

When Johns got upstairs Frances Strauss, an intimate friend and secretary to *New Masses* director Walt Carmon, and truly general manager of the magazine's financial operations, greeted him with a grin.

"Did you see Dorothy on the way in?"

Johns nodded.

"Well, she really came across this time. I wouldn't dare tell you how much."

She didn't, but pushed Johns ahead of her onto the fire escape where they could have a cigarette and start a fund-raising campaign. It didn't take Johns long to prove that he had no money to spare for anything but the magazine he edited. As Frances Strauss crowded him closer to the railing of the fire escape, he assured her that paying proletarian writers for their unbiased words was the only

NEW MASSES

A Monthly Publication of Workers Art and Literature

MICHAEL GOLD
Editor

112 E. 19 ST., NEW YORK, N. Y.
ALGONQUIN 4445

WALT CARMON
Managing Editor

FRANCES STRAUSS
Business Manager

May 14, 1931.

**CONTRIBUTING
EDITORS**

PHIL BARD
EM JO BASSHE
HELEN BLACK
SAMUEL BRODY
JACOB BURCK
ADOLPH DEHN
ROBERT DUNN
JOHN DOS PASSOS
ED FALKOWSKI
KENNETH FEARING
JOSEPH FREEMAN
WANDA GAG
HUGO GELLERT
HORACE GREGORY
WILLIAM GROPPER
CHAS. YALE HARRISON
LANGSTON HUGHES
JOSEPH KALAR
GAN KOLSKI
I. KLEIN
MARGARET LARKIN
LOUIS LOZOWICK
H. H. LEWIS
NORMAN MACLEOD
A. B. MAGIL
SCOTT NEARING
HARRY ALAN POTAMKIN
PAUL PETERS
LOUIS RIBAK
BOARDMAN ROBINSON
E. MERRILL ROOT
MARTIN RUSSAK
WILLIAM SIEGEL
UPTON SINCLAIR
AGNES SMEDLEY
BERNARD SMITH
JESSICA SMITH
OTTO SOGLOW
HERMAN SPECTOR
MARY HEATON VORSE
KEENE WALLIS
JIM WATERS
ART YOUNG

357

Subscription rates:
$1.50 a year - Foreign $2
Canada $2.50

Richard Johns,
9 Gramercy Pk.So.,
New York City.

Dear Dick:

We stewed a lot about it and then suddenly decided: "Hell, it's our birthday, they <u>can't</u> turn us down! "

So we decided to write our closest friends for $5 apiece.

We've been lustily alive for five years now: created some darned good reading and a lot of swell drawings. We've helped make life worth while.

But we are in immediate need of funds now. We're not making a fuss about it, or wasting good space in the magazine.

We know that we've got good friends who swear by us. (Allright, occasionally at us too.) So we are writing <u>you</u>, among them for that five ($).

Times are tough. Swear at us if you have to. We hope however that you decide: "Hell, it's their birthday...here's the $5." (We're risking a return envelope on the gamble.)

Here's wishing us a happy birthday, and to you, thanks in advance.

Frances

For the board and editors.

contribution he was about to make. Johns knew that Dorothy Parker was a woman always generous of herself and the money she made as a writer, but he couldn't help wondering whether her back had been pressed against the cold iron of that fire escape on this contributional afternoon.

It was through his friend George Rittenhouse of *Publishers' Weekly* that Johns selected his first New York printer. This was a small, select and expensive printing shop on West 34th Street almost at the edge of the Hudson River and had just converted to offset printing. The second *Pagany* for 1931 is still regarded as the most attractive in the quarterly's series, but it was also the most expensive to produce. Costs for printing this issue were twice what Johns had paid Simonds in Boston. Despite better graphic reproductions and faster service, Johns' budget really did not permit this kind of expenditure on production, even if the results were distinctively better.

From the third issue of 1931 until *Pagany*'s conclusion early in 1933, Johns was forced to use small, undistinguished print shops in New York. The quality control of the Simonds pressroom was lost and replacing it were musty one or two man operations where anything was printed if paid for on time. Now *Pagany* was printed along with proletarian leaflets, weekly Chinese and foreign newspapers, menus, playbills, and other ephemera of the age. Generally these printers ran slovenly shops and Johns realized that added concentration would be required when proofreading and pasting up proofs. Many times there were arguments between editor and printer over alteration and correction fees, the printer refusing to acknowledge errors made when setting type.

NUMBER 1 *January–March*

CONTENTS

PAGANY

THE FIRST YEAR OF "PAGANY" AND THE POSSIBILITY OF CRITERIA

Ezra Pound

The function of the editor is to select. He has a limited surface of paper at his disposal and his job is to fill it with the most vital stuff he can find.

The function of the *critic* (benevolent and beneficent) is to select.

The function of the *writer of critical articles* is to make manifest his dissociations.

Literature does not exist in a vacuum.

Critical writing is ancillary. It is the shoe-horn not the foot. The attempt to pass it off as peer to creative writing is rooted in inferiority complex, the jealousy of the eunuch for Don Juan.

"Critical dicta are points of departure not limits or circumscriptions" (present author 20 years earlier).

The good editor picks by flair. Well and good. He is not looking for finish or for work done to specifications, and he has, as editor, no need whatever to analyze his flair either for himself or for anyone else. Nevertheless he must in course of time become more or less aware of what he is looking for—and even aware, more or less, how he finds it.

SHERRY MANGAN

In choosing (supposing it did choose) a critical spokesman I don't see that PAGANY cd. have done better than accepting Mr Mangan. His general position re/ the relation of criticism to other writing is so sound that I am all the more ready to argue certain phrases that seem to me either questionable or erroneous, or if you like, to insist on certain dissociations, which he has neglected to make. For example

COCTEAU

I see no resemblance whatever between Mr Eliot's fatigue and M Cocteau's adventures. Cocteau will try anything once. My ikon of Cocteau is that of a frail man balancing a two ton weight on a peacock feather and taking the risk that this weight will at any moment fall on his head or his shinbones.

Eliot's leaning against a church or a king or any convenient lamp-post is merely part of the general post war fatigue. It is all or mostly poppy-cock. It is of no importance or interest save in so far as it is transported from a weary Bloomsbug to the vast open spaces etc.

Cocteau takes to catholicism. Very well. It means that he takes to a catholicism *à la Cocteau,* when he finds that this isn't exactly what the good fathers want he looks around for the next day's activity.

While the present writer withdraws from the changing follies of the world to contemplate the more or less tideless sea and the more or less changeless mountains, M Jean jumps from the "opium of the people" to the simple material "hop," by the time the gossips have him "detained" in a maison de santé one finds him not in a maison de santé but sitting in bed perfectly lucid, he is getting himself unpoisoned. It happens to be rather painful but he now knows about "hop." I have known M Jean for a decade and if there is one impression I have had from that slender and nervous figure it is the impression of a fine and high courage, of a man using his strength to the last absolute limit. Another early impression (comparative) dates from the day I was going through Jean Hugo's english version of Le Cap, namely that the difference between me and these Parisians was that I cd. do four hours desk work at a stretch and that they were good for about 15 minutes.

Nevertheless my last sight of Cocteau (April 1930) was Cocteau in the midst of producing a film. He had just discovered that he needed 40,000 francs for a snowstorm (made of borax).

Nothing cd. be more superficial that the view of Cocteau as snob. M Jean played a jazz drum in 1922, the second-rate literati sat near the door of the cabaret with envious ee. etc. He did not play the drum like a black buck or real American college boy, he played it as if he were performing an excessively delicate mathematical operation. I suspect he stopped as soon as he understood it.

Mr Hemingway is preeminently the wise guy. Mr Hemingway estimated M Jean's religion quite wisely in his

Neothomist Poem.

The lord is my shepherd.
I shall not want

    him for long.

Yet both Hemingway and Picabia underestimate M Cocteau.

PICABIA has the finest philosophic mind I have ever encountered. He is one of the very few men capable of dealing with general ideas *at all*. At the time when (oh whenever it was) when Picabia lived out there by the Porte Maillot he used to tease M Cocteau. He used to pull M Jean's leg to the length of twenty good feet of rubber and then watch it snap back and M Jean had no mechanism to deal with that situation.

Picabia denounced M Cocteau: Il abime tout, c't homme là. C'est la Tour Eiffel de Delauney.

This last was for Les Mariés. It contains an injustice. There is a definite act if not of invention at least of carriage in getting a subject *from* the easel picture to the stage.

Brancusi who has no mechanism for dealing with the Parisian top-mob can sit back and admire Cocteau for his energy in getting about and dealing with the dambastuds.

Natalia Barney who is certainly the best thing that ever came out of Dayton Ohio has written somewhere in her desultory scribblings: *I have got a great deal out of life. Perhaps more than was in it.*

Cocteau has certainly extracted interest from a great variety of heteroclite objects (à la Picasso if you like) but . . . are we here to deal with the life around us? Do these things exist? celluloid imitations of glasses of cherry-phosphate etc.

You can not limit Cocteau to the fashionable producer. You have Cocteau, the man who in France in the years just after the war cd. write a straight plain simple essay relying on nothing but its lucidity and good sense. Cocteau the refresher of the french language. Cocteau who stays within his own limitations but has never been stopped by any keep off the grass signs; by any "chi tocca al filo muore"; by any poison label.

Cocteau always with a new toy, because it amuses him, Cocteau, always talking and always saying something that he was not saying when one saw him the week or the year before, Heracleitan if you like, c'est la vie, the perfectly natural life of Jean Cocteau.

And as for snobs, there is no doubt that they wd. like to nest in his tail feathers, but this assiduity does not . . .

"Mais, mon cher!! Les X . . . , mais mon cher, dans AUCUN pays du monde!!"

The feather is no longer attached to the bird. Hence the high frequency in the frequent denunciations of Cocteau.

HENRY JAMES

"the snobisme that followed Henry James." No my dear Mangan. Or yes, snobisme may have followed dear Henry BUT:

If there is one thing that H J did it was to warn his compatriots against being taken in by the English. My first explosion was: did he do anything except warn us?

My second is: at any rate how much of the work is a warning? the vacuity of public men (Tragic Muse, Private Life) the vacancy of Lady Barberina?

At any rate he warned me. With a phrase, a tone (given the ambience and the situation) an expression all-comprehending, abysmal, without any need for specific, in fact under circumstances when specific utterance wd. have been impossible.

Mr James was dissatisfied with the American literary life of the "80's." For this neither Mr Mangan nor any other sane man will now in moments of lucidity blame him. It is not necessary to follow this statement by the really dastardly assumption that H J was satisfied with the English.

CRITERIA

Literature does not exist in a vacuum. My commendation of "Morada" was largely due to Morada's seeming to be aware of literature as part of the general and social existence, whereas The New Masses group seems rather in need of a declaration analogous to Mussolini's remark: *Possession of a Fascist membership card does not confer literary genius on the holder.*

The condition of man in social organism and the working of the latter, are parts of legitimate subject matter. All major literature has taken count of the relation of the one to the rest. If you have a potato-faced premier or a pot-bellied usurer or agglomerate of the elected in place of a (in reality probably unpicturesque) "tyrant" you must adjust your terminology *ad rem*. And you must be ready to learn how the damnblasted thing functions.

The realist (in the Maupassant line) short story is a most useful form. The changes effected or effectable in its technique have been and are very few. Technique does not consist solely in playing about with verbiage. The major part of technique consists in shaping the material into the FORM. There is more technique in a novel or in a vol. of stories by Edgar Wallace than in a year's issue of the Criterion and of all the highbrow weeklies on the market.

As to possible criteria. You can go back to the original Imagist manifesto and find enough criteria to keep you busy for some time. Custom doth not stale, because the practice is not common. Every ten years or so someone ought to git the boat up into dry dock and scrape off the barnacles.

One of the simplest tests or criteria that critic or editor can apply is the perfectly simple: Use no word that does not contribute to the presentation.

This sentence does not provide the Bloomsburgers with a subject for unbounded yatter. There is nothing to be said about it. The writer either does or doesn't. The saying has never become popular. Not even Amy cd. popularize it. Imagism was never, if I may interrupt Mr Mangan, Imagism was never popularized, Amygism was popularized. The Amygist manifestos omitted this troublesome clause. It meant too much work. The Amygists dug out the longest word they cd. find in my published writings. I had used "polyphonic" with a definite meaning applicable to rhyme-schemes of Arnaut Daniel. I had, I think, indicated that there was a difference between the term so used and polyphony as a technical term in musical text books. However it was a long word and it was used to start yatter concerning what turned out to be dilutations of Paul Fort.

That second clause of the first manifesto is as useful to the prose writer as to the poet. The editor finds a ms. unsatisfactory, he doesn't know quite why. There are dead twigs on the tree yet the tree doesn't seem dead all over. The author had, perhaps, something to say but went to sleep while saying it. The page is sprinkled with words that don't function.

I can't see that this clause has ever hindered a first rate writer. It is however an instrument for measuring voltage.

Most contemporary verse (a.d. 1930) seems to me rather unsatisfactory. Not, you understand, *wholly* unsatisfactory but rather unsatisfactory. The third clause of the first manifesto was a rather general reference to melodic line. You can't get a whole technical treatise into a manifesto. I ref: the reader to Boris de Schloezer's remarks on melody in his book on Stravinsky.

I have heard that poetry is an art in which the art of words and that of music are fused or welded together. It wd. be better, and wd. show more historic and factual sense to say that it is an art that occurs before these two arts have split apart from their parent stem.

It is undoubtedly possible to exercise either art separately, as a violinist may do finger exercises for the left hand for half an hour and then turn to practice bowing. One does not expect the violinist to separate these two activities during a concert. The difference between poetry and prose is due to a different proportion of the musical element. Most versifiers are today (as they were in 1912) too god damned lazy to study the musical side of their craft. Some are not interested in it all. There is no use in talking to what Mr Mangan calls the "never-had-its."

Mr Mangan uses the term "abundance," possibly the old term "copia" wd. satisfy his requirement. But there is pseudo-copia. Just as there is pseudo-experiment. We have had a flood of pseudo-experimenters who are merely there in granpap's laboratory fooling around with the test tubes. They haven't learned any chemistry, they don't mean to learn any chemistry. Haven't great discoveries been due to accident?

There are two questions the critic or editor can ask himself in the presence of a new manuscript:

1. Has the author studied his metier?
2. Has he investigated his subject?

I note in Pagany for its first year a very good case of defect in the second of these. A most estimable and serious young man whose career I have watched with attention though I have never been satisfied with his work, has tackled a public subject. But he has tackled it without knowledge. Uncouth reporters have done the job better.

I repeat that a frenchman has written a treatise to prove that Homer was an army doctor. He tries to prove it from Homer's knowledge of wounds. Some other guy has written an essay to prove that Shakespeare must have served as a lawyer's clerk.

The subject matter of an author in the year 1931 is man, a savage, governed largely by avaricious barbarian blahbooers, in an age where the focus is economic (not political) and in which the economic factor is extremely Heracleitan because of the rapid movement of practical science.

The reds, let us say, try to construct an ideal community for cab-drivers. In five years there will be no cabdrivers left. Cabdrivers' para-dise is unfit for chauffeurs. The serious author has got to look for the permanent equations or at least he has got to be interested in the relative durability of the equations. It is just as floppy for an author today to ignore economics (finance, distribution, distribution of purchasing power, distribution of the benefit accruing to society as a whole from machines) as it wd. have been for an early greek bard to ignore transport by sail.

Mr. Mangan is quite right in saying that we can afford to ignore Dresden china theology. Aquinas is hardly a serious (in the modern sense) character. (I suspect that Scotus Eriugina was.)

MR ELIOT

Literature does not exist in a vacuum. Neither is it actually printed and published in an Utopia. Utopia for the duration of this essay can be taken to mean a community of lively men loving justice and eager to see and understand the literary manifestations of their contemporaries. In so far as Mr Mangan hammers Mr Eliot for his kindly introduction to the castrated British edtn. of my poems I must point out that it is just that, a British edtn. Mr Mangan is quite fair elsewhere in his essay in pointing out that after all Eliot is in England writing for the Bri'sh and that the damage caused by his hobbies has been caused more by their transporta-tion to an unsuitable milieu than by their inherent nature. Let him enter-tain for a moment the following propositions:

It does not matter a tinker's damn (or one faint Bloomsburried sigh) what anyone in England thinks of me or of Mr Joyce or of Mr Lewis (author of The Apes of God). It matters quite considerably to anyone resident in that island that the best contemporary work can not get printed there without continual fuss and botheration. If a certain amount of the more active work was printed in that muck hole in 1917 and 1918 it was due largely to a sort of quakeress nun who subsidized the Egoist and who was willing to sit for a number of hours daily in a sort of cell labeled "office." (Someday I shall perhaps do a monograph of the british woman of letters from Harriet Wilson to Harriet Weaver.)

When it became impossible to get contemporary work printed in Eng-land and when Ulysses was merely sequestered and its importer put under official blackmail that island appeared to me rather as the nethermost parts of a privy. A place not to be dwelt in.

Mr Mangan may legitimately take that preface as symptomatic of some of Mr Eliot's mental habits, but for sake of rendering justice he shd. also consider it as a diagnosis of the Bri'sh public. That preface shows the measures which an admittedly acute and intelligent editor thinks it necessary to take (I believe quite rightly) in order to insert even the more anodyne parts of my writing into a circle of Bri'sh readers large enough to pay the bare expenses of printing the volume.

The book shd. not have reached America at all (save for the research work of bile specialists). The American reader is provided with Liveright's edition of my Collected Poems.

The Bri'sh public is hardly our public, it is in a limited sense a subject. Mr Mangan is welcome to study it. He shd. realize that my Homage to Propertius is not only a "Persona" but a Persona which implies that one empire going to hell is very much as another (Bri'sh as Roman). Mr. Eliot knows that the Bri'sh reader won't like this.[1]

---

[1] So far as I know only three Englishmen have either understood or liked the poem. And one of them (The late Thos. Hardy) suggested a means of "making it easier for the reader." Which you can, if you like, chalk up against Life's L'il Ironies. Mr Hardy's comment was filled with acute good sense. I can only hope that my later work has shown the effect of his lesson.

GRAPHOPHONE NICKELODEON DAYS[1]
Edward Dahlberg

> *'it looks like a big*
> *like a big night tonight*
> *a big night tonight . . .'*

And yet it all came back, the taste of it, the tang and brine of it, like the windy crispy newspaper afternoon air over the san francisco wharves. All that he was and could never completely unknow   all those down-and-out days went carousselling through his brain   ragtiming through his head the alleynights in back of the 8th street lady barber shop, a broken spiderweb, the barefooted nigger evenings in fall, *run-sheep-run,* the tough hot bakery independence avenue julys, wading in khaki mudpuddles sunk in vacant lots   locust, cherry, maple, walnut, wyandotte, the smelly leaves, the roots, the branches, the gutters of the streets, the water from the fire-pump swobbing them,—he could never erase them.

Still slides, *love me and the world is mine,* graphophone nickelodeons, slot machine phonographs

> it looks like a big
> like a big night tonight
> a big night tonight

a hot time
in the old town
tonight

one cent muscle machine: how many lamps can you light, can you ring the bell,
you ring the bell: penny arcade moving pictures:

> ladies night in
> a turkish bath

What the book
agent saw
punching bag, muscle builder, fortune teller, penny arcade postcard proverbs:

> a rolling stone
> gathers no moss
> (but who in the hell)
> wants to gather moss)

[1] Extract from novel: *Flushing to Calvary.*

george washington public school on independence avenue:
> there's some one tapping
> on the maple tree
> jackie frost, jackie frost
> came in the night
> who killed cock robin
> it was i with my little hatchet
> ring around a rosie
> a hot time in the old
> town tonight

get a peep at *venus* through the telescope for only a nickel! cheap at half the price but why through a telescope   it's a word beginning with f, strawberry pimples on her cheeks, drawers were always falling, *honey boy i hate to see you leave me,* kimonoes, garters, corsets, hairpins, perfume behind her ears, emma, loosely kimonoed, her thighs, a dream out of beverley of graustark, her talcum-powdered lotion-creamed breasts—a long moving picture soul kiss   hot tossing nights, her thighs whorling like an electric barber pole: the penny arcade automatic piano jangling away in spasms . . .

> call me up some rainy afternoon
> and we'll have a quiet little spoon
> and we'll talk about the weather
> i'll see that my mother takes a walk
> mum's the word, baby dear . . .

when he grew up he'd eat thirty lemon pies all at once . . . *oh, oh, oh don't be afraid*

dago bread, cheney watermelon hucksters, lyric moving picture house, open air tents, lawdie lawdie tabernacle sermons, halley's comet, the end of the world, bad rodent dreams in the 8th street flat, bohunk nightmares, blackhand barky trees, pimpish gaslight joints, the midnight ride of a can of beer, *ach du lieber augustin*

the kansas city west bottoms, a wiry and rusty rat trap, the bluffs, stale, gone-looking boxcar smoke in the back of his throat, red caboose bonfires, corn-stalk smoking, m.k.t., chicago & alton blakean alfalfa field midnights, *casy jones got another papa,* roundhouse cindery toe-stubbing noons, adobe main street 11 o'clock mornings, armour & swift packing-house summers, dusty hoofbeaten heifer clouds, kansas city stockyards, biting cement feedbag dust 4th of julys, dog-lolling street bum days, cool strawy bins, hosstrough waterpail stalls in stedna's liverystables, hoss swopping piddling saturdays, *pony boy, pony boy, won't you be my tony boy*, manurish heeled oklahoma stockmen, good tippers, got a haircut, egg shampoo, a shave, a massage, and a manicure, took the whole works in his mother's barber shop: street car conductors, cheap skates: stingier than a close shave, awful mashers, twenty three skidoo for you kid   the flatiron salesman was an old rounder

Bananas and cream kellogg's cornflakes sundays, dragging, ant-like bath sundays, grand pa's tar soap, dutch cleanser, gold dust twins, whiskbroom, scoured kitchen sink, carpet dusting,—he had to shoo the furniture polish rag over the postcard views of swope park, the old shanty union depot, his mother said he was more trouble than his measly help was worth: he was good riddance

the grand opera house, tige and buster brown, the funnies, in my old kentucky home, *massa's in the cold cold ground,* cecile was the orneriest chippy in the star ladies barber shop, had ten men on the string, you couldn't trust her from here to there

Mary was a still-water, never ate meat on good fridays, wore high top-boots, lace shirtwaists which concealed her flatiron breasts: her legs were lost in the amusement park grotto of her shroud-black clothskirt: she never cut up with the trade: when she quit lizzie's shop the saloonkeeper next door set her up in diamonds and lighthousekeeping and bought her all kinds of fancy cutglass: cecile said, you could take it from her, they never took out a license

the question girl, a week's run at the grand opera, the spokey bohunk umbrella factory across the way: he played around the wooden boxcar cases with ghizella who was too smart for her age but what could you expect, her mother always slept with another codger every night, her paw was a cranky roundshouldered old screw who ran a barber's itch college down on the lower commissionhouse main street, near the cowboy and indian gillis theater and the city carrot peas asparagus cream cheese vegetable and meat market, but lorry thought she was a regular peach: her watercolor hair, curly papershavings, was prettier than the coca cola girl on the owl drugstore anniversary sale calendar: when he was going on nine, with tantalizing mesmerizing *school days* in the back wings of his head, he hummed:—

> oh gee, be sweet to me kid
> i'm awfully fond of you
> i'm blue when you're cross to me
> come treat me square kid
> i love you for fair—for
> i'm crazy kid, crazy for you

love me the way you did—
fill me with joy, my honey boy
oh gee, be sweet to me kid . . .

. . . because she wouldn't kiss him   one saturday afternoon when his
mother was shaving and haircutting and joshing in the star ladies' barbershop ghizella helped him carry the provision basket up the steep hill to
the 8th street flat: they were in the lacecurtained cutglass parlor sitting
on the pianostool: don harney, the peroxide blonde, with the troublesome
appendix, who was kept by drew, a reporter on the k.c. journal, was in
the next room hotwaterbottling her right side: lorry was dead gone on
ghizella who told him how she and leslie had played house together: then
how leslie and his sister had done it: and how she and leslie's sister had
played taking turns doing the housekeeping and putting the sofapillow in
its proper place and folding back the sunday bedspread   ghizella played

i like coffee
i like tea
i like lorry
and lorry likes me

on the bass upright piano so that don harney in the next room couldn't
hear her   ghizella said it was good, so good, much better than cracker
jacks or taffy and lorry wanted to ask for it but he was tongue-tied and
couldn't get a word out of his mouth   then there was eight year old
mabel who he knew when they lived up on shady forest avenue who told
him how it was done but he was afraid   when mabel was seventeen she
left her husband and two kids in joplin and ran off with her uncle   the
last he heard about ghizella she was streethustling in windy chi.: run-
down at the heels, saving u.s. cigar coupons for a set of roger's silverware
and working in a turdy whorehouse: she had gone clean nuts, that's what
bud taylor said before he knocked up buella claire   when ghizella was
eleven a black stovepipe nigger dragged her into a vacant lot.   bud heard
his maw talking about it to mr. coffee, the flatiron salesman

The oblong pasteboard pictures inside *sweet caporal* and *hassan* turkish
cigarettesboxes of john l. sullivan, stanley ketchel (shot by accident),
william mc kinley, joe gans (kicked off with t.b.), golden goldfilling
smiling heavyweight champion jack johnson (railroaded out of country
for white-slaving), ad wolgast (the chicago stockyard boy), abe attel
(flashiest lightweight in ring), 3-fingered mordecai brown (greatest spit-
ball pitcher of all times), second baseman larry lajoie, casey at the bat
discus-throwers, polevaulters, olympic players, roald amundsen, arctic pole
missouri dairy refrigeraters, teddy roosevelt, big game hunters, rough

riders, *remember the maine,* commodore perry, don't shoot boys, the kansas city paseo, the spanish-american war, the u.s. armory, teddy roosevelt days, wide-open pretzel limburger cheese saloon times

> oh bring back those eggs
> at ten a dozen,
> bring back those wonderful
> days

bock, swiss, porterhouse charlie steak, hot tamale, chili con carne mexican greasers, the schottishe, *12th street blues,* the millionaire tramp, the candy kid . . .

all that was his boyhood louvre . . . phineas's dad's three gilded balled pawnshop on walnut street (that's the way to ball the jack: some day phineas would grow up and have three balls like his father had and be as strong as samson): phineas was rich and used toney words: *booty,* willis woods theater, country club district, fairmount park airs: he wore swell knickers and a button on his coatlapel with printing on back: *to hell with the maine* . . .

Peck's quick lunch, nickel lemon creamy suns, buttered oyster cracker packing lard tincan noontimes, two bits chicken dinners, chili beans, parchment yellow spuds, high yellow oleomargarine, the greasy crisco moon, upstairs, back, over tischa's licensed house: clean as a pin: all the switchmen and railroad johnnies went there for a piece of tail: 12th street was classier then   tischa had delicatessan winnie wurst sores in an anthill mound on her cheeks and beer-stained hair and ran around with a silk jazzshirted, lislesocked dopefiend with a brilliantine advertising pompadour: he had toney mint's breath: lorry chewed wrigley's spearmint: he wanted a sweet hightone hotel baltimore breath   he wanted to be the candy kid and a willis woods theater dude: . . .

> you've got me going going kid
> you are my little merry wid
> you are just the candy kid
> you've got me going going some . . .

*   *   *   *   *   *

> *'tickle me here*
> *tickle me dear*
> *tickle me love*
> *in these lonesome ribs'*
> > james whitcomb **riley**

Automatic pianola clinking rain, clinking clinking champagne alaskan eugene field ice, edgar guest shooting gallery verse

Lew Dockstader's minstrels, blackfaced coon nights, black stovepipe nigger alleys, ghizella, poor dear, ringling bros. circus, barnum & bailey, a sucker born every minute, and now that we have stop-watches, dockstader's minstrels better than sis hopkins:

if a body meets a body

comin' through the rye

people were buying tickets to beat the band, a packed house every night, bigger event than the priest of pallas parade, or the arrival of the millionaire tramp

A colored jokebook drop curtain: blackfaces in purity squad whitegloves, marching up and down the stage

keep time

keep time

An orchestration of seventy chairs; two comedians start in with a hick's barndance jig, turkey in the hay

turkey in the straw

Programs are still rustling. The lowney chocolates, hershey and bon bons candy-butcher has just died down. The minstrel joshing gets under way. It's still a horse on the audience.

say nigger, where wuz you born?

in virginia.

well, what part?

all of me, nigger, all of me.

The audience titters. Thin potato chip titters crackle in the theater *sweet caporal* dust.

so, you all comes of noble blood.

yes sah.

well, what kind of blood do you all come from?

i done told you, nigger, i comes of high blood

lookee, here, coon, the only high blood you got in you is high blood pressure.

The programs whiskbroom the hot air again.

A darky tenors

> mr brown, went around
> all around,
> with his violin,
> lawdy, how he played it,
> made it moan
> so beautiful
> fiddle up, fiddle up

then another jokester interrupts:

why don't you try an operatic air?

operatic air, what kinda air is that?

try madame butterfly.

you try her.

A fat man in the audience boo-hoos into his handkerchief, makes round circular liquid yodels, and gurgles up and down his galli curci coloratura stairs. The rest of the orchestra take him up.

A fellow in the niggerheaven gallery whistles through his fingers. The crowd is pulsing and motorthrobbing with the actors. The jokester waits and then goes on:

all right, i'll try her.

what you waitin' for, go on and try her.

all right. the next song, to please the ladies in the box, is entitled, madame butterfly, to her frigid husband: some day, he'll come.

Cattle stampeding stamping of feet everywhere. Thick yellow spud-blocks of laughter jam the air. The audience brings down the house. Then the jokester, like a referee in the center of the ring, holds up his hands for quiet, and continues.

now for the benefit of the reading-loving public in the theater, i'll recite:

'lilies are both pure and fair
growing midst the roses there—
roses, too, both red and pink,
are quite beautiful, i think.'
'but—
another runner-up interrupts:
roses, red, violets blue,
i can row, can-oe, can-oe.

A skinny toothpick cigarmanufacturer wipes the blobs of carousel tears whorling on his spectacles. Then he adjusts his chair in the box. He tries to remove the part that he knows is his from the adhesive tailormade cloth.

The minstrel ringleader makes a stab at another. The clinking clinking eugene field ice hoarfrosts the theater air.

the years had dragged a weary pace
since last those joys i tasted,

The fellow in the gallery sirens through his fingers. And then:

drag him out!

Lew Dockstader enters. Lew Dockstader who shook the country like the russian revolution of 1905.

*   *   *   *   *   *

'layers and layers of sensation
and no heart in it.'

peer gynt.

And now thousands and hundreds of lady barbershop female smells flooded him: witch hazel, bay rum, facecreams, hairtonics, talcumpowdered breasts, Emma, loosely kimonoed, her body damp and smelling of his thick bedroom imaginings,—all that flooded in upon him, but he was not there. And all the neuter odors of shoeleather, sprinkled streets, tar, lumber piles, stirred in his nose, but he was not in it. For he had not yet emerged from them, could not.

And from the american minstrel troubadour trouvere days: a bit of blank cartridge verse:

'the years had dragged a weary pace
    since last those joys i tasted
and i have grown so wan of face
    and oh, so slender-waisted!'
'o saw ye bonny leslie
    as she gaed o'er the border?
she's gane, like alexander,
    to spend her conquests farther.'

punching bag, guess your weight fortune teller lines:
'so now, in the prime of my manhood, i polish
        this lyric gem'
    'or shall i wear the bottom of my trousers rolled?'
'of the clink of the ice in the pitcher the boy brings up the hall'
up the hall up the hall of the memory-membrane tissues of the nose, clinking, clinking against metaphysical corridors and stirring up the museum—desolation in his blood—'o metaphysical head.'

*   *   *   *   *   *

'ist das nicht das weisenhaus,
ya wohl, das ist das weisenhaus . . .'

The cleveland orphanage, the old mother's home down the block, the green dollar bill blades of grass out on the front lawn, *es ist verboten,* fifty demerits for stubbing one's toes against them, the waterfountain mute as a stillborn child in soured and dried shrubbery february: ratty wet wooden chicken coop march: mick and gullyside januarys the slit of sky seen through the orphan asylum dormitory window, an enameled mush tinplate—snowblue enamel in summer the fountain played on 1st and 2nd picnics *ist das nicht das weisenhaus,* down the hill, the mill on the floss, snoring silas marner afternoons in the schoolhouse, around the bend over the diphtheria pond, becker's stalecakes, becker's heavy neck-boils, herman mush tate's dictionary of sure-fire words earthier than the bible, woodland avenue pushcart boulevard, goulashy every-other-wednes-day sausages, christine's drawer's, mick and gullyside january days, hospi-tal pruney sundays, *ist das nicht das weisenhaus, ya wohl, das ist das weisenhaus, we the people of the united states, i pledge allegiance, one nation, indivisible, with liberty and justice for all, ya wohl, das ist das weisenhaus, o wie schön es, o wie schön es, o tennenbaum, o tennenbaum, und die kuchen schmekt so gut,* every-other-wednesday sausages, gray pruney graham cracker sundays, we the people of the united states

The goddam potsdam court, unter den linden, milwaukee lager, schlager beer, donner und blitzen, *hail, hail the gang's all here,* conf. 1917, his first skylark blueserge long pants, virgin mary white immaculate american carnation confirmation day, *good bye j.o.a., i say good bye to you, with-out the least regret* . . . out in the city, a former inmate, out in the big wide world, the american playboy of the western world, raymond hitchcock—*hitchy koo*—*oh, oh, oh, it's the cutest little thing,* lake erie air, free free euclid avenue air, high tone air, vaudeville air, rockefeller park, wade park, Keith's Circuit 1917 . . . *if i only had your disposition, i'd be lovin' you all the time, if you're crazy about the women, you're not crazy at all, you're so pretty, oh, so pretty, you're some pretty doll,* that's the way life was out in the big city, The keith's circuit vaudeville slapstick war: *i may be gone for a long long time, over there, over there,* khaki forever, three cheers for, social criticism: *i didn't raise my boy to be a soldier, then what are you doing over here,* you goddam son of bitchin' bolsheviks, the big parades, the war, The War, THE FATHER, SON, AND THE HOLY GHOST: THE WAR: *all ye millions i embrace thee,* the redlight districts were shut down, puberty skyscraper erections, tallest building in the world, bigger and better wars, *all ye millions i embrace thee,* you goddam son of bitchin' bolsheviks, *then what are you doing over here, over there, over there*

The yanks are coming . . . the yanks are coming, puberty skyscraper erections, the vaginal walls of jericho are falling

* * * * * *

'*And upon her forehead was a name written,* MYSTERY, BABYLON THE GREAT, THE MOTHER OF HARLOTS AND ABOMINATIONS OF THE EARTH.'

the revelation

NEW YORK, the syphilitic body of god, its jaundiced electric lights diseasing the night, welfare island, a cancerous blurred negative, the stippled waters of the east river, over the queensboro bridge, faster, faster, faster, *eveready flashlight batteries, adams black jack, And upon her forehead was a name written, SOCONY, SOCONY, MYSTERY,* chiclets, *dentyne,* brisbane steel frame cottages, *BABYLON THE GREAT, SOCONY, THE MOTHER OF HARLOTS,* queens boulevard, welcome to long island city, *AND ABOMINATIONS OF THE EARTH,* faster, faster, *batter my heart, batter my heart*

MAIN st. FLUSHING to CALVARY, saul's *dead march,* the theater moon, *pomp and circumstance,* the stars strung telegraph-wise across a logarithm table in the back of a text book, coney island calvary cemetery nights, *and his son isaac and ishmael buried him in the cave of machpelah in the field of ephron,* mardi gras confetti seaside bathing saturday evenings, oyster house seaside brine, secondhand seaweed, the ritzy calvary cemetery leaves swing over the daily graphic slabs: the dream surrealistic theater leaves . . . the theater moon, an open can of armour & swift packinghouse lard, *batter my heart* . . .

It went carousselling through his brain. . . . He took the evening in the palm of his hands and rubbed his eyelids across it.

TENDER ADVICE

Romer Wilson

"You think because I ain't been to Oxford or Cambridge I don't know the colour of the sun. I'm sorry you went. I've been a fool and spoilt your education by 'aving you taught. Yes, my dear boy, I'm sorry. Put the mess you're in down to me. Put that jackass Jesmond with his spats and immoralities down to me. Put all old Whiskerando said in his impertinent indictment of you down to me. Sweep your 'eart out and dump the sweepin's in my bin. You're young, lad, and I don't exactly blame you for eatin' what I put down before you.

"I don't know what we are to do quite, though. You better draw a hundred or two and get off by yourself somewhere. Rome, what d'you say to Rome? I've seen the blue sky there over the ancient city and Saint Peter's sticking his nubbin up into it. Why not go to Rome for a bit? Your mother and I 'ad our honeymoon in Italy. You didn't go with us, but you came back with us, 'ardly noticeable you were, but we knew. I guess you've some southern heat in your blood. Your mother and I 'oped it would be so; and it was.

"After all, what do you care who the hell these old 'eros at Cambridge are or what they do to you? They can't injure you unless you stoop to them. You're an Englishman and a citizen of the world, not a pettyfogging bent-at-the-knee old schoolmaster's son that 'as to ask a scraggy lot of antique town clerks for a job teaching gutter snipes. Even if I'd give you nothin', you're a free man with 'ands and feet.

"You go to London and find a decent woman, and when you're right in that direction, see Rome, and well, needn't take it as a prelude to dyin', need you? Then go in the Peeny mountains, as your mother used to call 'em. Ha! Ha! My boy, don't be a fool. If you can't be a gentleman with a Cambridge manner, at any rate don't be a fool. Don't miss it!. Go to Italy, that's where you were conceived. They lift at every street corner and raise their hats to each other as if each was a dog and a duke. You go out there and forget this intellectual twaddle be'ind you. Don't read the newspaper. Sit in the sun. God's sake, sit in the sun! Give Cambridge a miss.

"Ah, my dear boy, I don't know what to say to you. You're in a pitiable mess. It doesn't matter a rap to me what you did. For your own sake, forget you did anything. Clean yourself out, go to Italy or Spain or anywhere, go alone, go with nothing. Look 'ere, I put it to you this way. Tom Foster isn't born. I 'avn't a son; shan't 'ave till you wire me— "Arrived Rome." Stay anywhere you like. Ah, you young chaps, you have read so much it takes the words out of my mouth. God help you! What do you do this sort of thing for? There's only the devil in it as far as I can see. If you go on that way among decent men—but you're young and, as I say, if I had to do it over again, I'm damned if I should educate you.

"Tom, your mother and I loved each other. It would be 'ard to tell where we loved each other most, but it certainly wasn't least in Rome. We never could take you travellin': you were always at school. Dursn't interrupt your damnable education to show a boy a new country. It was too 'ot in August, too cold at Christmas, and June—the one month I 'ad free—you must be sucking lollipops be'ind your masters' back, or loungin' away your time at a seaside resort preparing for Eton—preparing to prepare for Cambridge, pretending to be preparing to prepare yourself to make your entrance into this world; what is it—fully equipped for the Battle of Life? Bum show!

"Tom, I've been fooled. Education 'as inked your nose. Run, Tom, run away before it inks your cock. Tom, your mother and I liked Italy. We went there again and again. "If Tom were 'ere " Well, Tom wasn't.

"What's the good of sighing like that? Think me a dam fool, do you? A dam fool! I 'ave been but I'm not to-day. Perhaps it's you wanted to talk to me. Well, you did, and this is my answer. Take it or leave it. My answer is a cheque for two 'undred and to listen to you when it's spent.

"Ever seen a green tree, Tom, ever seen a tree out of day dreams, ever seen a mountain, ever felt a fresh wind blow? That's what is good to me. I can't help liking a good dinner. I can't help not liking Imperturbable Spats and Gloomy Grouser. Oh, yes, I've names for 'em all. Who's going to stick to you? Found that out? Never mind if nobody does. It doesn't signify with me what you did. What you did doesn't shame me now, it doesn't frighten me now. I was frightened by you, but I fought it all out, and some'ow I got back to Italy, Rome or Florence, never mind which, the Ponty Vecchio it was the sun on it, and your dear mother—oh, my Tom, oh, my Tom, I don't know how I bear her death but for you—said, 'Why, there's houses on it!' And I said 'Yes, across the river in the sun.' Like a rainbow.

"And I remember we took a carriage one day. Your mother felt tired of picture galleries on your account. She was beginning to. We drove up to a small monastery and had a view over Florence. Ah, magnificent! Tom! Tom! Tom! You're a great grown man—and no doubt—well, never mind—my heart nearly burst. Mother and I kissed each other up there.

"That is what I would like you to see. Stay away over June. June is the month. By the way, you can live out there if you like. Why not? I'll be out at Christmas and you can show me the changes the war made.—Come, my boy, there still is some shade of hope. Come to think of it my way! The green trees like growing and the sun shining. Why should men alone be black in the face with misery? Here is the world. It's men alone—

"By my soul, I believe you despise me. I believe you're infected to the core by the poison I had so expensively procured for you. God is not a ninny. He made the sea. God's off your menu, I suppose. Well, he's not off mine. However, I've no right to interfere. Silence is all you ask from me. I see it in your attitude—silence. And what else: You shall choose. You shall be father, I the son. Allow yourself sufficient money. You have carte blanche up to two thousand. You wish to sever our relationship, divorce your father, cut off your father from your regard with a moment's notice? I'm wrong to have burdened you with a father.

"Yes, my dear boy, I know I cannot for a moment understand you. There are no more sins these days. The world has simply done you an injury, life has insulted you—Allowed!—What next? God, what slop! That is not it, even. I know the intricate machinery of your sins is beyond paternal understanding.—Have you forgotten?—By Hell and the Abominations, who's the dog that started this smelly game? I'd tan him! I'd tan you, but you have a man's outside. My hands off your body, my hands off your soul. They shall be, they shall be, in a moment. We shan't meet for some time.

"For my sake as well as yours you must take a holiday, just for your health's sake. Go to a good doctor first. I expect you're sound. Not as if you had war nerves. What's this feminine weakness is rotting off our boys? Are there no good women? If I were a woman, I'd die a virgin before I had all the limpets of Eton on to me. And your long nosed dons? Do they marry? Can they breed? It seems a pity to me, when I see your beautiful colleges, that such cat's-meat spawns in their gardens.

"When you get to Florence, Tom, go to the Bobbly Gardens and rest there. Walk in the avenues alone or in company. I'd take some nice girl there. At the end of the vista you will see the blue sky. Your heart will start climbin'. Then it's deliciously cold in the shade of the churches. A cool drink on an 'ot day.

"And go where Michael Angelo—he's the biggest man they 'ad,— wherever he worked, go. 'Uge! He was a giant and he'll comfort you. But it's in their little pictures they ave 'eaven on earth, those Italians. All of a sudden a cypress tree against the sky! Your Mother loved 'em. Rude upstickin' trees makin' love at nothin' in June.

"And then if you're done with that, there's Lugano on a summer night for you. All that with a friend. If you care to take a friend, you are welcome. I can smell it all again. Or over the border near the snow line. Innsbruck! Before the war—or the Black Forest—in June, always in June! Or further north, Stockholm even, to roam at will and be young again. I should not care if I had pupped all the sins of Adam if I was young again and had what I have had.

"Well, my boy, good-night! I don't expect nor hope nor want. There is a blank cheque to you on the mantlepiece under the clock. Wire me if you happen to pass through Rome. I should really appreciate that. Good-night. God bless you. I daresay I shan't write. Don't draw less than two hundred. I'd make it nearer three—for immediate uses. I'll make up your account quarterly, of course. When you fancy, come in the office. Come to work, mind you, though. I'm pressing nothing. Good-night.—Good-night—From Rome. I should appreciate that wire."

FOUR POEMS

(1924-1928)

Louis Zukofsky

I

Buoy—no, how,
It is not a question: what
Is this freighter carrying?—
Did smoke blow?—That whistle?—
Of course, commerce will not complete
Anything, yet the harbor traffic is busy,
there shall be a complete fragment
Of—

Nothing, look! that gull
Streak the water!
Getting nearer are we,
Hear? count the dissonances,

Shoal? accost—cost
Cost accounting.

□

II

(Awake!)

Propped on the earth
And from where, what sleep, awake! Your head—
And kissed the center of your forehead—
Knowing we have escaped from death
Of sleep; and as on aerial curtains wrought
Of morning with the wind and one more kissing thought
Death's words are naught:
'Now like two lamps irrelevant upon the road
Short-circuited before blue morning go out!'

III

Tall and singularly dark you pass among the breakers—
Companionship as of another world bordering on this;
To the intelligence fastened by the senses you are lost
In a world of sunlight where nothing is amiss:

For nothing but the sun is there and peace vital with the sun,
The heaviest changes shift thru no feature more than a smile,
Currents spread, and are gone, and as the high waves appear,
You dive, in the calming are as lost awhile.

How in that while intelligence escapes from sense
And fear with hurled human might darkens upon bliss!
Till as again you stand above the waters
Fear turns to sleep as one who dreamt of falling, an abyss!

□

IV

Passing tall
Who walk upon the green
So light they are not heard
If never seen;—

Willow above in spring haze,
Green sprig and pendulous;—
Wind, white lightning
In branches over us;

Sun;
All weathering changing loves,
In the high grass (kiss!)
Will not uncover us.

Feb. 8, 1931.

Dear Johns:-

Up till now I haven't received a single copy of
Pagany. If you remember, you were to send me seven copies.

I saw Dos Passos again. His address is: 571
Commercial Street, Provincetown, Mass. You had better send him
a couple of issues of Pagany right off as he is going to Mexico
City very shortly. He thought Pagany as a name of a periodical
was rather unfortunate. However, the book racket has not in
any way made him uppish. He is a first rate person and Wilson
says his stuff is extraordinary. And another thing. Although he
has a publishing market for all his books, he is quite unable to
get parts, chapters or fragments printed by the magazines. This
I think is a first rate opportunity for Pagany. I wish myself
that you could change the name. Dos Passos feels as I do and as
a number of others do that there are so many goddam mushroom
halfassed periodicals around town that one is leery of all of
them. I told Dos Pasos that the only way to make a magazine
good is to have first rate writers contribute to it.

I hope you'll get something of Joe Gould's for this
issue. The New Reoublic is printing the first chapter of
Flushing to Calvary in a forthcoming issue. This is their first
venture in fiction. Have read Mc Almon again and still think he's
lousy. Told Pound so. Mc Almon's use of the idiom is just
garish, bad and sloppy. If you write Gregory, he will do a
critical article for you. His book of pomes has just been
accepted by Eliot for English publication.

2.

You can tell him what you want. I should think he would do a good piece for you. I'm always asking people for stuff and as soon as I come across people with a Ms. that has some real merit in it will send it on to you.

With all good wishes. Do send me the Paganys, will you?

Edward Dah Elang.

Jewish Community Center,
Bergen and Belmont Avenues,
Jersey City, New Jersey.

Mar. 22, 1931

Dear Dick:

Here's something interesting (enclosed).
Please consider the communication a confidence and re-
turn the letter to me. Should anything come out of it
I'll let you know .

Keep hammering (with Pagany) for another
year (this year) at least . I think people are just
now beginning to pay serious attention . Perhaps it
may not seem that way to you but I catch words here
and there from unusual sources that interest me . Do
you think we could in some way attack (in a summar-
izing way) the french, german, english views of what
is alive, what dead ? Some letter from some lively
American abroad - not Pound, someone in Germany perhaps - I don't know whom . Geo. Antheil may have something to say on the general situation (Villa Mas
Mirason - Cagnes-sur-Mer) Perhaps there is some painter
- Hillaire Hiler has written something recently on
Neo-Realism (la Ste. Sebastienne, Cagnes-sur-mer)

Perhaps the bunch in Cagnes-sur-mer would
get up a not too wordy symposium on the situation
abroad - each speaking out - Kay Boyle might engineer
it . I dunno .

Or their view on the American thing? Or does
this not attract you.

The talk at the bookshop last Friday went
off like a wet cracker. No, that isn't quite true . It
wasn't so bad . Everybody seems amused tho' there was
some dissatisfaction with ## the selections I read .
You wouldn't consider giving a Pagany party before
leaving N.Y. would you - have someone (not me) read
some new stuff .

Can't wait to see the next issue .

No news of moment from Nantucket . I had
a letter but nothing much in it . I believe that the
only thing to do is to go down and look around as
early as possible . No use trying to do it bt letter.

Return any short stories of mine which Bob
sent you and you don't want - unless they are out .
In that case forget it .

Yours

Bill

EZRA POUND *res publica, the public convenience* **RAPALLO**
VIA MARSALA, 12 INT. 5

22 Marzo

Deer Bull

Thanks fer nobl effusion. Am always gratified
~~tha~~ by proof that someone has comprehended what I am
drivin' at.

Apropos yr/ pages 25,27 or thereabouts. I am
g/lad to state that canto 33 had just come off the
machine , in fact IT had JUST come off the machine ;
with only 8 lines of my accompanying note to Johns. intervening
between it and the perusal of yr/ crizism.

Notes / one NEVER can tell what people will find obscure.
NEVER occurred to me that " tovarisch " (kumrad) soviet
salutation corresponding to " Citoyen " in the french revulushun
wd. be incomprehensible to ANYone.

glad to get someone to state that IF they don't understand
the greek etc/etc.etc/ let 'em GO ON , and they will
find that they have been told just the same without
readink the greek..

Funny you shd/ have picked what seems to me a prime
ezampl of the faults you say you dislike , which you
will see by revised XXX (which has been sent you) I
have removed from ᶜanto 6 ~~XXXXXXXXXXXXXXXXXX~~. Always
~~thhuugh thaat~~ canto too stiff , but cdnt. take time out
or do revise until I had ~~gXXX~~ got on further.

///

EZRA POUND   *res publica, the public convenience*   **RAPALLO**
VIA MARSALA, 12 INT. 5

As to practical uses//

The crit/ divides into two
sections // P. I/I6 the analysis , and I6 to 28
your criticism.

The first part is from my pt/ of view
(wiff all due respect) the most useful to get printed.
I mean merely from point of view to getting the ^{C}antos
enough read to overcome the resistence of the god damn
printers to getting my stuff into print at all.

Nevertheless , see no reason for someone not printing the
WHOLE sassay. I dont see how you can cut it to IO
pages of typescript (?? Symp/ wanting ten pages in typescript
OR IO of print).

This circumstance is reported to me. Mr/ namely and VIZ /
Mr ^{B}andler the academical drag has eliminated himself
from Bitch and Bugle ::

possibly , though I affirm it not ,
because Mr Kirstein was showing signs of conversion
(or something like it) to , to my (and more nearly
our W.C.W. and E.P. in so far as etc. can be supposed
and DO in fact represent something non/Bandlerian.

At any rate Mr K. professes desire to more=animate his
review . I dont know whether his desire to please me
wd. carry him to 28 pages MORE , just after he has
pubd. the Fitts.

^{H}e axd fer my opinion of Fitts . and

EZRA POUND *res publica, the public convenience* ろ **RAPALLO**
VIA MARSALA, 12 INT. 5

I complied three days ago : on the UNFITTness of the Fitts
, " if F. understood ANYTHING he completely failed to manifest
any trace of his understanding ".

I believ K/ and Sympozzeeum are at daggers . (rumour).
Whether you wd. think it worth writing Kirstein and asking
whether he wants a refutation of Fitts , I dunno. I shd/
say quite plainly that Symp/ had requested , and that you find
you have far exceded their limits. That you wd. (under seal
of discretion) let him see the ms/ IF he wd. get you an
answer within a week.

OR there is Pagany / as Johns has asked for Cantos , especialy
and as I am sending him three by tomorrows post.

            This merely to save yr/ labour. As you
have done 28 pages , seems waste to slash it down // especially
as I cant see that it wd. condense. And the two sections
obviously make more sense together than they wd. separate.
            Zuk/ tells me Harriet after asking Fitts/ and
holding his ms/ three months has now chucked it (alledgedly
because of H & H.

        or/and/or/either/or/both

I mean re/ Pagany that Johns , in using cantos 31/33 might
find it excusable to insert the lead/up. as "summary of
preceding chapters " instead of crit.
                all of which shd/ I suppose
be veiled with the hypocracy of NOT being my suggestion.

EZRA POUND   *res publica, the public convenience*   4   **RAPALLO**
VIA MARSALA, 12 INT. 5

glad SOMEONE admits a reason for the Hell. As to the
faults //

if I stopped NOW to doll up every line I wd.
never git the job done. I wd. rather leave the MMMM
mass in the rough than quit in the middle , Also
some of the details can't really be decided until it is
all down on paper in someorother bloodydamn form.

I dont mean to imply that I see ALL of 'em.

Here ZOW . I hope you have a carbon. Anyhow
will take yr/ ms/ to Paris.

ADDRESS

co/ Chase Bank
4I rue de Cambon

yrs/

P.S. French slang has passed Leger's inspection . I spose he
knows his own language. On the other hand ..... Not very
slang anyhow.

Historically speeking Cantos not strictly done it Italy.
I to 7 and some now chucked out ;
       or I to 6 while   done before leavin
   England// Malatesta ; still living in france and rushing.
   down to italy fer a few months per year. allo which of
no crit. val. merely privik life of orfer.

IN HIS ATTRACTIVE SECOND ISSUE for 1931, Johns was able through Julien Levy to present four photographs of New York City by Berenice Abbott. Selected with great care to give variety to Miss Abbott's portrait of a city, these photographs were to be included in Miss Abbott's exhibit marking the opening of the Museum of the City of New York in 1932. Johns also had the opportunity to reproduce three paintings by artist Hilaire Hiler, who more than any other American artist captured in his work the spirit of the French people and their milieu. The kinship of his detail to that of Breughel was a frequent topic of conversation in art circles.

Of the graphic reproductions represented in *Pagany,* Johns was most impressed with four watercolors depicting scenes from Henry James' "Turn of the Screw," by American artist, Charles Demuth. Demuth held a highly respected position in American art at that time. For Johns, studying the original watercolors was like looking through the reflections of the sun on water and seeing the clear mysteries of the deep shimmer far below the surface.

Starting in this second issue was Albert Halper's three part novella, "A Farewell to the Rising Sun." Actually, Johns was undecided about printing this work, since it had to be serialized and he had purposely avoided the serializing of Caldwell's *Tobacco Road.* Of course, *Tobacco Road* would have run for many issues; this piece would take only three. Johns, thus, decided its serialization would not be a hindrance to *Pagany.*

It was clear that seeing his work in print meant a great deal to Halper, and the combination of satire on the popular Hemingway style and a rich, warm understanding of the caricatured human beings involved made it for Johns an extension of the awareness of humanity that showed in Halper's less adorned stories.

The correspondence for the period clearly indicates that there was much argument over the novella. Letters of criticism and praise came across Johns' desk from Robert McAlmon, Erskine Caldwell,

264-266

                                        Mount Vernon, Maine
                                        May15th 1931

Dear Johns:

        I want to write and tell you of one reader's
reaction to the new Pagany: probably it's worth isn't worth a
god damn, but maybe you can put up with lay-critics by now.

        Is A Farewell to the Rising Sun the sincerest form of
flatery, or is it not so good as the drip-drap in Judge? By
God, I couldn't get anything out of it but a little boyish
entertainment; therefore there must be something wrong with my
appreciation of a writer's emotions. A Farewell is all right,
but I would rather read something like Sisters in an earlier
number with the sister who couldn't leave brother-in-law alone.
Miss Daisy is something to talk about longer than a day. I
wish I could write like that even once. In-Between Ladies is
something like something else. McAlmon and I have formed a one-
sides friendship: he doesn't like me, but I like him. I wish
he would sticj to USA, because like somebody wrote he cane make
a culture in a country where there isn't much yet. He is about
the only one capable of doing it, too; there is culture in
picking potatoes and binding wheat. Next time to write him tell
him I said that in all sincerity. I want to live in a country
where there has been made a culture by McAlmon. Soccogee Country
is fine. Perhaps there is a dramatic quality in west of the
Pecos that nobody else can explain. It's a rotten country, but
people live there; therefore there must be something to write
about. Edge if the Next is pitiful, at least to me it is
a pitiful, because it missed being good. The same story could

-2-

never be done again, ant it's a pity it wasn't done better
the first time. Boyand girl never turn out right unless there
is an element of the life of Nature in the things they do. But,
with that story out of the way Armfield ought to do some great
work, just about as great as anybody has done. I hope he does
do it. The Old Gentleman is , I think, the best in the number:
don't you think so? It is a a river of emotion that gathers
force until it floods the pages at the end. I hope he writes
more. White Mule gets better and better. It is apparent to me
that the book will be a monumental thing, and the xx book should
place Williams at the head of writers, where he belongs. There
is no one else doing what he does. Figure, is I think, almost
up to where you left off with your story in #1. And that one
was, to my way of feeling, just about as good as a man can do.

Probably this has been a little too frank. But
if you knew, you would know that I nearly always say what I
think(makes a lot of trouble for me, too)and very few people
like to hear what a person actually thinks in his mind. But
everthing I said was with honesty, and I hope you will read it
for that and nothing else. Of course, my criticism is better
than it sounds, because I was judging Pagany with the standards
of Pagany, and not with the standards of The Bookman, New Masses,
or This Quarter. You understand now, don't you?

Best wishes, and try to come up this summer.

Sincerely,

Erskine Caldwell

###I over-looked Joe Gould. By all means. And I wish somebody
would publish the history in books, too. The thing is one of
the most deplorable slights today: every word of it should be
in print---between paper covers, or boards.

112 E 11 St
N Y C
May 19 1931

Dear Johns

     I see where the Sunday Times handed me
a gentle but not very subtle razzberry. Taking
the edge off a guy like Hemingway ruffled their
maiden hair the wrong way. And the little dig
they give the smaller magazines is pretty petty
stuff.

     At any rate if you care to send me about
five or eight copies of Pagany I think I know
where to place them so that they would do some
good. Robert Herrick of Chicago University wrote
a scalding attack on Hemingway in the Bookman
that brought a typhoon over his head and there
are afew more people who I think will be interested.

     Hve you tried sending Harry Hansen a copy?
He might give a paragraph to Pagany in his column.
I liked the stories by Pauline Leader, Chapman and
March very much.

     If you think my idea is worht while drop me
a note. I could call for the copies or you could
mail them to me.

     I will be out of town over the Decoration Day
week-end, holding down a waiter's job at a big
camp upstate but will be back by June 1st.

       yours,

       Albert Halper

Edward Dahlberg, and others. What right had anyone to satirize Hemingway? Wasn't it anticlimactic after Hemingway's own satirization of Sherwood Anderson in *Torrents of Spring*? Didn't a deft manipulation of Hemingway's style deteriorate toward the end into a bathos of sentimentality?

Whatever the literary value of this work, Johns recognized that he had made a serious mistake. The novella should not have been cut into three sections, to be picked up and continued after a three months' hiatus. Read at one sitting, everything fused into a progression from satire to a warm recognition of human values. This sense of continuity was fatally disturbed in the disjointing.

Albert Halper was a man whose whole energy was directed toward the goal of becoming a writer of consequence. His working experience had been both wide and varied, and if he knew little of the sophisticated life pursued or pretended to by so many creative workers of the period, he did know people, not superficially but deeply.

With no steady income to depend on, he would work in many different places, spending dedicated hours on his writing whenever possible. Generally, in order to build up a cash reserve so that he might give full time to his writing, he took jobs with little responsibility so that they could be changed easily and at will. At one point, he had spent many months working in one of the great mail order houses in Chicago, and his novel *The Chute* makes a close and valuable record, not only of the mechanics of the operations but of the lives of those people who worked in and for it. The vitality at the core of Halper's short stories was wedded to a true virtuosity in using simple words expressively, and these qualities made them popular among the contributions printed in *Pagany*.

Quite different from Albert Halper in personal and written style was Joe Gould, a favorite among characters in New York during the Thirties. He is well presented in a *New Yorker* "Profile" by Joseph Mitchell and even more directly by Alfred Kazin in his *Starting Out in the Thirties*. Gould looked like a dried up little gnome and his unwashed head showed clearly through the thinning gray hair. But Joe was at home in any situation. He would ring the bell at 9 Gramercy whenever he was in the neighborhood and, disregarding

July 30 1931

Dear Johns

    I hope this letter doesn't spoil your
appetite, or anything else.

    Well, Johns, I am out here at this adult
camp as a waiter, you know, working from 7:30 in the
morning to 9:30 at night, wring wet with sweat after
every meal and if I get a free hour or two off between
meals I have to donate that free time to the drama
group which puts on shows for the guests. The heat and
the goddamed job is getting me at last, iron man tho
I be.
    So far I have made, by the sweat of my
balls about $100 here. If I can get ahold of a few
dollars more I will be able to quit this grind and
get back to New York and resume work on my novel.

    If you are flush with money (which is an
awful assinine statement to type) and if you are in
a good mood and feel as though you could pay me on
publication for the second instalment for "A Farewell
TO the Rising Son" it goes with out saying that I would
appreciate it very much.

    I am aware that you do not pay some contributo
rs at all, and you have been damned nice to me in that
respect, but this goddamed job out here is making me
desperate.

    Dont feel, however, obligated. If you are har
d up yourself, never mind, the world wont crack if I
sweat a few months more out here .

    With best wishes,
        your comrade in sorrow,
           and waiting for some kind of a
           revolution,

Albert Halper

Central Hotel,
149 E. 14 st.
New York City,
Sept 24, 1931.

My dear Mr. Johnson—

I have not received any check for the two chapters from the Oral History which appeared in Pagany and you did not reply to my letter.

It is rumored that in order to get money from Pagany one must either— nag or tell a sob story . I realise that you have your difficulties but such a policy seems to me rather a mistake . I wish you could do a little better in replying to your correspondents. It gives a bad impression .

I presume that my need of money is as much as that of your other contributors but it does not seem to me consistent with the dignity of literature to make your contributors fill out a social worker's questionnaire to get what is coming to them.

If you wish I will make arrangements for other chapters of the Oral History to be published in Pagany, and since localism is coming into its own. I might give you a selection of my distinctly New England material.

Sincerely yours,
Joe Gould.

whoever might be there, hold the floor and everyone's attention as well. Always in his hand was one or another of the brown-covered school notebooks in which he was writing his Oral History, which he felt certain was greatly superior to any part of Emerson's or Thoreau's Journals.

It was amazing to listen to this sociable, unselfconscious tramp talk of the old days as a young gentleman at Harvard and then in the same breath gossip about what had occurred at last week's Joe Gould party. Joe had a genius for juxtaposition in issuing invitations, with the affair generally taking place in someone else's home or apartment. But eternally, Joe was the host, and when asked to Joe Gould's parties, one went.

Wherever you went in those days, you would run into Joe. If you were going to the Yiddish Theatre on lower Second Avenue and dropped into the delicatessen next door, there would be Joe, ensconced at a little table behind a pyramid of books to review with the grubby notebook for the Oral History near at hand in case some important entry came to mind. These were working periods for Joe because reviewing books meant cash for food and various necessities. So he would content himself with a wave and a nod, a smile crinkling the dirt around his eyes, and remain at his table. Often appearing in *The New Republic* or the newspapers, Joe's paragraph reviews were succinct and to the point.

Johns had neither the money nor the wish to do anything about Joe's dreams for the publication of the Oral History, but he did want at least one small part of it in *Pagany*. Johns picked two short selections from the notebooks, one on insanity and the other on freedom to be published under the title "Me Tempore." He knew Joe Gould probably as well as anyone did and had talked about him at some length with Horace Gregory, who had just completed a study of Gould's work for the Spring Book Number of *The New Republic*.

299-301

What became of Gould's page on page of self-expression, the almost indecipherable wavering lines of penciled observations which kept pride in the heart and head of a very dirty old man? No one knows. It is good that a few pages were printed in *The Dial* and *Pagany,* for Joe Gould, in his unsoaped individuality, was a part of America in the Thirties.

284-287

Since no criticism appeared in this issue of *Pagany,* there was more room for what Johns felt was distinctive fiction. Pauline Leader's "Hired Girl" and William March's "Miss Daisy" were each exceptional portraits of very dissimilar women, while William Chapman's "The Old Gentleman" was a consummate exposition of a young boy's recollections of his grandfather, their love for one another and the positive impact of the old man's death on the child.

Johns always believed that a wide variety of material should constitute each issue, but it was no accident that these three stories of an adolescent's reaction to an older person were included in one issue. Although each story was entirely individual, each one raised itself high above the spate of would-be sensitive and touching encounters between the generations, which had become wholly commonplace in the escapist slick popular journals of the day.

For his own story, "Figure," Johns borrowed from himself by developing his own poem "The Sphinx," which had been printed in Louis Zukofsky's one Objectivist issue of Harriet Monroe's *Poetry.* As did the poem, this story stemmed from a beach incident when William Carlos Williams and his family had visited Johns in September of 1930 at Cape Ann on the North Shore of Massachusetts. After the mistaken personalizing of both "Solstice" and "Sorry Lady," it was refreshing to be able to use the actual reactions, in a relaxed moment of friendship, of Williams and himself to a figure of a woman made of beach sand on Good Harbor Beach. It was most satisfying for Johns that the story later won him another place on Edward J. O'Brien's Roll of Honor for the American Short Story for 1931.

The poetry in this second issue was highlighted by "Three Poems" by Callman Rawley, whose poems were appearing under the pseudonym Carl Rakosi. Rakosi had been born in Berlin but educated in this country and, while working toward a Master of Arts degree at The University of Wisconsin, influenced by Louis Zukofsky. Zukofsky was teaching in the Department of English and probably engaged Rakosi in numerous discussions of his objectivist theories of poetry. Johns had followed Rakosi's poems as they were printed in *The Little Review, The American Caravan, The Nation,* and *The New Masses.*

Other poetry in this second issue of 1931 included Yvor Winters' "The Journey—Snake River Country," and Norman Macleod's "Shadowbox: In a Milltown." Winters painted an empty, desolate landscape of a particular western terrain. Macleod gave a desolate but vivid portrait of a creative man tied by necessity and the pressure of the depression to working as "a checker for some lumbermill" who used the intricacies of his imagination to override the bleakness of his situation.

288

During the preparation of this number, Johns met a number of contributors whom he had previously known only through letters or occasional telephone conversations. Robert McAlmon proved the biggest surprise since his correspondence gave little indication of the character that descended upon New York. Judging from the quality of his editorial skill and writing, Johns had always pictured McAlmon as a vitally alive, robust though somewhat condescending individual. The man he met, however, was cold, bitter, and reptilian.

276-277

Thin almost to the point of emaciation after many years in Paris, McAlmon was still charged with a restless energy which gave him little chance for repose. Although he had been away from New York for some years, he still knew some crannies among the craggy cliffs of skyscrapers where there were bound to be unusual and interesting people to talk and drink with.

But this was the social side of McAlmon, and well before the dinner hour was over he was chafing to get away from any need to be polite and hit the trail for the livelier speakeasies of Third Avenue or Greenwich Village. Some such individuals develop a physical warmth once they have sufficient liquor in them, but McAlmon only became more waspishly angular. He was not impelled to warm personal involvements with others, only to enough knowledge of them to uncover their flaws. He was a boisterous drinker, but not a happy one. It was no pleasure to make the rounds of night places with this argumentative and scrappy man.

William Carlos Williams had talked enough about McAlmon for Johns to realize that in the literary area of Williams' complex life McAlmon was considered a close friend. As a doctor, Williams displayed a warm confidence which relaxed and gave assurance to his patients and carried over into his personal relationships as

May 2, 1930

Dear Johns :

      Well, if you mean that you have turned down what McAlmon has sent you - all I can say is that you haven't read it through . From page 28 on to the end it is about as good as anything you are likely to have sent in to you for the next twenty years   .

      What in hell <u>**is**</u> the matter with you younger chaps ? Are you hunting for "beauty" or a "solution of the universe" or what in God's name is it you want anyway . It surely isn't writing you're after .

      I'll keep McA's thing for a while . If you want to use some of it on my say so , all right , if not I'll use it otherwise .

        Yours

      William

well. He certainly was an intense and challenging influence on Johns, both as a person and as a literary mentor to a younger man. However, sitting at the same table with Johns and McAlmon, Williams, almost as a chameleon might, took on essentially the same gray tones as the latter, occasionally lit up by sharp flashes of wit through the off-color gossip which ordinarily was McAlmon's forte.

Johns always enjoyed being with Williams, except when McAlmon was there. He shied away from them when they were together, for the cruel tongue of McAlmon's gossip frequently drew falsetto giggles of leering amusement from Williams which were neither native to him nor in any way attractive.

Johns did not see McAlmon very often while he was visiting New York but he was as disturbed as all McAlmon's friends at the editor's inability to settle into any sustained work. When he was sober, which was only at the beginning of any evening, he was introspective and discerning, but he drowned any recognition of responsibility or purpose usually before the dinner bell had sounded. One day he left the city to resume his constant and undirected wanderings.

Two contributors who occasionally appeared at 9 Gramercy Park were Horace Gregory and Kenneth Rexroth. Gregory was an intensely modest and reserved individual who differed greatly from the other poets whose work appeared in *The New Masses*. He belonged to no particular school of poetry, nor was Johns altogether convinced that he was as much the proletarian as an adherent to a highly personal sense of justice. Johns was sure, however, that his ability as a teacher equaled his skill as a poet. Although Gregory had some difficulty getting started in a conversation, once he was engrossed in a subject he spoke quickly and vividly.

Of Rexroth, William Carlos Williams wrote on May 6, 1931:

> . . . he seemed vague about his destinations and inclinations—he's rather a nice chap—somewhat bitten by the prevalent Anglo-Catholicism drift but that isn't a fault, really,—any more than anything else which serves as a temporary belief. He was inclined to find some fault with me over my pagan inclinations which all these spiritists—if I may call them that—find limiting. But yazus! why argue.

                                    12 rue de L'Odeon, Paris.
                                    May 26th, 1931

Dear Johns:

          Here is the end of a novel, but I think it makes a
complete thing in itself, and if you will, use it as the next
thing of mine, unless you have already something else in mind,
such things as Bill has.   Ezra Pound is in town, Sam Putnam
is editing the New Review, Transition is to start again, Front has
passed out, but other new magazines are in the offing, Less and
less do I think I'll bother about a publication now. There are
only, so far as I see about six people about, and they can get
printed, if they aren't arriving with the commercial publishers, and
I don't care about publishing a magazine unless I can discover new
or print neglected talent. Paris is much better than it was when
I arrived, but there has been a good deal of lousy weather. Now
we are getting some sunshiny days, and I go south in three days.
However when you write me, and do, to let me know you get this and
where you are, use the above Paris address, which is always good.
I liked the last Pagany very much as do some others about here.

          If you want use the Indefinite Huntress instead of this, but
let me know. I won't bother altering the passages I intended to
as I am unto new work and it is hard to get myself back into that
frame of mind. Anyway it isn't bad as it is.

          When I get south I'll see Hiler, Kay Boyle, and several others,
and if you want reproductions of photography and paintings, I can
get a hold of some for you. They touch up the magazine, I think,
and as regards photography the sort that Berenice is doing and that
Atget and some others have done, it is becoming a type of visual
document or literature. Let me know if you want things from over
here. Hope you feeling well.

          I send this to Grammercy Park, but gather from what you said
that you'd have moved back to Boston by now. But they'll forward it,
I hope. Berenice sent me some twenty small photographs of New
York, but not such clear reproductions. Anyway you can get things
from here there if you want more of her things for a later issue.

                                    Sincerely,

                                    Bob McAlmon.

June 6th/ Hotel des Colonies, Cagnes sur mer France. Down here,
and have one marvellous photos of Hiler's, old manner, and one, new
and present manner, which I'll send you later, with other things.
Use the enclosed, the Indef. Huntress, if I don't send you something
new or newly revised before you need something or want it. The
Halper burlesque is great, and he certainly ought to have no trouble
placing it commercially. I'd recommend it wholeheartedly to Moss
and Kamin, but think he ought to arrive by having it published by a
commercial house. He is doing better on Hemingway what Hem. did on
Sherwood Anderson in the Torrents of Spring. It is the best
criticism of H's fake hardboiledness concealing tripe that has been
done. Tell Halper to try Liverright on it, as H. broke his contract

with them by sybmitting <u>Torrents of Spring</u> after they had just
published Anderson's <u>Dark Laughter</u>. They had in their contract
the refusal of his second book, and he wrote that to be able to
go to Scribners, who offered him a better contract. The last is
the best Pagany printed, and strangely more people like my story
the best of any as yet, and I don't, but that's that.

I never received a copy of the
last Pagany. Please send me
three here —

    Hotel des Colonies,
Cagnes- Sur- Mer—
       A. M. France.

Here for Sometime.

Rexroth had hitchhiked in from California, and when Johns first met him, he seemed to him like a free-flying gull momentarily trapped in the corridors of New York. Johns noticed that although his talk was wide and spacious, there was the same precision in his words as in the architecture of his poetry. Rexroth was always willing to help Johns, and frequently, visitors to 9 Gramercy Park would find the shy, lanky poet hunched over a table "specking type" for the ads which were to appear in exchange with other little magazines.

As far as his own personal life was concerned, these were free and easy days for Richard Johns. From under the clock at the Biltmore or the Astor, there were innumerable directions to turn for fun. Johns moved from the theatre and such productions as Gershwin's *Of Thee I Sing* and O'Neill's *Mourning Becomes Electra* to cellar speakeasies in the Village where girls would slip off their girdles and check them along with their coats. At Cora Livingston's swank Small Paradise, besides girls and more girls, there was an eighteen-hole miniature golf course filling three ornate rooms all leading to bars and 100-proof bootleg liquor available until daylight.

Despite this enjoyable entertainment, Johns missed the companionship of Eleanor Herbert. He began to travel back and forth to Boston and its neighboring North Shore to be with her. By late Spring they both thought seriously of marriage and their engagement was announced. But soon after the announcement, fears of confinement began building up in Johns almost to the point of suffocation. There was no question that Johns loved this woman very dearly, but he did not have enough confidence that he could forswear the excitements of light promiscuity and his freedom in order to marry a devout Roman Catholic. Johns did not feel that he was ready to be forced to channel all of his affections to one woman in what he was sure was her interpretation of the sanctity of marriage. The engagement was broken; Johns was a much-relieved young man, and Miss Herbert resigned herself to her duties as a schoolteacher.

Dear Richard Johns,

I was awfully glad to see that
The Editor announces for future publication......
You have satisfied one of my ambitions. I always
wanted to see myself on just such an annpuncement
page.

You might be interested to know
that Titus of "This Quarter" has just taken a
story also, rather longer than Hired Xxxix Girl,
called Aunt Mary Louise's Lover.

I had a baby, a girl, Dec. 27th,
It was, I think, my most poignant creative effort,
although I don't know as I consider it my greatest. Iam too much the artist for that....Now I
am trying to get back to work, altho raising a
baby and washing a million diapers a day are
terrible time eaters.

I wrote a novel the first
seven months of 1930 in spite of being at work
on the baby at the same time - or shud I say in
spite of the baby having been at work ak on me?
Anyway, it has been rejected only 10 times - so
far. Knopf who rejected it wrote the typical
letter of rejection: it was very well written
but so stark and vivid he was afraid to take it.
They all seem to be afraid to take the book, damn-
it. It's at Vangaúrd's now....

Well, I hope you will like the
enclosed.

Yours,

Pauline Leader

NUMBER 2 *April–June*

CONTENTS

PAGANY

HIRED GIRL

Pauline Leader

I came home from school one winter day to find her in the room back of the market, sorting clothes from one big laundry basket into another. I was seven or eight or ten then. I stopped at the door and stared at her. My first sight of her was mixed up with the smell of lard being rendered to sell in the market. The smell always made me sick and I used to run away, returning only when there was no more smell to come creeping from the back-room into the market and even out to the sidewalk. But Nellie just went on sorting clothes from one big laundry basket into another. She didn't seem to be aware of the smell at all.

She was a nigger, but if it were not for her light brown and yellow skin you would never have guessed it. Her nose too, perhaps—the nostrils were wide and flaring and turned up like a pig's. But her lips were thin—thinner than mine. She wore glasses—the kind you pinch onto the nose. She was very particular about her glasses. She liked them rimless although the rimless kind broke more easily than those with hard protecting rims. She wore them as if they were jewelry—she had a lot of jewelry and was always buying more at the five and ten.

She was twenty-five that day I first saw her and came from a farming village where she had a lot of brothers—real black niggers. On Saturdays they all came to town with the money they got working for the white farmers and you saw them on Main Street eating pop-corn out of five cent bags. Nellie was small but her brothers with their wonderful lithe bodies looked as if they had come straight from some African jungle. Nellie's hair was different too—long and straight. Her brothers' heads were close-cropped and kinky. Nellie was ashamed of them, called them niggers, and said they were just half-brothers.

"I'm part Spanish," she used to say mysteriously.

After a while we forgot that she was a nigger. She was one of us. I forgot the time when she hadn't been with us, and I couldn't see the time when she wouldn't still be with us, and I only called her nigger nigger when she wouldn't braid my hair in the morning before she braided my sister's. She had her favorite and she was always changing it. Sometimes it was I and sometimes one of my sisters.

Her room was a cot in the corner of one of the two rooms upstairs that made up the rest of our living quarters. In that room there were three other beds where we kids slept. Under Nellie's cot was a suitcase where she kept all her things. Sometimes when she was downstairs in the room back of the market we would ransack the suitcase and try on her dresses and high-heeled pumps and pretend we were grown-up.

Our life revolved around the market. Its hours —the opening at dawn and the closing after midnight—were our hours. There was no "time for bed, children"; mother and father were in the market shoulder to shoulder engaged in the desperate struggle for existence. Nellie's job was to feed and clothe and wash five children and keep them out of the market. For this she got four dollars a week and the cot bed upstairs and the privilege of putting her suit-case under it.

There was no "evening off"—never in the four years that she was with us. Sundays, once a month, my mother let her off to go home and see her mother. We all considered that this allowing Nellie to go away for a whole day was doing her a great favor.

Yet she could laugh. Mother and father were always "in the market," so we five and Nellie were alone together most of the time. She entered into our jokes and we entered into hers. She joined us in our conspiracies until we forgot not only that she was a nigger but that she was a grown-up.

Nellie prided herself on being a "good girl." When a colored girl who had come from a farm as Nellie had come to do housework for white people in town was raped by the head of the family and had a baby, Nellie was loudest in accusations against her. Her particular negro words for bitch and bastard were more naked than any white ones. There was no pity in her.

Yet Nellie liked men. There was the traveler from the meat-packers. Every time he came around he'd drop into the room back of the market to see Nellie. Sometimes he'd put his hand down the back of her neck inside her waist and tickle her. Nellie would giggle loudly.

On Saturday nights, *the* night of the week, after she had put us to bed upstairs and locked the door on us so we couldn't get out, she would take a stand in the market and watch the customers. More than once, when my mother was at a loss for pennies with which to make change, Nellie would suddenly produce from her pocket an envelope containing sometimes a hundred pennies and nickels which she had found, one by one, on the floors of the rooms and when sweeping up the market. She'd said nothing at the time but had quietly saved them all up for this moment on Saturday night in a market full of customers when she could suddenly hold out the money to my mother and say, passing it off as nothing,

"Here's some pennies and nickels I found on the floor when I was sweeping up."

My mother had the sense to "act up"; her expression of surprise and pleasure was perfect, and Nellie's face would glow as people looked at her.

On these Saturday nights the foreign population came in to spend their money. Most of them traded at our place for we alone kept black bread and the spiced bologna that they loved. My mother had learned to speak Polish to the Poles who numbered the greater part of the foreign population. Among them was one John. His last name was unpronounceable so he was known as John the Polak. On Saturday nights he would come over to the corner where Nellie was standing and speak to her in his broken English. He was about thirty-five, tall, and his face was even darker than Nellies's. When he talked you saw a lot of broken yellow teeth. He did not seem to understand that Nellie was a nigger as we used to tell him when we were mad at Nellie and wanted to get even with her. She hated more than anything else in the world to be called a nigger; at best she would admit sometimes that she was colored. But John didn't seem to understand that she was different, as the white people were always looking at her with that understanding in their eyes—even when they were praising her for her honesty in the matter of the pennies and nickels. John the Polak persisted in talking to her as one lonely human being talks to another.

We kids went to the movies as often as we could lay our hands on the necessary dime, but I can't remember that Nellie ever went. Probably she asked my mother but my mother would never let her off so she and John the Polak were never alone. He would come to the room back of the market and talk to her clumsily while we kids looked on and made fun of them both. Nigger Nigger!! Nigger loves a Polak! Polak loves a Nigger! We kids thought we were being very funny and shrieked with laughter at our wit. Sometimes he was welcome in the back-room and sometimes he wasn't. My mother was jealous of Nellie "wasting her time." But if the Polak bought something in the market it wasn't minded if he went to the back-room to talk with Nellie. It was "good business."

My mother and father prospered and bought some houses. The market was given up, so was the room back of the market and the two rooms upstairs. We went to live in one of the houses my parents bought —the others they rented.

Nellie came with us. But in the new house she was still alotted only a cot and a corner. My mother wasn't especially hard—it was the way most of the hired girls in the town were treated and particularly the colored ones.

The new house wasn't to be ours alone. The front room was rented to John the Polak, but there was no fear now that Nellie would waste time on him with my mother always around. Nellie's life was a round of work from dawn to midnight, only with more to do than during the market days. There had been time for laughter and stopping to whisper and conspire when my mother was out to the market behind a counter, but none now with my mother watching all our movements like a hawk. All of us felt the new vigilance, and no less than Nellie we grew sullen.

Then my mother went to the hospital for an operation; we kids understood obscurely. With her out of the way, Nellie suddenly rebelled. Strange that there should be any spirit left in her after four years of us. But there was. You could see its sick struggling in her yellow face, around her lips, when she set herself against us sometimes.

Work slackened. My father had to go away. The "moral fibre" of the house relaxed. We all relaxed and had time once more for laughter and jokes. Meals became irregular. We ate when we pleased, went to bed when we pleased. We knew it wouldn't last long and no less than Nellie we were making the most of it while it lasted.

John the Polak shared in our fun. Nellie and he were the ring leaders. The door to his room was left open and he was more a guest than a tenant. With Nellie we went in and out. Nellie sewed the buttons on his clothes. They kissed each other and we laughed and danced. Nigger Nigger!! Nigger loves a Polak! Polak loves a Nigger!

One night my father came home unexpectedly and found John the Polak sitting in the kitchen with Nellie on his lap. Nellie had brought up some of the wine from the cellar and we were all a little drunk.

My father told John the Polak to go to his room. He told Nellie to "get out." It was winter and Nellie didn't have any money so she went with John the Polak to his room and so the door was shut again.

She stayed in his room all night.

The next morning they went away. I never saw Nellie any more, but on Saturday nights sometimes I saw her brothers on Main street eating pop-corn out of a five cent bag. I grew up to the accompaniment of Saturday nights on Main street, barber shops, drug-stores, clothing "emporiums," grocery stores, lasciviously full, and in the middle of a block catching the eye suddenly of a Nigger god, confusion in a fifteen year old breast and desire looking quickly away again.

THE JOURNEY
SNAKE RIVER COUNTRY
Yvor Winters

I now remembered slowly how I came,
I, sometime living, sometime with a name,
Creeping by iron ways across the bare
Wastes of Wyoming, turning in despair,
Changing and turning, till the fall of night,
Then throbbing motionless with iron might.
Four days and nights! Small stations by the way,
Sunk far past midnight.   Nothing one can say
Names the compassion they stir in the heart.
Obscure men shift and cry, and we depart.

And I remembered with the early sun
That foul-mouthed barber back in Pendleton,
The sprawling streets, the icy station bench,
Rodeo pennants, the latrinal stench.
These towns are cold by day, the flesh of vice
Raw and decisive, and the will precise;
At night the turbulence of drink and mud,
Blue glare of gas, the dances dripping blood,
Fists thudding murder in the shadowy air,
Exhausted whores, sunk to a changeless stare.
Alive in empty fact alone, extreme,
They make each fact a mortuary dream.

Once when the train paused in an empty place,
I met the unmoved landscape face to face;
Smoothing abysses that no stream could slake,
Deep in its black gulch crept the heavy Snake,
The sound diffused and so intently firm
It seemed the silence, having change nor term.
Beyond the river, tree nor grass, but stone
And rolling hills; the river moved alone.
And when we started, charged with mass, and slow,
We hung against it in an awful flow.

Thus I proceeded until early night,
And, when I read the station's name aright,
Descended—at the bidding of a word!
I slept the night out where the thought occurred,
Then rose to view the dwelling where I lay.
Outside, the bare land, stretching far away;
The frame house, new, fortuitous, and bright,
Pointing the presence of the morning light;
A train's far screaming, clean as shining steel
Planing the distance for the gliding heel.
Through shrinking frost, autumnal grass uncurled,
In naked sunlight, on a naked world.

THE OLD GENTLEMAN
William Chapman

The thing that I was more afraid of than anything else when I was very little was that the world was coming to an end, and I used to lie on my bed looking up through the skylight and praying that God wouldn't let it happen that night.

I think someone had told me that the world was coming to an end any day now, and that if I had happened to have been bad during the day before I would be in a serious fix.

It was my belief at the time that the world would come to an end either at noon or at midnight—someone had told me that, too—but I always had the feeling that the end would come at midnight. I knew about Gabriel and I had a vivid picture of an angel, with brass horn about four feet long and no stops on it like a cornet has, standing on the turret of the armory around the corner blowing great blasts. The armory was the largest building I had ever seen and it was by far the most logical place for Gabriel to go to let people know that the world had come to an end.

And so I used to lie there in my room on the top floor looking up through the skylight praying that the world wouldn't come to an end, because I don't ever remember having felt that I had been good.

Sometimes I would start off to sleep and wake up suddenly thinking that I had heard the horn and I would be scared stiff and lie rigid waiting for the next blast and after a while I would think that maybe I had been dreaming and go off to sleep.

But the night the Old Gentleman died I forgot all about the world coming to an end. I think that I really felt so badly that nothing mattered and it was the first time in my life that I had ever felt that badly except maybe the time I thought Captain Jamison was going to take me to the North Pole and didn't. But when grandfather died I was older, too, which made it worse.

When I was much younger my mother and father and an uncle had died but I was too young to know much about that. It was just mysterious, with people crying all around the place and patting me on the head. I didn't mind it because I didn't know what was going on or what it was all about and I was glad to have the people patting me on the head because it made me feel good.

I was only six when the Old Gentleman died and so of course I hadn't had a real long time to get acquainted with him. But I remember him better than anyone who was around me when I was very little.

He wasn't very old—not more than sixty, I guess—but he always seemed to me to be very old. I thought he was about a hundred. He seemed to me to be one of the oldest gentlemen I had ever seen and even now when I try to think of a real old man the picture of my grandfather comes into mind.

And he was old because he was all through. He was like a baseball player standing at the plate with two strikes on him and knowing that the pitcher was going to throw another strike and that he wouldn't swing at it. To hell with any more of this swinging, he must have felt. Ever since I could remember him he looked like a man who had had enough.

I don't know much about what happened to him before I knew him because nobody ever talked about him much, and when anyone in my family starts telling you anything they always get the facts all balled up so I don't suppose I ever would have learned anything much about him even if they had talked.

The first time I remember him was seeing my sister Jenny sitting on his lap and pouring perfume on his bald head and into his moustache. I know it was perfume because my sister told me later what fun she had putting it on.

He was kicking up pretty much of a fuss but he was having a good time. He had a moustache that looked like the Kaiser's only it was white instead of black like the Kaiser's used to be before he lost the war and got that beard; after which, as you know, everything turned gray.

My sister would pull his moustaches down and ask him who had a moustache like that. And he would say Robert Louis Stevenson only he has a chin-piece, too. Then she would twist it another way and ask him who that looked like and he would say Teddy Roosevelt or somebody else. And once, when she had nearly all the bristles jammed up his nose and asked him who he looked like, he peered over his glasses into the mirror and said—I hope to God nobody looks like that!

Another early thing I remember is that whenever we had cranberry sauce with dinner and it was passed to him he would say—No I thank you, it gives me heartburn. I could not make out what he meant.

I've told you my first impression of him and so I suppose it would be only fair to him to tell you his first impression of me.

It was a little while after I was born that he saw me. He regarded me seriously and after a thorough inspection he said—My God, where did he get those hands and feet? And when they told me about it a long time afterward it only increased my respect for him. I never was one to believe that new babies were pretty. And if you have to say something you might as well say something that makes sense.

I did have big feet and a big head. I remember when I was six I wore a size six hat and my uncle said that if my head grew a size a year that I would have a hell of a big head when I grew up. I did not think that was funny and I did not like my uncle.

The real reason that I didn't like my uncle was that he was bad to the Old Gentleman. He didn't work and lived off grandfather. Grandmother was snooty to him, too, and I think the reason for it all was that grandfather had had a lot of money once and my three uncles and my father and my two aunts and grandmother all lived extremely well.

They had a seventy-five foot yacht and a big house. They lived next to the Governor up in one of the New England states. They knew everybody and had everything they wanted and then when grandfather went to New York and was cleaned in three years in Wall Street and had to take a position in a shipping concern they were all pretty bitter. They all had to move into a brownstone that was just starting to go to seed. Later on my father, who was self supporting and lived by himself, and one of my uncles died quite gracefully, and one of my aunts married, not quite so gracefully. That sort of cleared the air of the financial tension but things were never good again.

It must have been a pretty tough spot for him because I guess they were as complete and thoroughly knit a lot of snobs as ever worried an old man to death.

Every night the Old Gentleman played solitaire. Hunched over a little table in a corner, all by himself, he turned the deck of cards over and over, and I don't believe it really mattered to him whether he won or lost.

He always dressed beautifully and at the end he didn't have many clothes so I guess that's why he always wore the alpaca jacket when he played solitaire.

He was not musical although the rest of the family were all pretty good at one thing or another. But he sat and whistled as he turned the cards. He didn't really whistle. He couldn't. But what he did was to make a gentle sort of blowing noise. And he repeated the same tune over and over. It was the only one he had mastered and it was the first line of *Shoo Fly! Don't Bother Me.* That was all he knew and that was all he whistled.

People came in and out of the room without paying any attention to him and he didn't pay any attention to them. There seemed to be a tacit agreement that he was in disgrace like a child standing in a corner with a dunce cap on and the strange thing about it was that no one ever talked about it.

He made one mistake as far as I was concerned and I was never sure whether it was a mistake or whether he was covering up his embarassment. It was one night when he was putting me to bed. My mother had died when I was two and my father when I was four so somebody had to put me to bed and he usually did it. I think it was the only domestic function he enjoyed. And although he was not demonstrative he had a deep-rooted sort of affection for me and I did for him, too.

As I said, he was putting me to bed this night when all of a sudden someone made one of those noises, which, in the good old days would have got a good laugh, but since has become the last word in misbehavior among so-called polite society. I didn't do it so I took it for granted that the Old Gentleman had done it.

I was taking off my long woolen underwear at the time preparing to get into the fleece-lined outfit with feet in it which he held in his hands. All of a sudden it went.

Grandfather straightened up and looked down at me with undeniable amazement and horror on his face. I laughed, and then he said that it was a very bad thing I had done and that he would never again put me to bed if I did such things. I told him that I had not done it; that he had done it himself. That made him furious and it was the only time I ever really saw him angry. We had a bad time of it and he insisted that I apologize and I wouldn't because I was sure I hadn't done anything. He went off without saying goodnight and I felt pretty badly. But in about five minutes he opened the door and said goodnight.

Now, looking back on it I'm not quite sure. Although I have never heard of anyone doing anything like that and not knowing it, maybe I did do it. Maybe he did. But if he did I'm sure he didn't know that he had done it any more than if I did it I knew that I had. But he is the last person in the world I could conceive of doing such a thing and so I'm inclined to think maybe it was I.

One other time he got angry but I didn't see him. He was down stairs and I was up in my room on the top floor and I could hear his voice but I felt so badly at the time that I didn't even try to hear what he was saying.

One of my uncles was a great kidder and he spent a great deal of his time playing practical jokes on me. He was always sending me post cards from President Taft and Uncle Mon, who was a funny-sheet character, and when I asked him why they didn't have stamps on them, because he just used to throw them in the area way without stamps, he told me that people like that didn't have to put stamps on their mail. I believed it because at that time I didn't believe that anyone ever told a lie. I never did, and I was sure that no one else did.

That is the reason why I believed a lot more of his foolishness. I remember he told me that Brigadier-General Corbett, a retired army man who lived down the block, kept his white horse in the front living room and that if I would watch carefully I could see him peeking out of the window sometimes. We would go walking down the block and I would watch carefully for the horse but I could never see him. When I looked away for a moment my uncle would say There he is, and I would turn quickly but my uncle would say It's too bad, he's gone. So I never saw the General's horse and I was very disappointed. Furthermore, I discovered that Corbett wasn't a general at all. He had merely been to the Spanish-American war and everybody called him Colonel, all, that is, except my uncle, who called him Brigadier-General. But that was long after.

The Old Gentleman disliked all this business but he never said anything when I was around.

One day my uncle told me that his friend Captain Jamison, who belonged to the Seventh Regiment, had been ordered by the President to go to the North Pole and he said that Jamison was anxious to have me go with him. Of course, I thought that was wonderful and my uncle said that the regiment would march through our street about five o'clock and pick me up.

I was home all alone that afternoon and spent my time going over my effects diligently, selecting the things which I believed necessary for such an occasion as a trip to the North Pole.

Very carefully I went over all my things. A pair of rubber boots. Yes, they would come in very handy. A sweater and my gray chinchilla coat with the velvet collar were included without hesitation. Stockings and my second best shoes, woolen underwear, a picture book with a slight amount of text which I knew by heart, presumably to be read during the long Arctic nights, a badly made Indian suit, and other items which I have forgotten.

Then I did an ingenious thing. I solved the problem of carting all this luggage, for it is quite obvious that it would require considerable skill for one such as I to manage all this.

First I wrapped each item in newspapers which I collected from all over the house. I got a ball of string from the cook and tied each package separately and lined them up on the floor in two rows in between which I laid a long piece of rope I had gotten from the back yard.

I attached each package to the rope by a piece of string about a foot long. When this was finished I took the rope by an end left long for the purpose and slung the bundles over my shoulder so that they hung down my back like a bunch of bananas. I walked back and forth in my room with the bottom package trailing on the ground but otherwise everything worked very nicely.

It was just the thing for carrying one's belongings on such a trip and I wondered why no one had ever thought of it before.

I had the whole business down in the front yard when my other uncle came home and he asked me what I was doing out like that and dragging all that rubbish around on the string. I told him that I was waiting for the Seventh Regiment and Captain Jamison who would be along any minute now to pick me up so that we could all get off to the North Pole according to the President's instructions.

He made a funny noise in his throat, looked at me for a minute and then went hurriedly into the house without saying anything else.

Well, one by one they all came home and they all wanted to know what I was doing and I told them all the same story. I knew what direction the regiment was coming from and to this day I retain a picture of those soldiers led by Captain Jamison, who was the only one on horseback, turning the corner, and, with an unnecessarily large number of flags flying, coming down the street toward me.

They all knew something was up but it wasn't until the joking uncle got home that the thing got out. He hadn't had any idea that I was going to get so worked up about it all. He came into the front yard and saw me there and I asked him where the regiment was because it was then almost supper time. I think he must have been pretty upset because he stalled me off and said they would be along later and went into the house.

By this time the bundles were coming apart and I had to keep tying them up again and again.

Then the Old Gentleman came along from the shipping office. I could see him walking slowly down the street looking at the ground. He always looked at the ground when he was walking along the street.

He came into the yard and said good evening to me. Then he stopped, and asked what in God's name I was doing with my overcoat on because it was August.

I told him all about it and he got sort of purple and funny-looking and said something about a damnable outrage and went into the house with more vigor than usual.

It must have been about fifteen minutes later that my uncle came out and said that the whole business had been called off. It seemed that the President had called up Captain Jamison and told him that the regiment was not to go for the time being. Captain Jamison had just called on the telephone and paying his compliments to me had conveyed through my uncle the unfortunate news.

I was stunned for a moment. The whole bottom was gone from things and I didn't know what to do. My uncle said he gussed I had better go up and take my coat off and get ready for supper.

I dragged the packages upstairs to my room on the top floor and took my coat off and sat on the bed and began to cry. I could hear my grandfather's voice on the floor below and although I didn't know what he was saying I knew that he was awfully mad and was making some sort of a scene.

It didn't matter much to me because I had a feeling that there was something wrong inside of me. And although I didn't think that my uncle was a liar I was pretty sure that he had made a joke out of me and I was terribly ashamed. I lay on the bed and cried. A long time later one of my aunts came up and asked me if I didn't want some supper and I said that I didn't.

And it was a long time after —the skylight in my room was no longer light—that the door opened and the Old Gentleman came in. He didn't light the light but just came over to the bed and sat down on the edge. He put one of his hands on my forehead and stroked it a couple of times. He didn't say anything but I was glad he was there. He was the only one in the house I was glad about. He didn't say anything but I knew how he felt. He didn't say everything would be all right and he didn't promise to buy me anything or he didn't promise to take me to the Aquarium as he usually did when I felt badly. He just sat there quietly in the dark with his fingers in the roots of my hair gently rubbing my scalp. It felt awfully good and later I fell asleep.

Well, the night that the Old Gentleman died they sent me off to bed early. He hadn't been up for a week and I wasn't allowed in his room. Everybody kept talking about sinking spells and his being delirious but no one ever thought about taking me in to see him and we were really the only ones in the house who had any real affection for one another.

It snowed a lot during that week and they were glad to let me stay outdoors most of the time cleaning the snow off the sidewalk. I don't suppose I was much help, but Fred, the negro furnace man, said that I was awfully good at it and he said that he didn't know how he would get along without me.

Then when the snow was all cleaned off I would work trying to get the packed down ice off the steps and pavement. I liked to wear my rubber boots and it would have been a lot of fun if I hadn't been bothered about what was going on inside of the house.

When the weather was too bad I spent most of the time in the big, dark front parlor and I used to sit under the big square piano playing with some lead soldiers. Then I could hear people walking up and down the stairs but nobody ever came into the front parlor to see me.

The doctor came a couple of times a day in his top-heavy electric runabout and I was very much afraid of him and was careful not to encounter him.

I ate my meals alone in the kitchen, and Helen, the cook, was mysterious and scared, too, I think. She never said much but once in a while she would cross herself and say—Oh, Mother of God!

So that night I went to bed early and I went all by myself after I had been told by one of my aunts. I went up the stairs and into my room and I don't think it was more than six-thirty. I didn't light the light because I was not allowed to touch matches but there was a light in the hall outside the room and besides the skylight was so large that quite a bit of light came in there although there was no moon.

It was cold up there and I put my sleeping clothes with the feet in them right on over my underwear because there was no one there to see and it wasn't as cold as having to take the underwear off and hurry into the sleeping clothes.

I said my prayers, skipping hurriedly over the first people I usually prayed for an got to grandfather and all I said was—Please, God, don't let grandfather die. Oh, please, God, don't let grandfather die, don't let grandfather die, Oh, please God—and for a long time I went on like that. That is the way I used to pray looking up at the skylight when I thought the world was coming to an end. Please, God, don't let the world come to an end tonight, I'll be better tomorrow.

Finally I lifted my head up from the blanket. I must have been there for a long time. I got into bed and there were clean sheets and they felt good on my face and hands. I couldn't feel the cool on my feet because of the feet in the sleeping clothes. I was sorry I couldn't feel the coolness but I knew it would be cold and I was glad to be warm.

It must have been sometime early in the morning when I awakened. It was dark and very still. I had to go to the bathroom and I didn't want to get up because I would have to go to the floor below and it was cold. I would doze off and dream that I was down in the bathroom and that everything was all right but then I would wake up again and find that everything was not all right and that I was still very uncomfortable.

Finally, I did get up. The light had been put out in the gas jet outside my rom but the ligh twas on in the landing below. I went down the stairs as quietly as I could. I had to pass my grandfather's room on the way to the bathroom and the door was open. I looked in and saw what looked like some sort of a white canopy erected in the middle of the room. It frightened me but I didn't stop and went right to the bathroom.

But on the way back I stopped in the doorway of the Old Gentleman's room. I stood there for a little while trying to make out what had been put up in the middle of the room but I had never seen anything like it before. The light from a street gas lamp in front of the house shone on the ceiling and part of the walls making the room quite bright.

I walked into the room and walked up to the thing that looked like a square tent made of sheets. There was no one in my grandfather's bed and then I saw that there was someone lying in sort of a cot in the white tent, covered up by a sheet.

I was very frightened but after I had stood beside the cot for a minute I pulled the sheet down a little way and saw my grandfather. He did not look so old and I thought he looked very handsome.   I knew he was dead.

I stood and looked at him for a little while and I did not feel as badly as I thought I was going to.   What really bothered me was that someone would come and find me there.   So I put the sheet back and went up to bed.

I was terrified that someone would come out and find me and know that I had been in my grandfather's room but I got to my room all right. I got into bed and lay there very quiet.   I did not cry and I was surprised because I didn't.   I was surprised because I didn't feel more badly.   I was not afraid any more and I lay on my back looking up at the skylight. For a long time I lay there very still with all sorts of things going through my mind.   It was getting light when I fell asleep.

ME TEMPORE
A SELECTION FROM JOE GOULD'S ORAL HISTORY
Joe Gould

I.

INSANITY

Insanity is a topic of peculiar interest to me. Despite my theory that people with strong will-power and a sense of humor never go off their nuts, I almost have first hand information about it. There have been times when the black mood was on me. I needed every bit of self-control that I possessed to refrain from shouting aloud or waving my hands in wild gestures that would have brought a curious crowd around me and eventually have landed me in the police-station. I could very easily imagine myself locked up as a maniac. Yet all the time, the real me was not in sympathy with these impulses. It made me feel that perhaps there was a basis of truth in the old idea that insanity was caused by forces external to the soul, such as witchcraft. Science affirmed this once. It may do so again.

It seems to me likely that many who are held under observation or in detention are in just this pitiable state. They may be adjudged lunatics because of the unconventional antics of the outer body, with which the mind may not be in accord, and may consider absurd. The grim part of it is that the line which divides sanity from insanity has no logic in it. The wildest ravings of any lunatic are no more incongruous than the creeds which are solemnly held by sober, unimaginative people.

If a man claimed to be George Von Kaiser Wilhelm he would be locked up. His pretentions would border on sacrilege to many people. Yet the attitude of the normal person toward royalty is equally crazy. Think of the high honor which is paid to him who inherits a throne, and yet he eats and drinks in the same way as the rest of us, and his dead carcass will feed no more maggots and fertilize no more weeds than that of any other mortal.

The insane person is a victim of self-deception. Yet in a measure we all have this virtue. One is his own imaginary creation of himself. Before our soul-mirrors we strut and swagger. When we are not actively enhancing our importance in the scheme of things we indulge in self-pity. Every man Jack of us has some mental trickery to justify his instinctive feeling that he is the center of the universe. Texas Wilson said to me once, "If we could only see ourselves as we really are, life would be insupportable."

One of the commonest delusions is when a man feels himself to be Jesus Christ. That is not altogether absurd. We are all of us a part of the godhead, portions of the everlasting miracle of the continuity of life. The man who says that he is Napoleon is merely dramatizing the sublime egotism of human nature. Who does not aspire to some dominion over others, even though it be in petty matters? Nevertheless the person who seeks to alter by one iota the personality and conduct of another is fundamentally on the same footing as he who seeks to conquer a continent or lay toll upon the commerce of the sea.

Consider that woman whom I saw in the insane asylum at Central Islip. She hid under the bed all day in the alternate belief that she was a cat pursuing a mouse or a mouse fleeing from a cat. At first sight it would seem as though we could all afford to laugh at her and pity her at the same time. How many people are there who neither spend their lives plunging into darkness in search of more futile prizes than mice nor fleeing shadows as fantastic as her fear of cats?

The fallacy of dividing people into sane and insane lies in the assumption that we really do touch other lives. This is a matter open to serious doubt. Our physical senses differ so much with respect to sight, hearing and so forth that we have no certain means of telling whether any two of us live in the same tangible world or not. When we use words we cannot be sure that any of us apply the same meaning. Even more personal and private to each individual is his thought-process and spiritual texture. Hence I would judge the sanest man to be him who most firmly realizes the tragic isolation of humanity and pursues his essential purposes calmly. I suppose I feel about it in this way because I have a delusion of grandeur. I believe myself to be Joe Gould . . .

II

FREEDOM

When a very charming young lady nearly sent me to jail for a letter I wrote during a nervous breakdown, I did not look forward to the experience at all. I felt rather ashamed of my bashfulness and modesty. Heretofore I had welcomed adventure. I had been democratic enough to meet the Chief-Justice of Nova Scotia socially. My theory was that I should always avail myself of the opportunity to study new types and here I was passing it up.

At first I had no terror. There were times in my life when I had envied prisoners. I knew that they had enough to eat. When they were depressed with their own problems no burdens of others were thrust upon them. It seemed to me that for a while prison might be a place of freedom to me because it would release me from the heavy ball-and-chain of economic worry.

Faced with an opportunity to test my theory, I weakened. My principal reason was that I was told that they served rotten coffee in jail. That seemed more than I could bear. Fresh air, sunlight, freedom of motion—these are almost as necessary to me as food and drink. Yet I felt I could be deprived of them and retain my balance. Through sunbaths I have absorbed a surplus supply of solar rays and ozone. Sunlight is always inside me. I love the beauty of the outdoor world but what I have had of it can never be taken away from me. Were the bars to lock me inside grey walls, my soul would still traverse the Canadian Rockies where my weary feet once trod. Freedom of motion that is partly mental. No barriers of space or time intrude themselves upon my ever active mind. I can live in a glorious past and an exciting future. My memory is sufficiently full to keep me from boredom.

It is true that in a jail I could not move about. That would be arduous for one whose social life is as varied as mine. I am a part-time member of several diversified social groups and at home wherever I go. Much choice is mine. Restricted into narrow confines, I could not eat chitlings in Harlem, wander through the woods, visit art galleries or flirt with all the women I meet. Yet, after all, only freedom of choice would be mine. That is a delusion and a snare. No man can eat at two tables, walk on two paths and sleep in two beds at once.

When I had all the sunlight that filtered through Western mountain peaks I had moods when I wanted the gloomy coolness of libraries. When I was gorging myself to repletion with facts sufficiently useless to be interesting I would all of a sudden be seized with an intense longing to be again on horseback speeding into the sunset when the ice was breaking up in the Missouri river.

Miss Moore, who thinks that millionaires as such are important, was shocked when she realized that their life was not completely Elysian. She said that even they had to submit to the common tyrannies of time and place, and appetite. An unjust cosmos did not honor their triumph of the acquisitive spirit as did their fellow-mortals.

It would seem that no finite mortal can be free unless he is so single of purpose that he knows what he wants to do and wants only that. The indecisive wavering man is unfree no matter what wealth is at his command. He who can neither be bribed nor threatened is free and only he; God is not free because he has to pay so much attention to bores and stupid people . . .

April 31, 1931

Dear Dick:

Great stuff! surely this is the best issue
yet. The Demuth illustrations are astounding - and
astonishingly well reproduced.

You have lit me all up#, like a skyscraper.
It has made me want to again .   .   No doubt the
"lefters" have something to talk about . But what do
they not leave behind driven by the necessity (perhaps)
for making a new start that must bring them inevitably
back to the point of departure. But to hell with that.
Pagany has a tone of its own that is cultured and
begins to show a weight of intelligence - or a froth
of intelligence -   Blooie. It's a pleasure. It's
good.

Your own story has an interesting pattern
A becoming B and B, A - in the end. Nicely done.

Halper, Gould - enjoyable. But I'll bet you
have worked.

Florence is particularly delighted with the
Hiler reproductions and I myself think that as pictures
these small replicas illuminate the originals in an
interesting way .

Write when you have time and let me know
your plans . Come out any time you feel like it, we
are always glad to have you .

Yours

Bill

IN BOTH THE Summer and Fall issues of Volume II Johns printed "Eveline Hutchins," by John Dos Passos, a selection from his forthcoming novel *1919*. Eveline Hutchins was a new character for Dos Passos, and this lengthy section gave her personal life from childhood to her days in France during the heat of the war. For this second novel of an eventual trilogy entitled *USA*, Dos Passos' technique was similar to that in *The 42nd Parallel*, breaking the personal narratives into short sections, interspersed with portraits of famous people done in highly stylized capsules, as well as the emotional *camera eye* from the author's psyche. Johns was positive that the uninterrupted story of one character's life would make an effective contribution, which it did.

Due to the length of this first section of "Eveline Hutchins," and the second part of Albert Halper's "Farewell to the Rising Sun," as well as the continuing of Williams' *White Mule,* there was little other prose in the Summer issue. The most important was certainly Edward Dahlberg's "Coney Island Angelus Bells." One constant reaction to Dahlberg's writing was that it was either liked or hated. It wasn't meant to be easily accepted as average run-of-the-mill work. For Johns this was a prose poem of horror, dredged by a sensitive, loud-speaking man out of the scraps of recollection during one searching and indelibly etched day. A period piece about the present, it had tremendous impact, and Johns looked forward to meeting Dahlberg at some time during the months ahead.

Although it was short, Joseph Vogel's "Counterfeit" gave a long term view of the pains of the depression and delineated the sickness of it. A story about a working man paying for a cup of coffee and the consequences when unable to come up with twenty cents, this work portrayed the delusions and instability of a time challenged by social revolution.

319-322

Like Vogel, Norman Macleod was a widely respected spokesman for the proletariat. Vogel was strictly urban both in his personal tastes and in the subject matter for his writing. Macleod was a literary nomad who had roamed throughout the Southwest and Europe before coming to New York during the early Summer of 1931. He was the American Editor of the bi-monthly little magazine *Front* edited by Sonja Prins from The Hague, as well as Editor of *The Morada,* the home base of which was The University of New Mexico in Albuquerque.

Macleod was an earnest young man, and Johns went with him once to a Sunday picnic for workers and their families held in the Bronx. There he met Jack Conroy and Harry Roskolenkier for the first time. Johns was impressed by the consuming sincerity of all three men. They were the spokesmen for this welter of people transported from small, cramped quarters into the open air of Van Cortlandt Park, where the dusty, yellowing green of grass seemed as opulent as the tended lawns of such local playgrounds for the rich as White Sulphur Springs.

Johns couldn't help but reflect that this simple but enjoyable outing was far removed from the comforts of 9 Gramercy Park and the excitement surrounding it. Watching Macleod, Conroy, and other workers passing out box lunches of ham sandwiches, apples, and milk, he had visions of dinners at the Brevoort, the Lafayette, and Luchow's, polar opposites in a world divided by economic chaos.

Such proletarian recreation was far removed from the sumptuous service of the new Waldorf Astoria where Johns went frequently these days in preparation for being an usher —along with such rising literary lights as Wolcott Gibbs and Ogden Nash—at the wedding of Frances Reyburn, daughter of Lord and Taylor president, Samuel Reyburn, to his old friend F. Everett Abbott. This picnic was different, too, from any activity of Village intellectuals and poseurs in the arts, and the educated connoisseurs of modern writing and criticism, pacing the stone quadrangles of colleges and universities, they would have been amazed at the literary significance of a workingmen's outing in a run-down park in the Bronx.

That Sunday in the Bronx was rewarding for Johns as he watched the sharp eyes of Macleod and Conroy study these one-day-off-from-poverty reivers. He knew that some of the feeling and expression used to describe these people and their condition would appear in the pages of *Pagany* between such extremes as Mina Loy and Kenneth Burke. During that season Johns felt an increasing sense of pride in the assemblage of dissimilar individuals who became a part of *Pagany*. No one contributor was more truly American than another.

The poetry for the third issue included "Three Cantos," XXX, XXXII, and XXXIII, by Ezra Pound. Johns did not pretend to understand the erratic economic theory presented in Pound's earlier cantos or later in his "Money Pamphlets," but he did appreciate William Carlos Williams' enthusiasm for the poetry as a whole. Williams had shown him proof copy of the Hours Press limited edition of *A Draft of XXX Cantos,* not to be published in this country in a trade edition until 1933 by Farrar and Rinehart. Then, after Johns had carefully studied this work of energy and imagination, Williams asked if he would like three unpublished cantos for *Pagany*. Were they political, economic, or historical in their didactic discourse between Mr. Adams and Mr. Jefferson? Johns was not sure! He was, however, swept into a raging sea of genius, and frequently capsized by Pound's loss of self-control. When the complete edition, *The Cantos of Ezra Pound,* was published many years later, Johns realized a mistake had been made in the numerical sequence of these poems as they had appeared in *Pagany*. The canto Johns printed as XXX was cited as XXXI. He never knew whether this error was an oversight on the part of Pound or Williams, or whether Pound made a textual revision at a later date.

Other poetry included "Four Preludes" by Conrad Aiken and "Six Poems" by e. e. cummings. Here was certainly enough material for one fifty-cent literary quarterly, but Johns also included the brief "A Cracked Record (*Cum Tu Lydia Telephi*)," Basil Bunting's biting commentary on the leisured rich and the emptiness of the human life. This poem was followed by Mina Loy's portrait of a similar world in "Lady Laura in Bohemia."

310-313

323-325

It was indeed an issue of contrasts, and two other poems clinched that fact, Dudley Fitts' mannered, patrician sensitivities displayed by "The Bust in the Vestibule," and the sharp freshness of lines like:

The maple fits upon the joist like a flower,
a picked beam,
a great wood to plane and saw.

326   in Carl Rakosi's "The Founding of New Hampshire."

May 5 1931

Dear Bill:

Tickled that you like the new Pagany. It pleases *me* more than any has for some time. The next one, too, promises to be good. I'm sorry that I do not believe I should possibly have room for your notes on Pound's first thirty Cantos. The number is muchly crowded as it is and your White Mule interests me a lot more than anything anyone could say about the Cantos. I have yet to have any great interest in any sort of critical surmise. Such work belongs to The Symposium and H & H, which are different in most ways from Pagany.

My plans are very indefinite, still include a thought of marriage and, I hope, a fairly lazy summer in all events. No particular place however as having signed a lease in New York I can't afford summer quarters anywhere. Nantucket I decided to be too remote and expensive, although I hope to get down there for a week.

My best to all of you. I shall have to go to Boston the last of this week but will get in touch with you on my return. The weather sets up a great nostalgia for the sea.

Yours,
Dick

NUMBER 3 *July–September*

CONTENTS

PAGANY

331

Errata—On page 65, beginning with line 20, the German should read: "Ärmes mädchen, lass mich Dich lieben—Ich kann Dich glücklich und zufrieden machen."

SIX POEMS

E. E. Cummings

I

come a little further—why be afraid—
here's the earliest star (have you a wish?)
touch me,
before we perish
(believe that not anything which has ever been
invented can spoil this or this instant)
kiss me a little:
the air
darkens and is alive—
o live with me in the fewness of
these colours;
alone who slightly
always are beyond the reach of death

and the English

II

if i love You
(thickness means
worlds inhabited by roamingly
stern bright faeries

if you love
me) distance is mind carefully
luminous with innumerable gnomes
Of complete dream

if we love each (shyly)
other, what clouds do or Silently
Flowers resembles beauty
less than our breathing

III

speaking of love (of
which Who knows the
meaning; or how dreaming
becomes

if your heart's mine) i
guess a grassblade
Thinks beyond or
around (as poems are

made) Our picking it. this
caress that laugh
both quickly signify
life's only half (through

deep weather then
or none let's feel
all) mind in mind flesh
In flesh succeeding disappear

IV

lady will you come with me into
the extremely little house of
my mind. Clocks strike.   The

moon's round, through the window

as you see and really i have no
servants. We could almost live

at the top of these stairs, there's a free
room. We almost could go (you
and i) into a together whitely big
there is but if so or so

slowly i opened the window a-
most tinyness, the moon (with white wig
and polished buttons) would take you away

—and all the clocks would run down the next day.

V

somewhere i have never travelled, gladly beyond
any experience, your eyes have their silence:
in your most frail gesture are things which enclose me,
or which i cannot touch because they are too near

your slightest look easily will unclose me
though i have closed myself as fingers,
you open always petal by petal myself as Spring opens
(touching skilfully, mysterious) her first rose

or if your wish be to close me, i and
my life will shut very beautifully, suddenly,
as when the heart of this flower imagines
the snow carefully everywhere descending;

nothing which we are to perceive in this world equals
the power of your intense fragility: whose texture
compels me with the colour of its countries,
rendering death and forever with each breathing

(i do not know what it is about you that closes
and opens; only something in me understands
the voice of your eyes is deeper than all roses)
nobody, not even the rain, has such small hands

VI

my darling since
you and
i thoroughly are haunted by
what neither is any
echo of dream nor
any flowering of any

echo (but the echo
of the flower of

Dreaming) somewhere behind us
always trying (or sometimes trying under
us) to is it
find somehow (but O gracefully) a
we, entirely whose least

breathing may surprise
ourselves
                    —lets then
despise what is not courage my

darling (for only Nobody knows
where truth grows why
birds fly and
especially who the moon is.

Two mediocrities:
That is to say, without the high-strung moment
Which in the transition, the passage,
Undoubtedly occurs.
We are running again
Where we ran once,
This time along the parallels that meet.

THE BUST IN THE VESTIBULE
Dudley Fitts

Don Giovanni,
a cenar teco
m'invitasti.

i

Then Cosgrove took out a blue handkerchief
and twilled it about his thumb. 'Have you lost your key?'
he said; 'Have you decided? Come, time to be going.'

(But my belief

is: Cosgrove died a week ago next Labour Day.)

So sorry, guy, to make you wait

They say
(they knock at my door, scratch at the lintel, they
push their fierce voices over the transom, they
say:)

"It's time Mr Fitts. Didn't you know? Its
time Mr Fitts. Time.'

Time?

—But

of all men else

I should never have come out, I
should never have mislaid my key
So sorry guy

of all men
else, I have avoided thee.

I have kept him waiting in my vestibule.

. . . though he is patient Though his eyes are blue . . .

'Only look' he said 'how it's all subdivided:
'30×50, down as far as can be.'

Or up (I insist)

—'Or

'up,' he said; 'and posted (look) NO TRESPASS
'&
PERPETUAL CARE

(I suppose that means they cut the grass)—'
So sorry

That means the elevator's on all night.
But it's only a flight;

            I'll walk up
and ring at their door.
             He said:
'I was just going to suggest that myself.'
Time. Time to be going. Time.

(Though he is patient. Though his eyes are blue   rock.)

                ii

Sally there's a man named Cosgrove waiting for me downstairs in the
          vestibule
Sally I don't know him at all well He was there when I came in just
          standing there Sally
I slipped by him I said *Good evening Mr Cosgrove* he said *Have you
          decided?* he said *Time to be going*
But I came on upstairs Sally Sally he's a strange person his
Mouth hair nose eyes ears his whole head and his neck down to the
          shoulders is stone Sally
His old grey topper his eyeglass and embroidered scarf are marble
Sally
His legs bestrid the Oceans   his left wrist
Spun golden pucks like planets across the crystal floor
And worlds over a chaos of brown space
His right foot was a burning triangle against the base of the outer door.

His face
          I saw him in Acoma:
                    Staff in hand, the Governor
came down from the Mesa (and the drums shuddered) and
for five simoleons from Cosgrove's largient hand
led us up into the Tower:
and all beneath us the topaz-lighted plain
below us all the dancing: blue cornmeal
or sacred pollen or chromatic serapes
littering the Plaza
                  (*O Cosgrove*
      in the Avenue the deft Isottas wheel
      south under twilight
            but I
      remember only the Seventy-Ninth-Street throat,
      amazed that marble was flesh):
The Pueblo clangs brass at brass noon.
                    Look,
      your eyes also Your eyes—!

Sally is there ice in the frigidaire Are there guest towels enough?

Cosgrove: he will be up he is coming I know he'll be up He'll want a
    cocktail
He'll want the evening paper Sally Sally he'll want Grandfather's Revere
    snuff-
Box Sally he'll want me and you you too Sally he'll
Want he'll want

(Time to be going.   Time.)

Cosgrove Cosgrove: Alas he is dead he's just died Alas he's dead when I
    saw him standing there topper Alas and eyeglass and stone scarf
He's dead and that's why I sha'n't get in without ringing because he will
    have my key And had been here
Wanting a cocktail (he has drunk your heart) and the evening paper
    (he'll read your brain tomorrow) and you You
He has known you Lain with you Known you love Love love (and planets
Whirled plattering from his tangent brows to burn
Yes where there's (No), in my tongue my heart eyes here, Here, I say
    Here—

iii

No, not here, not in my house, Not here, but somewhere,
Somewhere, there are they whose eyes follow
The line of winds shattering against red windows, high up
In sunset of steel and concrete; there, not here, not here, somewhere,
Somewhere, there would be the way of saying these things: this
        I saw him just last night at Michel's this *He was so young* this
        He was standing in the vestibule only tonight, top-hat and scarf:
        it was late: the scrubwomen had piled all the chairs up on tables,
        rolled aside the rugs; he looked right at me, said nothing
Somewhere, somewhere Not here: there are those whom thought
Of Cosgrove hurts; there, his death swings
Around inward around channeling the hot gyre of brains
And hearts where dancing is,
Piercing throughly cortices of marble, here,
Eyes of stone: till the stone eyes ache, and the aching
Thin glaze encyst them over, the small nerve stiffening:

There, they will say *Good night Cosgrove, Good night,*
And only a girl's voice, only a fireside story,

Remember that we have suffered much, that we
        must go to bed, since he is dead)

Since the annunciator is broken downstairs, since the 'phone
Is out of order, double-lock the door, lock each window, draw the shades

    Good night Cosgrove

Carefully, so: Carefully, redouble
Partnership in what really must have been quite a shock really.
Say that Death is no respecter of persons.
Comment that his wife may sleep lonely now.
                If he knew, if
(and sleeping may dream perchance,
            Somewhere: *of what places?*)

          iv

So there would be the way of these things: Travel.
You travel. You know the alleys then; or, alone
walking the wood at noon,
      or cycling through the hot Devon fields after luncheon,
or at dusk maybe,
      penny buns and jam in a haystack by the roadside,

or, turning up a side street
in New York or London, the
flare of a cigaret: his face twists back to meet
your face, in a heartbeat, in a raindrop swift on your forehead,
strangely cold, strange,
            or, his name is called
in a Kansas town, suddenly, from the corner drug-store,
in the chime of ten, casually, in a chord,

or later, or very late that night,
we registered as man and wife at the Haarlem House
(a huge oldfashion unclean room with two beds)
and, staring out from the crazy scrawl
his eyes blue stone in the desklamp:

his eyes between us all the long night,

star light, star bright,
no other light

> (*Did you know?* he sailed away in a Dusenberg
> over the twilight asphalt *Do you*
> *remember?* and left me furious with remorse
> for having delayed him, standing there in my vestibule
> *Do you believe?* or where he is now or
> where he is *Do*
> *you* he will not ever come back for me
> again *hope?* not again, not
> ever, not again)

The bust of Cosgrove in the vestibule,
niche'd between ranks of name-discs and pushbuttons,
    I SAID I HAVE COUSINS IN PARK AVENUE
repeats stone-eyed the annunciator's denial:

> OR I COULD GO TO MY AUNT'S IN FIFTY-THIRD STREET

In the Avenue the smooth Isottas flow
south and north after midnight. Somewhere, a softer
voice at a drowsier hearth (somewhere, darker
than this dark vestibule) he is remembered . . .

Of Cosgrove and his bust, what remains now
but a mouthful of ashes, but words, but a girl's crying

COUNTERFEIT

Joseph Vogel

"Nobody's sick, nobody's sick."   Carl thought he was walking along
Fifth Avenue. "Mister, can you spare . . . "   His soft collar was soggy
and stuck to his neck.   There were too many people on Fifth Avenue.
The shoppers were all right when you had a crippled twisted hand or
black glasses and *Help The Blind*.   The young men were all right but
they didn't understand.   "Say, what's the matter with you, are you blind?"
The autoist let go of his brakes.   "Help the blind, all you sick people,
help the blind."   Carl thought he had crossed the road.   "I'm sick,
lady . . . "   The lady brushed by him.   "Need a quarter for a meal.
Here's the Manufacturer's Trust Co.   Put them up, quick!   Keep quiet."
He thrust his hand behind the cage and seized a bundle of bills.   The
teller suddenly sank below the sill and a siren shrieked.   "All right, you
got me, but I need a dollar.   All right, but hold me easy, I'm sick.   Everybody's sick, everybody's sick. "   Carl thought he was gliding along the
sidewalk.   He saw a man he wanted to speak to.   Looked like a banker,
one of the old school.   He tried to stop, but the sidewalk glided under
his feet.   "Mister . . ."   He turned and walked back.   The banker had
stopped to hear him better.   "Can you spare a quarter for a meal?"   Carl
thought he was saying, "Can't walk, sick, want to lie down . . ."   The
banker was talking . . . "usually go with a man so he won't spend money
on a drink . . . look honest . . ."   Carl closed his hand over a quarter.

On Sixth Avenue he entered a Coffee Pot and invited the head
shipping clerk to a meal.   The head shipping clerk always made him
laugh, he was hopelessly stupid, so Carl told him to go to hell.   "You
ought to be working under me by rights.   I know more about this job
than you."   The head shipping clerk's face turned red.   "All right, if
you know so much, then find yourself another job."   Carl laughed.
"You're so dumb, you never know when someone's kidding you.   What
did I say?   I only said you're a nice guy.   All right, you can go to hell."
Carl picked up his own check and thought seven months slipped by.
"Don't fool yourself, don't fool yourself."   He rose mechanically from

his chair, went over to the counter, pointed at a dish. The counterman called him back and asked for his check. "Huh . . ." he didn't know what to say. "Pardon . . . forgot all about it." He carried a pork sandwich back to his table. "Hello, Joey." Carl turned around. "Still working for Bloomingdale's? How's the broad in the silk underwear department?" Joey blushed. "Pork is bad food for a sick man." Carl thought he was speaking. "It's cool, though. Good for fever. Hello, Joey, how's the broad in the silk underwear department? Ha, ha, that's a good one. It's bad for a sick man." The food was tasteless, but it burned in his stomach.

It was hot in the cafeteria. Carl pushed the plate away from him. His sticky hand rose to his forehead, wiped away beads of sweat and left his face hotter. The cafeteria was a little purgatory. Not a napkin in sight. Dishes clattered loudly and sent darts of pain through his body. The little ugly Jew with a small black moustache was telling loudly about his experiences with the blonde called Jeanette. He smacked his greasy lips. All the little black-haired Jews with little black moustaches. Carl rubbed a finger across his lip. He needed a shave. His hand was greasy. He pulled over a loose newspaper sheet and noticed that his fingers trembled. Might see a doctor, a little black-haired doctor with a little black moustache. Son of a bitch. "Go to hell. You're so dumb you can't take a joke. Sure, I'll get a job tomorrow. A better job. Damn it, go throw your little lousy Jeanette into the East River. See if I care about Bloomingdale's." Paper good enough. He wiped his hands on it, crumpled it in his fingers. Counterfeiters Caught . . . He threw the ball of paper away from him. It struck an old woman's legs. She looked at him angrily.

"My father was a counterfeiter in Warsaw. He was a tall crazy Swede who served six years in jail and then drank himself to death. He killed himself with home-made booze."

"That's news," thought Carl. "Counterfeiters caught. Thousands of ten dollar bills, then freedom and booze." Carl's eyes brightened. Free, free, he banged his fist on the table and bent double as a pain shot through his spine. The pain of living free, eating in the best restaurants where dishes clanking did not drive you crazy, the pain of having Jeanette for yourself and a cool bed to stretch your body in, a nurse to put a glass of ice cold water to your parched lips and a banker of the old school pouring cool shiny quarters over your hot aching body. A nurse with a white apron stood beside him. "Finished with your sandwich?" Carl raised his head. "Bad for a sick man." He thought he was speaking to a waitress. "Pay the cashier?" He might pull out a ten dollar bill and hand it to her. Suspicious? No, he had enough to pass out right and left without discrimination.

Carl passed them out, threw them away at beggars, but he spat into crippled twisted hands. He rode endlessly on trains, ships, ate in restaurants where waiters walk on carpets, then passing through Genoa he helped construct a white-walled hospital and on the top floor under a skylight he put himself to bed but the fever would not go away. Then he walked down to the street and found himself in the north and his teeth clattered loudly, sending a pain through his spine. He wanted to buy a warm coat with his ten dollar bills but he could not find a clothing store. The snow exploded.

Carl raised his head. He saw a man opposite him eating black beans, moving his jaw up and down. There was a rotten odor of beans. A fork scraped the bottom of the plate and carried the black beans to the man's mouth and the man swallowed the beans. Carl gazed into the man's small black eyes and the man moved his eyes over to the left. Carl watched the black beans in the man's eyes.

The place stifled, heat, heat from the kitchen, heat from cooking foods, heat from beans. Coffee Pot. "Better get out. Nice and cool outside." Carl wanted to move. "Better get out. Feel too sick." Ten dollar bills. Freedom! Now only one ten dollar bill. Pay the cashier; nine dollars and eighty cents change. Suspicious? "I got a friend who is a banker of the old school and he makes a specialty of counterfeiting quarters." Cashier suspicious? "Ten dollars is all I have. Got it from the Manufacturer's Trust Co. Bigger bills too. Change a bigger bill?"

"I gotta lotta money." Do me re ti la fa . . . Marlene Dietrich no dress singing " I gotta lotta money." Song hit of Broadway. "Throw me a rose I love you give me key to your room I good boy marry you first I gotta lotta money." Suspicious? Ten dollar bill for twenty cents worth of food. American cheese sandwich. Get arrested, sit in jail. Hot jail. "Better get out, too hot, oh, weak, sick." Carl stretched out his hands, grasped the edge of the glass-top table and pushed himself to his feet. Not so sick after all. Pay cashier now and get out. Nice and cool outside. Pull out bill from wallet, pay ten dollars for twenty cents sandwich keep the change. No suspicion. Ten dollar bill. Counterfeiter caught. Sick counterfeiter put in jail. Quivering like an aspen leaf. Longfellow. Carl thought he had a ten dollar bill.

The cashier looked at him sharply. "Where's your check? Watchudo, lose your check? Yuh better see the manager."

"This your check, mister?" Carl turned around and saw the waitress. "You musta left it on the table, mister." The waitress smiled.

Twenty cents, mister," said the cashier.

Carl fumbled for a wallet. His hand trembled. He felt sick. The cashier looked suspiciously at him. Can't get arrested now. Too sick. weary, weary. Want to sleep, get in bed . . .

"Twenty cents."

Carl remembered a banker who gave him a ten dollar bill. It was a blind beggar with a crippled twisted hand.

"Don't stand in the way!"

Carl watched the cashier's face closely. He thought he was saying, "Ten dollar bill. Got bigger bills. Change a bigger bill?"

"Say, Mimie, call the manager over here, quick. Here's a guy trying to get away with something."

Counterfeiters Caught. Carl thought he was caught. He wanted to get outside. The manager threw his arm around Carl's neck and held him. The diners rushed from their chairs and surrounded them. "Here, you hold him," said the manager. "I'll search this guy." The manager slipped his fingers skilfully through Carl's pockets and pulled out a quarter. He grinned, baring his teeth. "Good thing for you, sonny. Cashier how much is his check?"

"Hell, he's got a nickel change comin' to him yet," said the cashier. She threw a nickel at Carl and it rolled away under a table. "Now get out and stay out," said the manager.

"The guy looks sick," someone said.

"That don't cut no boners with me," said the manager. "Go on, beat it."

Carl walked out of the restaurant. He wanted to lie down, but he thought the manager would catch up with him. He kept on walking. He thought he was walking on Fifth Avenue.

LADY LAURA IN BOHEMIA
Mina Loy

Trained in a circus of swans
she
proceeds recedingly

Her eliminate flesh of fashion
inseparable from the genealogical tree

columns such towering reticence
of lifted chin
her hiccoughs seem
preparatory to bowing to the Queen

Her somersault descent
into the half-baked underworld
nor the inebriate regret
disturb
her vertical caste
"They drove 'em from the cradle on the curb"

This abbess-prostitute
presides
Jazz-Mass

the gin-fizz eucharist dispenses
—she kisses and curses
in the inconsummate embraces
of a one armed Pittsburger
"Here zip along out of that, Laura!"

"I can't come to Armenonville with you-u
I want to stay here and behave like a grue-u"

Her hell is
Zelli's

Where she floods the bar
with all her curls
in the delirious tears from those bill-poster eyes
plastering 'court proceedings' on the wall
of her inconsiderable soul

A tempered tool
of an exclusive finishing-school
her velvet larynx
slushes

"Glup—you mustn't speak to me
I'm bad—haven't you heard?
I'm Orful—o—g'lup I'm Horrid"

She gushes
"——know young Detruille?
Isn't he di-vi-ne
Such a sweet nature
that boy has

The other night when he tucked in with me
we talked most seriously
we have the same ideals
My dear he has
the eyes of Buddha
O I think he's simply di-vi-ne
The only man who ever understood
everything—   If I'd liked
he would'a'
married me
O I think he's simply di-vi-ne"

Out of the sentimental slobber
Lady Laura—momentarily sober
"How queer—that Detruille
said that he
once was introduced——
Well, I do wonder
how on earth ever such a bounder
happened to meet *my people*"

Sobs on my shoulder—
the memorable divorcée
and christened by the archbishop of Canterbury
Sixteen co-re—
Well let that pass!

She is yet like a diamond on a heap of broken glass.

THE FOUNDING OF NEW HAMPSHIRE

Carl Rakosi

A slender plank above a waterhole,
planted on end to meet my wants,
let me hear it whisper in the stock,
or sway a hair's breadth, and out it comes,
Another stake driven in and well shaved
points against the light from the layout.
The maple fits upon the joist like a flower,
                    a picked beam,
a great wood to plane and saw.
I tell my wife the walls are up,
the strips nailed at snug right angles,
                    the floors are oiled.
The Yankee poles are almost columns.

Braced against a gloomy magnitude,
I loiter civil on my soles and buffetted,
killing time in these traditions.
Are the woodsmells getting sweeter,
or the broker working at my back,
so that all the concord in the timber
can not warm this house?

EZRA POUND   6 Nov.   **RAPALLO**
VIA MARSALA, 12 INT. 5

Dear Johns
     This chap Caldwell seems to be a good egg.
You seem to know that already. I read the strawberry
in first issue without noting the name. HoWWevver. Thass
that.

Wdnt. it be a good thing to have Mangan do a narticle on
THEIR EXCESSIVE CUNCTATIONS and polish off a list of
five or six of the worst old trained seal that are now
obstructing the traffic. Idea occurs to me from interest
taken in W.L.Root's debunking of old Lyon Phelps in
Paris edtn. Chi. Trib.

I dont know who the seal are at the moment. I mean the
worst cases. I spose Barry Wendell is dead ? and
Mr Woodbury is dead ; but Ed. Wilson isn't ; and the
fungus in the N.Y. controll stations is getting to be as
bad as that in London (different , measles not paralysis
but still). Mag Mangan cd. do a cheery bit of sweepin
and define his own ideas in contrast.

What bekum of ole Bill"z White Mule . I await the rest
of thet animal.

///

Some day the ? will arise . Shd. the free reviews
aspire merely to feed to greed of Scribner and the big
purse holders. Wdnt. it be better for people like Caldwell
and Halper (and retrospectively Hem. XHH (of the
short bits of In our Time ; and the poems ; and
Torrents of Spring ; and Callaghan) to be able to afford

EZRA POUND

RAPALLO
VIA MARSALA, 12 INT. 5

to stay in a l'i'erary mag. instead of its being one's
human duty to bid 'em god speed for the gate receipts ?

I admit the case dont immediately rise.

Re/ yr/ remark on group. equality cant maintain itself.
open question whether a group of a few names each meaning
something isnt more effective than a list of 30 names.

At, any rate you've got Caldwell , Mangan ; ole Bill
getting better (and damn few do go on gettin better
at the a dvanced age of 47) ~~HHHH~~ and Bob.
(shd. think best way to deal with that case is
ḥ when poss, to get hold of as much of his stuff
at a time as he will let you , and pick the strongest.

I saw mss/ of two excellent longish things of his
last spring (butitmustbeadmittedthattheSUBject ....

You've done a good year work.

WITH THE THIRD ISSUE printed and distributed, Johns drove back to his home in Lynn for a brief vacation with his father and friends on the North Shore. It was there in East Gloucester that Johns through his friend Ross Burton, brother of designer Virginia Lee Burton, first met John Cheever. Cheever seemed quite innocent, not because he was several years younger than Johns, but because up to that time the range of his experience had been somewhat limited. Ross Burton had first known Cheever when he was a student at Thayer Academy before his expulsion. Out of this incident came his first published work, an article which he sold to *The New Republic*.

Now Cheever was turning out a number of extremely sensitive stories, primarily of the young adolescent confused by the strangeness of the many adults who impinged upon his life. Even then, the writing of this youngster showed superb craftsmanship.

At that time in East Gloucester there was an evening gathering place called The Wharf, presided over by Doris Rich, a young actress who made her summer pleasant by setting up a number of tables and selling set-ups for drinks as well as coffee and sandwiches, while she herself displayed her qualities as an actress in a number of short one-act plays or dramatic scenes from larger works. When Doris did a scene from Sir James Barrie's *Twelve Pound Look* the tables were full and an overflow stood watching from the public wharf outside.

One evening Doris Rich was planning an informal after-closing party for her friends, and Johns was asked to come and to bring someone with him. Being personally quite fond of her and wishing to give such time to Doris as was feasible, Johns did not want to bring a girl. Therefore he asked John Cheever.

It was a typical evening of partying, with perhaps a little too much to drink and fairly overt expressions of sexual affections. As it was coming to a close, Johns was surprised to feel Cheever's hand on his arm drawing him outside. Cheever had only one thing to say, repeatedly and with vehemence: "What are you doing here with all these horrible people?" Momentarily, he was like a child crying out in consternation against the conduct of adults.

357-361

Johns printed Cheever's story "Late Gathering" in the fourth number of *Pagany* for 1931. He also took the liberty of returning the "h" to the "Jon" which was the modified first name Cheever used when submitting the story. Cheever later wrote to thank him for this.

"Late Gathering" was a young and searching story. Years later, as Johns read the intricacies of physical affections handled so masterfully in Cheever's collection of short stories, *The Enormous Radio,* or in his *Wapshot* novels, he would recall with a chuckle the young hand on his sleeve and the impassioned, "What are you doing here with all these horrible people?" Indeed, John Cheever did learn his way around in a confused adult world, and has always expressed the fact consummately.

Quite different from John Cheever was Edward Dahlberg. Johns had never met Dahlberg and was delighted when the author invited him down to Provincetown on Cape Cod for a weekend visit. Dahlberg had been born in Boston, but spent much of his boyhood in Kansas City and Cleveland. Johns sensed a deep resentment in Dahlberg toward American society, and wondered why this man had not fled the United States years earlier to take up permanent residence among the expatriates living in Paris. But Dahlberg, despite his feeling toward this country, was too American to leave home permanently. Johns admired his slangy, back porch style of writing, and was amazed at his ability to link so clearly classical allusions with home-brew folklore, which made for an earthy yet continental Americanism in his writing. Dahlberg possessed the ability to draw from his native experience, fuse it with great themes of western man—suffering, insecurity, loneliness—and produce a burlesque which mirrored present-day America, yet in an entrancing, distorted glass.

Johns enjoyed this literary weekend with Dahlberg and his wife, Sara. Provincetown was something quite distinct from the smaller Cape Ann, where the atmosphere was alert but peaceful, neighborly and friendly. The summer visitors in Provincetown were sharply

this is a very bad story but because
you are an editor it is your
duty to read it ——

    I am very sorry that it is so
bad but I could'nt help it —
— It is a horrible condition
to be in.

             Jon Cheever

November 28, 1931.

Dear Dick Johns:

Wrote you some time back. How is Pagany shaping up?
Anything new happening. I've been terribly scattered myself,staying
here in Cleveland, biding my time, and more or less in a dull
flat stupor all the time. My Ms. is still going the rounds, although
I've gotten a good deal of encouragement from different sources since
I last saw you. I think I told you Covice Friede wanted to take it,
but the agent wasn't satisfied with the terms. I believe had I been
dealing directly with the publisher that I would have relented.
However, I have no criticism to make of the agent, for she is really
highly competent and has very much belief in the book. Then Harcourt
Brace were undecided for quite a time. I sent their letter and report
onto Edmund Wilson, who is now in Provincetown and he wrote me as
follows(as you've been so helpful and interested in the Ms, I thought
you'd probably be interested. Am enclosing excerpts from letter and
report of Harcourt Brace):"I'm sorry to hear you haven't got your
book placed yet, but the opinions sound pretty enthusiastic. Wouldn't
Liveright take a chance? I don't suppose Pagany has enough money
to do publishing on their account, have they?"
Before continuing, I hope you will understand,
Johns, that I have never thought of discussing the above with
anybody. Whether you have or haven't the money to publish is
something that I've never thought of talking about, since I know
nothing about it anyway. Only after quoting this, did it occur to
me that perhaps you might consider it intrusive on my part, although
Edmund Wilson suggested the entire thing out of a clear sky. As a
matter of fact, E.W. said he would write to Sylvia Beach if I didn't
get the book placed here. Anyway, here is a part of the letter from
Harcourt Brace to the agent, Miss Bernice Baumgarten:
"Finally, we are returning Edward Dahlberg's
manuscript because we feel that few readers would appreciate the
book for what it really is. FLUSHING TO CALVARY might add to Dahlberg's
an element of notoriety, whereas it should enhance his deserved reputation as a serious writer....Perhaps the best way to explain our
attitude to the novel is the enclose one of the opinions that was
written about it. I don't know that it would be wise to pass this or
any of our comments onto the author, but I should be glad to leave
that decision in your hands.". ..

FLUSHING TO CALVARY.

"Here is a disciple of John Dos Passos, a realistic follower of
D.H. Lawrence.
Dahlberg is a writer of undeniable sincerity, with a passionate conviction and interest in his work that are as rare as they are apt to
be unappreciated. There is a lyricism, and a religious intensity,
about the most bitter of the passages in this work and it redeems page
after page that deals with the filthy, the unutterably degraded moments
of life.

2.

For most people, this book would be simply what it appears to be, an uncommonly gross and detailed story of revolting, filthy, unmentionable people. The central characters are an old woman named Lizzie Lewis, formerly a lady-barber, and her son, Lorry, clerk in a commission house and worker in a subway newsstand. Incidental figures are an Argentinian bicycle-dealer, a boy who writes ads, Irish neighbors, Jewish shopkeepers, all the rundown godforsaken shabby and abysmally ignorant people who---we are dimly aware---live somewhere in or about the suburbs of New York.

There is an endless procession of these people; the nasty harlots of Coney Island, the diseased waiters, the stupid clerks, the spiritually crippled, and the emotionally bankrupt. Dahlberg guides this sullen parade with feverish activity; it is a crawling, masslike, indescriable stream. But Dahlberg is able to marshall it, to pour a steady cleansing stream upon this human material. It takes shape, the details are clear and unforgettable, and against our will, against one's taste and choice even, sympathies are aroused for these most miserable, these godforgotten.

I cannot understand exactly how this happens. I know that one is held by the exuberant relentless style of Dahlberg and that one feels profoundly unhappy for the Argentinian who is sent to jail for five years "for assault" that was farthest from his thoughts; one is moved by by the terrible fate of Lizzie, the stupid and ugly, the clumsy shoplifter and amateur abortonist and disgusting mother that she is; one thinks there must be something, hopes there must be something, for the patient overburdened sickened Lorry, the defenceless youth whose only memories are filled with poverty, wretchedness, shame and sickness; and so on. It is this stir in the reader's mind that distinguishes this book and this author from all the unlovely imitators of Joyce and Lawrence and Dos Passos. The book has sufficient reason for being; it is not another meaningless photographic reel of the seamy side of life, but an artist's testimony and a man's honest version of certain truths of life."

Now Cape and Smith have the Ms. I don't know what will happen there. Anyway, all this waiting is very dispiriting and leaves me low. Some one here I think may do "Kentucky Blue Grass Henry Smith." He wants to possibly print privately about two hundred copies of it. However, I've made no arrangements. Lawrence Drake wrote me sometime back that he wanted to print one of the sections of the novel, but he was waiting to take it up with Titus who was abroad at the time. Haven't heard from him further since. When is the next issue of Pagany coming out. Wonder if you'd mind sending me a copy of Graphophone Nickelodeon Days, if it isn't too much bother, and The Coney Island Angelus Bells. If you're going to use Ja Wohl, etc. you can take it out of whatever you may think there is coming to me, if you don't mind.

Meanwhile, all good wishes and friendship, and hope all this · doesn't bore you.

Edward Dahlberg.

General Delivery,
Cleveland, Ohio.

divided into three groups: the working artists and writers, the tourists, and the growing society of deviates of both sexes who had established a free and flourishing colony in this harbor town.

Certainly, however, such men as Edmund Wilson and John Dos Passos who had homes a few miles back from Provincetown could work well and industriously in the private atmosphere of dunes and sunlight. The Dahlbergs were eager to show Johns the entire range of summer living, and Johns went back to Cape Ann with a kaleidoscopic picture of beaches, art exhibits, night clubs where the entertainers were generally transvestites, and finally the quiet simplicity the Dahlbergs had set up for themselves in the midst of the seasonal jamboree.

As Summer progressed into Fall and the depression deepened Johns sensed an entirely new sort of writing being submitted for consideration. This was a younger, more agile sort of prose work charged with ambition and direction, a clearing through the fog of excessive experimentalism and colorless defeatism. Johns sought out this new guard.

Johns felt that he had printed enough material by Ezra Pound, who was now having his say in every little magazine in America and Europe, and with little distinction. Pound's "The First Year of *Pagany* and the Possibility of Criteria" in the first issue of Volume II had diffused in all directions. Now his even less-controlled writing in other magazines appeared as pointlessly vehement opinion.

Johns was surprised, therefore, when he read Iris Barry's "The Ezra Pound Period" in the October 1931 issue of *The Bookman*. This article summarized Pound's years in London during the First World War and included anecdotes of the literary people in Pound's circle, from Arthur Symonds through James Joyce and T. S. Eliot, to Mary Butts and Iris Barry herself, soon to be the young cinema critic for the *London Daily Mail*.

In 1931 Iris Barry was curator of films for the Museum of Modern Art in New York, and both Johns and his friend William Chapman frequently met her for luncheon. Johns was upset about her article on Pound; he brought a copy to one of these noontime meetings and read aloud to Chapman Iris Barry's closing words:

Pound himself is invisible and, save for his own poetry comparatively inaudible nowadays. He pontificates rarely, has few disciplines, as though with that immense effort of his from 1912 to 1919 he has done all that (has in truth done more than) could be expected of anyone and were glad of the years from thirty-five onward to till his own plot.

Johns showed Miss Barry Pound's review of *Pagany* in the first issue for 1931, plus other reviews, criticisms, and statements published in other little magazines. He assured her that the plot Ezra was tilling was world-wide by now and that he was giving much time and thought to helping many promising young writers, not only of England and America, but of the Continent as well. If anything, Johns went on, Pound was doing too much pontificating, wearing his name thin, almost to the point of appearing slightly mad through a maze of unrelated statements and thoughts.

Throughout the first two years of *Pagany* Johns had given Mary Butts' decadent sparkle a full display. By the time the fourth issue was ready to be printed, Johns knew he would no longer accept further contributions from her so that space might be available for newer and lesser-known writers, who, in his opinion, had something more vital to say. Somehow in her shorter than usual short story, "Green" there seemed to blow a tempering wind through one of the untypically English country homes which generally housed an amorous imbroglio. Now Mary Butts was writing with tartness, almost as if she felt there might be a healthy future for a young couple in the heterosexuality of marriage, cleansed of the emotional friendships of other young men for the husband and the influence of a conniving, mantic mother who would willfully destroy the confidence of a son's young wife. Though Butts' props were as plush, the narcissism was less posturing, and there was the hint of country health to come.

344-356

Mary Butts was always brilliant, and Johns was pleased to have had the opportunity to publish her works, regardless of the guise she might choose to assume. But this sign of good health on a generally fevered cheek was new and promising. One of her stories finally looked forward toward a balanced living, and Johns considered this story, one of his favorites printed in *Pagany,* an apt swan song for Mary Butts.

In 1929, Johns had rejected an inanity submitted by D. H. Lawrence. Now, William Faulkner had submitted a story which Johns was certain he could not accept. When Johns first saw William Faulkner's name on the title page of the story, "Divorce in Naples," he was excited, for in his opinion here was an author who was certain of a place in American letters. Johns had been fortunate in securing first editions of each Faulkner title prior to the sensational success of his novel *Sanctuary,* either as a review copy, or, within a few months, as a remainder. Although Faulkner's first book, *The Marble Faun,* did not impress him as poetry, he salted five copies away as possible investments. These along with five copies of Wallace Stevens' *Harmonium* were remaindered for eighteen cents each on the bargain table in the book department of R. H. White's, an old and seedy Boston department store.

However, as Johns read beyond the first page of "Divorce in Naples" he was chagrined. This was the story of the falling out of a couple of bed buddies among the sailors of a tramp steamer, because the effeminate one had lost his heterosexual virginity to a seaport whore. Later the buddies reached a reconciliation, dancing together on the deck and surrounded by the balance of the crew, intrigued and stimulated by their renewed relationship. This seemed a fairly trivial anecdote, especially when compared to the art of writing Faulkner had developed for his own best work. The final words of the story, spoken by the pretty catamite, tore the texture of the incident into ludicrous falsity:

> When we get to Galveston, I want you to buy me a suit of these pink silk teddybears that ladies use. A little bigger than I'd wear, see?

Despite his personal feeling about Faulkner's work Johns knew he did not want to print this particular story. It was not because of the homosexual theme—there had been many pieces printed in *Pagany* submitted by defensively proud and overt deviants and accepted on literary merit—but because Johns remembered the reception given his own story "Solstice," which seemed to arouse the compulsion of certain readers to personalize the main character. The substance of "Solstice" was intended to be more than a homosexual episode, while all the literary know-how of Faulkner only served to dress up a trivial commonplace of nautical sexuality.

When he returned "Divorce in Naples," Johns asked if there might be another story available, since he wanted a Faulkner story included in *Pagany*. When he was told that nothing else was available, he trusted his editorial acumen and formally rejected this inferior piece of work.

There was no longer space in *Pagany* for the twittering of such birds as Ford and Tyler. Gertrude Stein's translation of Georges Hugnet's "Enfances" in the first issue of Volume II was an interesting experiment, but by this time Miss Stein's nonsensical couplets had begun to pall. It was time now to heed newer voices, a little more inept in phrasing perhaps, but more true to the day and age in America. At that time there were two literary agents in New York City with a wholly unselfish interest in their clients' work, and they both respected what Johns was doing with his magazine. These were Maxim Lieber and Carl Brandt of Brandt and Brandt.

Carl Brandt welcomed *Pagany*'s publication of the poetry of Aiken and e. e. cummings, and it was he who made the "Eveline Hutchins" section of Dos Passos' *USA* available, all at the same low rate of three dollars a page.

Maxim Lieber handled an entirely different crew, writers whose names were not yet well known. It was through him that James T. Farrell was printed in *Pagany*. In the slimmer days soon to come, Lieber never lost his sense of balance. He asked for payment with regularity for those writers who had earned it, but he had sympathy and understanding of the fact that the driblets of cash which came into *Pagany* must be dispersed in several different directions. He knew that, whenever possible, payments would be made, and that Johns was grateful for his polite patience.

The phasing out of Mary Butts and the introduction of John Cheever indicated that *Pagany*'s fourth issue for 1931 was one of transition, a final encore for a number of writers, yet far too subtle for the reader to notice. Certainly standard names were included, writers who were performing excellently well in their craft. In the

338

339

MAXIM LIEBER

A U T H O R S '   R E P R E S E N T A T I V E

PHONE WICKERSHAM 7836

SUITE ~~1902~~

55 West 42 St. ~~509 MADISON AVE~~

NEW YORK CITY

December 22nd, 1931

Dear Mr. Johns:

     Many thanks for returning Farrell's "L unch Hour". I did, as a matter of fact, send you another piece by him which is now doubtless in your possession. I hope you will be able to use it. The difficulty with Farrell seems to be his inability to disentangle himself from all phases of biological function. I do believe, however, that some of his references might be deleted without injuring the quality of his narrative and the pungency of his style, the combination of which seems to create a type of fiction which comes closest to being a reflection of modern America.

     Will you be good enough to let me know whether you would care to examine a novelette of some twenty thousand words by Meridel LeSuer. It is, in my opinion, a combination of the emotional and cerebral and depicts the mood of a youth on board the night boat from Los Angeles to San Francisco. I shall be very glad to send it to you if you are in the market for a novelette.

        Very truly yours,

        Maxim Lieber

I05 Oakley St

Chelsea.

8. II. 3I.

Dear Mr Johns:

I have just received your letter of
October 27. I shall be very glad to receive the copies of
'Pagany' containing my work. But you do not tell me, as I asked
you to in my first letter, how you came to be able to print
them atall. I never sent them to you presonally, and if a friend
of mine, to whom I gave copies of my poems some years ago with
leave to find a publisher if he thought fit, sent them to you,
I heard nothing about it, either from you nor from him. (Nor
do I know at the moment how to find him and ask him.) If he
sent them to you, I should wish to thank him. Anyhow; how did
you get hold of them?

Also, I understand that though you sent me copies
of the poems as they came out, you did not send me a cheque.
(As you did when you published my story 'The House Party'.)
You say in your letter that you are going to send me one; for
the poems, I presume, and I hope for 'Green' also. I hope you
will do this as soon as you can. All writers wish 'Pagany' well,
 but they must insist on knowing on what terms they are dealing
Surely even if in treaty with a foreign author, it is not good
policy to be so inexact.

Yours very truly

selection of poetry, which included contributions by Conrad Aiken, R. P. Blackmur, Emanuel Carnevali, Horace Gregory, and Louis Zukofsky, Johns was proud to be once again able to present such an outstanding variety of themes, methods, and moods. One new poet to those pages was John Waldhorn Gassner, whose "Ocean Automobile Road" was clear and visual in its objectivism. Gassner's great enthusiasm was the theatre and the techniques of building an enduring play. Already he had notebooks filled on the subject, and he looked forward to writing intelligently on the theatre of America.

NUMBER 4 *October–December*

Contents

PAGANY

363

GREEN

Mary Butts

"Don't you think, Madame Nick, that it would be better if I went down to see?"

"I'll think of it," she said quickly, and he noticed a slight hauteur in her voice.

"We are sure, alas! that she takes too much to drink, and I am sure that my son does not. And you have heard what people say about her friends. Nick would never allow me to know the Taverners, so is it likely that he will have them to his house unless she insists? And if she does and he refuses, as he certainly should, she will fall out of her own set, and most of his friends will have nothing to do with her. The Derings have hinted to me that they might have to drop Dick. I hardly like to tell you Ambrose, but they said—" A paraphrase followed for several sexual and social irregularities.

"Don't you think I might go?" Ambrose Alexander said this with loving earnestness, with whimsical adoration, leaning over a narrow space towards an old woman, upright by the fire in a dull gold London room. Inside her tight silver wig and her mask of paint, she was yielding to treatment. In one hollow centimetre of her mind she knew she was, and that she would send Ambrose because he would bring back an exciting story, a story that would justify malice and moral indignation: that could also be repudiated without strain. He owed her a good deal, she thought. He was a Jew. His function was to please. He did please. A slim supple young man to run about was essential: to confide in: to reassure her.

For his part he was willing to oblige her. There were good pickings in that family, and, benefits apart, she was giving him what he wanted—a chance to get his own back on her son and his wife. For the six months before, for the six months since their marriage she had been ravenous for its discredit. The discredit it was for him to supply. But a full meal this time, and more than a meal, a provision, on which she would never satiate of the wife's blood and sap. What she wanted would serve his turn; but when he thought about her, and he preferred not to think about her too much, he misunderstood her degrees of consciousness, the balance of her scruples, her ignorance, her appetite and her fears.

"If you are to go down and see her, how can it be arranged? It mustn't look—"

"They had better not expect me. If I could have a car and it should break down, then I could simply be there, and they would put me up for the night."

"That's a good idea. I'll pay for it. But, mind you, Ambrose, it must be a real breakdown. I won't have any lies."

"Madame Nick, it shall go up in flames to make my word, since it is really your word, good."

She looked away from him, a little sentimental smile disturbing the corners of the old thin mouth. If only in her life she had heard more men say things like that. He meant it. Ambrose was a good and noble man. Of course he would not have to burn the car. That would be too extravagant. Even for the most disgusting news of her daughter-in-law.

Splendid that Ambrose was going. Her son might be in agonies about his wife: her son might be wanting his home again. She would give Ambrose messages to make it easy for him to come home for help. She foresaw decent divorce, and when Ambrose was gone, walked up and down the long room between the·azaleas and the chinese jars, rehearsing a long, hideous and wholly satisfactory scene with his wife.

Until the nature of the interview from being a source of pleasure became a kind of pain, and she noticed that she was not sure how far she wanted to be able to trust Ambrose there.

Later she rang him up.

"Of course I'll pay all your expenses, but don't be too extravagant. I've just thought: we may need all our money later." She had said "our money" out of romantic delicacy. Ambrose relished it differently. It had been share and share alike with Nicholas, who usually forgot about his own share. Then, a year ago, Nicholas had found out that intermittent rebellion is exhausting and had conducted an entire revolution instead. Six months later he was married. Now his landmarks were off both their maps. Only their dèbris remained—nothing but skeletons and broken boards where his places had been. A devastating escape, but his mother had herself to thank. And hatred of his wife, which had been her refuge, was to become her revenge. Against Nancy Loring, Ambrose knew nothing—had not heard much—"Le dossier accusateur de toute jolie femme"—But to be kept by Mrs. Loring, he must keep Mrs. Loring; give Mrs. Loring what she wanted, a daughter-in-law unkind, unchaste, and so far as possible, unkissed. It seemed that he might have to rely on his imagination. After six months they were still living out of London, in that small, remote house, where no one that he knew ever went. Without a car, a telephone, or a horse. With cats and an old boat and books. That did not promise disillusion yet unless the girl was bored. What was there to find out? Could he return and report bliss? A spring wind filled the curtains of his room; coal-dust from the unlit fire charged its delicate touch. With his eyes on the tree-tops breaking leaf he could only smell London. He did not particularly mind, but at night with the fire burning he could feel Mrs. Loring behind his chair. Boards cracked before and after her tread, step of a bully with small feet and ankles swollen a little with age, and there was a sound of gobbling already and appetite unglutted, and punishment for Nick shaping once she had got him back. Once they had got him back.

Need he go at all? Could he go in theory, or, if he went, in theory provoke Nancy to behaviour whose character could be decided on later, and Nick actually into appropriate disgust?

There is nothing more difficult to deny than a casual event whose importance rests on its implications.

It is said that you have been to Biarritz with friends of doubtful character.

You do not know them.

You have not been to Biarritz at all.

Prove it, if you have not been conspicuously with other people anywhere else. The force of your denial will fly loose, attach itself and strengthen the accusation. You will have been at St. Jean de Luz, where you met and were notorious with them there. It is this that lies at the base of all non-resistance to evil, that the resistance becomes a neutral agent, equally able to strengthen what it attacks.

Ambrose felt that he need not be too anxious.

There is always something wrong. If it were not yet conscious he had only to give the unconscious a name. While it was equally possible that the girl was bored, loose or a slut. If not, she was going to be. The elegantly-set problem absorbed him, in whose solution he ignored himself, his emotion for Nick, his curiosity about Nancy, his fear of the mother—about whom he assumed himself particularly cynical and gay.

Two days later he ran out of petrol on a remote road a mile from their house.

* * *

His wife asked Nick Loring:

"Who was it called the sea the "very green"?"

"The Egyptians, I think. The Red Sea and the Mediterranean. What about green wine?"

They were looking out at a green plain which lay as far as the horizon on their left, and their house stood on the shelf of a grass hill beside the plain, tilted in the sunlight to another green. High trees stood about the hill, and a short way outside, across a lawn, a copse crested its last bank. The plain had once been the sea, an estuary savage with tides, now narrowed the river, leaving at its flow and ebb, where all winter, for every hundred yards, a heron watched its pitch. There was no dust: no sound but birds and air: no colour but green. There was every green.

In late April the top greens were of gold. Across the plain there was a march of elms, open hands with blood inside them, tipped with saffron fire. The copse was a stuff woven out of the same green.

They went out. On the small lawn were cats, black and white enamel in fur. One watched its lover: the lover watched a bird: the third, bow-stretched and upright, ripped the bark of a tree. Two kittens tumbled over like black and white flowers.

They followed one another through the copse. Each willow-trunk was a separate man and woman. They came down the further side, to where, when it had been sea the plain had worn a little bay under the hill. There was long wet grass where the tide-mark had been. They came to a dyke and an old house. There were willows along the glass water very tall: along it and over it, one flung across and an elm-tree drowned in it; its root out of the ground in a flat earth-cake. The house was a deserted farm. An orchard reached it down a small valley between the rising of another hill. There was no path. They went up through the apple-trees, through a place wholly sheltered, where no wind came but only sun, where, when there was no sun, there was always light, so that in mid-winter, in the stripped world, the seasons did not exist there. They called it the Apple Land, remembering there something which they could not re-call, that seemed to have the importance of a just-escaped dream. The orchard ended sharply in an over-hanging quick-set, and a sharp climb to the top of the hill. To follow the valley to its head there was a glen on the left, sickly with flies and thin shoots and a scummed choked stream up to a short fall, almost in the dark, which was not quite wholesome, in whose pool was without stir or light. The way out of that was also sharp and steep but quite different—to a shut cottage on top and a garden with tansy in it.

Through lambs running in the up-fields they came to their village and bought a morning paper, cheese, apples and cigarettes. They came back another way, by a high road, by a lane, over the open grass along a ribbon their feet had printed, green upon green.

*   *   *

Ambrose Alexander reached the house as they had entered the copse. A shy country servant left him alone. He was pleased that they were out: stood back by the door from where he could see the whole length of the room.

Across the table an open ordnance map hung like a cloth askew. There was a chess-board beside it, and men half tumbled out of a box and a wide bowl of small mixed flowers. There was a stone bottle of ink and a dish with sticks of sealing-wax and stamps, pencils and a seal. There was a dog's lead and a pair of leather gloves. A red handkerchief was knotted up full of needles and wool. When he handled it, one ran into his palm. There was an oil painting of Mount Soracte and steel prints of forgotten gentlemen, and on the black chimney shelf a fishing-rod crossed with a gun. There were books on murder: The Roman occupation of Britain: Chinese Art. There was poetry. *Mr. Hunca Munca the mouse climbed to the top of the kitchen chimney and looked out. There was no soot.* Up to the age of five, every child laughs at this version of that joke; but to Ambrose it was as if the room was calling him, very plainly and in another language, an outsider. It was not what he had come to hear. He stared out of the window and up the hill. There was no one. Then he went upstairs. Under his feet the old boards had no friendly squeak. Like old servants who might talk.

Their bedroom had a rose-brick fire-place and a line of persian prints. Under the mirror, piled in a shell, were strings of glass flowers and fruit. Everything was in order, polished and very still, and the bath-room full of things to wash with. He went back to the bed-room. Supposed that in one of the shut drawers there was a shameful secret among soiled linen:

persuaded himself: opened it, and in it there were folded silks. Bedroom books: two more murders, a County History, *Per Amica Silentia Lunae,* Sterne. A cat looked in at the door and yawned before it went away. Under a scent flask was a receipted bill. He looked out of the window at the very green.

There they had been all winter long. They did not seem to want to go away. Told nothing: saw no one who would tell anything: asked for nothing. He was discouraged. Propriety, simplicity, the routine of country-house life. The house went on talking out loud; not without passion but with directness that annihilated. Down any passage there might be met a wall of fire. He looked at the bed over whose foot-rail hung a bright shawl and a fur.

The persian pictures were perfectly proper. In the dining room cupboard there had been two bottles of beer. He went downstairs, heard no approach on the soundless turf, so that they were on him in an instant, as instantly recoiled, and a moment later were overwhelmed in his cordiality and excuse.

Disentangling themselves from him, they exchanged a word together, out of the house.

"What has he come for? Car broken down? Whose car? Who's given him a car?"

Nicholas Loring was annoyed: his wife uneasy. There was nothing to do but feed him and not to go after the Swan's nest that day. Swans stay there but are more interesting than a townsman ill at ease, vocal and supple and full of admiration that did not try to be more than a display. Voluble and mobile, Ambrose had a trick of statement, one to each sentence, followed by a denial, a reversal of it in the next. So that which seemed, sentence by sentence, to be a vivid reaction to life, cancelled out to nothing. To no belief at all. Nicholas, folded-up in country quiet, was not without illusion and irritated by what had once stimulated him. No belief at all. And Nancy saw that everything Ambrose said would mean nothing and felt giddy in her mind until she felt sick. They were his hosts and they must stomach him, feed him and endure him to an hour they had not fixed. They were saved from spiritless invitation, and she from fear, by curiosity and the involuntary hosts' calculation of the time when they would be able to lose him. Ambrose understood this, and that he must stay the night and that at present no mere breakdown of his car would get him the invitation. He saw himself after lunch led by Nick, grim, courteous and embarrassed, to restart it at the top of the hill.

They came to the end of the lunch. Nicholas was listening to Ambrose, to what he had once heard, year in year out, and now had not heard for a year. And after a year there was no more pleasure in it or surprise at the changes. It was as if he knew them by heart: for the first time: at last:

Ambrose was trying hard with a parade of emotion, trying to praise marriage, their withdrawal, the serene country; displaying himself as the neurotic townsman, the alien, whose pride it was to humble himself, to look into paradise through bars. A peep he owed to them:

"Is that safe, Nancy?" turning to her from Nicholas.

"I think so," she answered civilly, not at all sure.

"He is trying not to cancel out," she thought. "Why?"

"He can't do it for long. Why is he here? He does not like me. Would like to have me—so as to hurt Nick. Nick he loves and hates." Then that he had once loved Nick and then hated him, probably for his marriage and now did neither, or in different proportions. What was he there for?

He said: "Suppose me at my role again—the old serpent. You used, Nick, to call me that, and any variation that struck you from 'you dirty devil' to Lucifer."

"Lord of flies" she murmured. He heard her. She was ashamed. He looked steadily at her and smiled. "You're right, my dear. I'm just as much that variation of the fiend. Only neither you nor Nick need the serpent in me any more. Serpents"—he added—"are not sentimental. That was useful once to Nick. While who has ever heard of a mother-snake?" They took that in.

"There was a time when Nick needed an old, contradictory bloke like me to leave all doors open and let a spot of reality in. His mother—" (the pause which left her unqualified perfected suggestion—) "she would have shut the lot, and everything open is the only answer to everything shut. But now—" He went on to explain that Nicholas, now he had welcomed the reality Ambrose had provided, had made his own freedom and been given love. It was true. But Nicholas must be re-persuaded that he owed it to him. Doors that have been opened can be shut. One implies the other. They could begin on him again, he and Mrs. Loring, and Nick would be well retrapped. The doors would be shut and the wife outside. Only it would take longer than he thought, and Mrs. Loring would not see the delicacy of it. He must find out how to persuade her that the cup of deferred blood is richer.

Rapt in these thoughts he stared smiling at them. Nick was moved, but remembered that once he would only have been moved. Ambrose had opened doors once, or he had thought so. Until he had noticed that he had only slammed them to and fro, chasing him between draughts. Until he had stuck open a certain number that he needed for himself. (Who wants to live with every door open?) His exits and entrances were now his own, and by one of them Nancy had come in: helped to fix open a few more, and by one of these, first Ambrose, then his mother had gone out. That was what had happened in terms of doors. He softened, feeling that he could afford to. Old Ambrose had come down for some sort of thanks. Or perhaps for a share. Share of the rich strength which made things easy with Nancy: easy to give and take: easy to go in and out: to live: Like music, all the musics. Ambrose was by himself as he'd always been. Nancy was thinking the same thing, that here was a man alone for good, and thought of him on a toadstool and with people round him on toadstools, and that he spent his time picking their stalks from underneath them and his own stalk.

Then, the strength mounting in her, also, she wondered if Ambrose had been necessary to Nicholas, to that old woman's only son. Was it possible that they had shaken Ambrose off his fence? Was this visit after all a no mean congratulation and praise, one of the mysterious triumphs of love? She forgot his subtle opposition to their marriage. Was this old Mrs. Loring's last defeat? She judged it most improbable and forgot her judgment. Only remembered that it would be good if it were true. If it were true, they might some day be able to forgive. She looked at Ambrose, very simply. It seemed a far cry to "mother's gigolo." He observed her, went to the piano, and played the letter-song from Figaro. Whistling softly *"and the sounds of beauty flowed and trembled until they seemed to triumph . . . over the hard hearts of men."*

She brought him over his coffee. There was not a cruel animal behind Nick, only a vexed old woman, who had been lovely, who would never feed on her son again, or with septic finger-nails scratch at the bloom of her own youth. She had been ungenerous about Ambrose. How hateful is the wife who does injustice to her husband's friends.

She lit his cigarette, and stood by her husband's shoulder, wholly herself and part of him and part of the very green. Part of Ambrose? Yes, for this moment, if this were true.

* * *

They took him out, a tramp across green, from green to green, entertained him with birds' nests set deep in thorned twigs and split light. There had been tea and toast and chess, an evening to get through and a night. He stood between them at evening at the door of the house. Now in the sky there was a bar of the green that has no name. He was standing on grass darkening beside dark green. She had said *"It was all Hermes, all Aphrodite"*.

He had been bored and concealed it, with the night before him becoming unsure of himself. Dinner, chess, music, country-talk. A drink? They had filled up his car and put her away in the village and refused to let him go.

They gave him a drink and a rabbit cooked in onions. He had gained nothing but the fooling of them, and if they did not know it, they were slightly bored. The worst thing that can happen to a liar is to be believed. If he did not notice that, he suffered as Nick indicated in intimate outline, his serene and final detachment from his mother. Confident they told him their plans, about excavations and gardening and Nick's new book which was not about himself or even about people. He had to listen and by that time it was night, grey, windless, with a squeak in it. The great chimney flared. Standing inside it one could follow the sparks up its square tower to a square patch of sky. Innocent as wine, as dew. He sneered. Outside was it innocent? Innocent for them and strong. His room was away from theirs. On that side of the house the night could do what it liked with him. The night would have him to itself. Nick and Nancy would have themselves to themselves. He would have nothing to himself but himself and night. Oh! there was someone who might come in and sit beside his bed. Madame Nick might come in and talk, smile and suck in her thin red lips. Keep him awake because she was hungry. She would not mind dark green night.

He would have nothing but lies to feed her on: have to invent her a meal because her sort of food wasn't in the house. He was getting childish. With their stupid innocence they were doing him down. What did Nancy want? To give him another drink: be sure that he was comfortable: a game of chess before bed. "Glorious game" he must say, but it took longer to play than he reckoned. A shy woman, what she did was better than her promise. Later she said: "It is good for your complexes, Ambrose, to win things and be praised." For that he should have let her win. God! But he could not bear to evade the game. And it put off bed and whatever it was that tapped outside on the windows its peculiar code.

But when he went up, the soft air surging in put him instantly to sleep.

They woke next morning with a distate for him in the house. He was to go after lunch and the morning seemed an hour-series that could not be lived through. There was no reason for it, only that they did not care now if his visit marked a triumph. They wanted him out of the way. There were interesting things to do and he would not do them. Nancy decided that she would disappear, on the excuse of leaving Nicholas alone with his friend, and came downstairs first to see that Ambrose had his breakfast in bed. There was a letter for her from Nick's mother. That hardly ever happened. She went outside to read it, barefoot on the cat-printed dew: split it open and read:

"My dear child,

I wish this to be entirely between ourselves, but I have an idea that Nicholas' old friend Ambrose intends to come down and see you. Please be very nice to him. You know how it is—he was so fond of my son and has suffered the break since his marriage. Of course it couldn't be helped and I am so afraid of emotional friendships between young men, but I am sure you have nothing to fear now. Don't tell Nicholas anything about this—and also what I meant to say is—don't be upset or offended if he should try and flirt with you. It means absolutely nothing. He has a very fine nature really and is not at all interested in women. Just want there to be no misunderstanding, not that Nicholas is likely to think anything as long as you are careful, only I do not wish you for your part to be led away. I explain this badly, but I am sure you will understand.

I hope you are both as well as possible.

Your loving Mother,

Angela Loring.

The crisp dew melted between her toes and their colour changed from pink to red. One hand held on to her curled, cropped hair. There was a moment when nothing happened at all, neither image nor concept nor sense impression. She came to, first to the small bustling wind: then to a bird. Then to a draught of other life, like voices shrieking from London, recorded on a square of thick blue paper. It was mad: it was comic: it was dangerous. She ate a light breakfast in silence. Anyhow it was tiresome.

She said: "You will want the morning with Ambrose. I'm off." But Nicholas had his plans also.

"Look here" he said. "I forgot that I said that I'd see that man about—"

"Take him with you."

"It's a trudge. I got mud to my knees last—"

"Am I to keep Ambrose?"

"I mean if you could be that sort of spirit—I'll be back before lunch."

"Very well. Do you mind what happens to him?"

"I'm leaving him with you—" He grinned and there began to be less of him, a hand or an ear or a foot left, and the rest out of sight and the whole out of reach.

After she had been alone for ten minutes she began to feel holy, and inside herself an immense pre-occupation with power. She went upstairs, put on a gayer sweater, and delicately painted her face. So Ambrose had come down to see if there was anything to be done about Nick. Through her. If she had been easy, to have her: easy or discontented or jealous of Nick. Very likely Mrs. Loring, mère Angélique, had sent him herself and repented and so written. She had thought such a thing possible? Wanted such a thing? Wanted her son's wife a whore and had not wanted it. Wanted Ambrose back? In her mind there was the old woman's name written-up and scored through. Then she went out and called lightly up at his window from the cool lawn.

"Come down, Ambrose, it's a perfect day."

With sweet animation and pretty phrases she made Nick's excuses, and took him the plain way up the hill to the village for a drink.

He had better go, he thought, there was nothing doing here. He was separated after the night's deep sleep, cut off already from what had been yesterday's preoccupations, and those of weeks and years and even of a life past. Indifferent for the moment to their re-assertion, like a man drugged, but not as though it was well with him there. So that the only thing was to get away. Go before lunch and cut its pointless coda. God! was Nancy, the woman beside him talking, running a primrose through his coat, trying to flirt with him at last? The gentle admiration of last night turned pert with a grin behind it. She went on like that all the way to the village inn. He had a drink. He needed it. He was imagining things. She was a gay baggage after all and he'd interested her. She wanted to know about himself, did she? She'd got rid of Nick. What was she saying?

"It's good of you to tolerate me, Ambrose. After you and Nick. What a marvellous friendship we might have. But oh, my dear—!"

"What do you do me the honour of thinking about me, wife of Nicholas?" There was another drink before him. Put it down. It was quick work following this up.

"This visit has cleared up so much, made almost anything possible. And now we are friends, I feel I must say anything to you that I think."

"Go on."

"Anything? You mean it. Then Ambrose, I shall begin about yourself, and first of all I'm going to tell you something you're to do and that you are not to do."

"I'll obey you."—Her voice had a light thrill in it.

Now she leaned across the Inn table, *dulce ridenteu,* a shadow in her smile, making him aware of her awareness of him.

"You are a great man, Ambrose, but oh, mon ami, love Nicholas, love me, but don't don't—"

"What am I not to do, lady of the place?"

"You should not, you must not—Ambrose, you are not to let people call you—you are not to be so mixed-up with old women who exploit you. I'm a woman and I'm not an old woman, but do you know what some old women are like? They adore your looks and your sweet manners and" she added "—how? They want you physically of course, but not simply physically, and they've their own way of getting that—And when they've got what they want or not got what they want—then they make comparisons.—"

What was this? She was serious, she was smiling. There was a smile set against him and eyes lit with cold fun.

"Whatever dowager takes such an interest in me?"

"Oh, my dear, with so many about, and you so liked and hard-up. Why this morning I had a letter from Nick's mother, for you to be returned intact. A perfectly wolfish howl. How did she know you were here?" The smiles were working easily on her lips, but her eyes were steady. Steady as two carved stones on rock.

"I think you should be kind to her: kind as you are to Nick: kind as you are to me." She was making a sing-song of it, her head drawn up, her throat strained a little under the high collar of bright wool. Then relaxing:—

"Forgive this candour" she said, "I know how they can be useful, these women. Only if you can't do without them, you must learn how to keep them in order. Nick was a little annoyed that his mother should write such a letter. Keep her in hand. You remember about Peter Carmin and how his friends got him out of the country—".

If she had been alone down there with him at the house she would not have been safe, in spite of the green. Odd to think what he might have been doing if he had her alone down there. Done the trick for **Mrs.** Loring.

"May I see the letter?" (He must say that.)

"Nick has it". That was what she must say. She could say what she liked. She was in her own land.

"I'll see Mrs. Loring and tell Nick I will write to him. I think I had better go up now since the car is here."

Its noise drowned her light farewells and excuses.

* * *

She dropped back softly, between the hills, by the first way, through the Apple-Land. Round the green bay, through the copse, until outside the house she looked at the plain and the trees, open hands. Her husband came suddenly round a corner of the house and saw that she was alone.

"Gone," she said, "and before I come in, take this letter into the house and read it."

LATE GATHERING

John Cheever

It had rained hard early in August so the leaves were off all the trees. In the sunlight the hills were like scorched pastry and when there was no sun the meadows were grey and the trees were black and the clean sky parted in firm lines down onto the smooth horizon. Most of the guests had gone away but some of the guests remained.

In the evening Richard and Fred walked down to the formal pond in the sand pit and watched the swans drift in the wind. Richard woke early every morning and looked at the hills. Then he shook off his pyjamas and caught his body swinging past the glass panes in the small window. His body was a lined angular whiteness passing the small panes in the window when he was not looking.

Fred did not get up until noon and the sun was hot on the roofs or the rain had stopped and the foliage was brittle with water. The coals in the small hearth were black and he had to heat his coffee. Amy told him that if he would come down sooner he would not have to drink old coffee. Amy ran her eyes down the length of red carpet and laughed like a gramaphone. Some of the guests were walking up and down the verandah wondering if it were going to rain, and the ducks came out of the grey shed and went to the small pool in the bottom of the sand pit.

A lady with a staff of black hair pulled back from her forehead and broken over the round of her skull spent most of the afternoons and a great many of the evenings eating sandwiches and telling everyone how beautiful Switzerland was.

"You have never really seen the fields I have. You do not know what a flowered meadow is. You have never walked into fields that were blue and white and yellow and every flower as perfect as the nipples on your breast. Curved just so, colored so lightly, and you have never heard the sound of running water. Oh no, you have never heard the sound of running water.

"You have never lived by a little stream that made a sound all day and all night. You do not know what it is to go away and not hear the little stream any more. It is like silence to you. Yes, it is like silence to you.

"And the stars? No. You do not know what stars are like. You have never been near enough to the stars to see the long streaming continuation of one line into another. You have never been so high that from your verandah the birds were like level wheels in the meadow and the meadows like patches of juniper. Oh no. You do not know. Enormous meadows like mere patches of juniper up on the hillside where there are no trees.

"And perhaps you have lived so high on a hill that the mist came up from the patched meadows like a pitted fruit and gathered in circles and little whirlpools? You have never seen a thick mist stream through the doorway and flatten on the ceiling." She would tap her foot on the flowered linoleum and lift up the corner of a sandwich. "You do not know how enormous things can be and I am afraid that you will never know."

Fred and Richard went for walks together in the hills and often stayed all day. They took their books and sandwiches and sometimes bread and cheese and bad wine. They bent their backs over the round of the hill and watched the clouds and, when there were no clouds, the trees break along the wind. There was no need of speaking. A gramaphone was a great responsibility. Resting on their backs against the flank of a broken hill they instinctively felt that the silence was going to lapse into the scratching of a gramaphone needle and someone would have to crank the machine. There was an enormous responsibility in choosing one side or another of the disk.

Sitting on the top of the hill they could see Amy lean from the cross windows and shout at the cows. The foliage was dead and the flagpole had been taken down because of the strong wind. In the long vacant drawing room the stiff twigs of the bridal veil pulled and scuttled over the clean glass.

On the other side they could see hills dropping onto hills dropping into the ocean. They could see Chestnut Hill and Break Hill ram one another and push the small scrub pines down over the beach. In the empty weather when there was no sun they could hear the ocean make a great noise on the rocks and speculate on the color and the formation of the waves. Often they did not know how they spent whole days in the hills lying on the sharp grass wondering about one another.

Amy said the russian lady with the broken hair had never been to Switzerland but that she had seen a great many milk chocolate advertisements. Amy said that the russian lady with the vacant eyes was simply waiting for her son to come from a college out west and take her back to Cambridge. People began to wonder if she even had a son who was coming from out of the west to take her back to Cambridge. She sat in her black brocrade pyjamas on the verandah and described the milk chocolate advertisements and everyone listened to her because she was so very, very beautiful.

In the delicate light of the early evening Fred and Richard came down from out of the hills and said good afternoon to everyone. Fred traced a white iris with the toe of his boot on the flowered linoleum. Richard bent over the whitewashed railing and said how beautiful everything was. Amy was in the corner talking to Jack and asking him not to bring down any more gin because she didn't like to start drinking down here because down here it was not like in the city and in the city people could not stand the pace and it was all right to drink but down here there was a pace that people could adjust themselves to and there was no need of drinking and it was going to be one place where sensitive people could come and stand the realization of being sober.

When Ruth played the piano it was very nice also and Fred and Richard dusted the whitewash from their trousers and stood close to one another listening to the music roll out of the doorway and heave over the stubble of unkempt lawn. Because the leafless trees made it look much later in the season than it really was the awning had been taken down from the verandah and the black metal skeleton shot off the roof and hung between the floor and the railing like a vacant elbow. Such muscle in the awning frame Ruth would say and drag her fingers over the dry ivory like little white rakes.

Fred and Richard felt that a clock was running down somewhere and that someone would have to wind up the clock in a little while. Amy sat on the blue wooden balcony with Jack and talked about how fine and lovely everything had been before people started to go to the city and get drunk.

"People who used to come out here eight years ago and find the place restful now went to get drunk after their first meal. They find the tempo of nature almost more unbearable than the tempo of New York. Instead of finding rest in the country they become nervous wrecks. I do not understand it no I do not understand it."

When Richard undressed, his body was warm like a well-lit room and he spent a lot of time jumping up and down before the oval mirror. He could hear Fred walking down the corridor in his leather slippers and he crossed his legs and and lit a cigaret. Fred came in and said good night and went away again. Richard noticed sharp colors, brilliant shadows and the manner in which the boards were placed in the floor. He remembered a great many numbered forms and objects with names on them so that he could tell them that it was half past eleven when the Huntington Avenue trolley car crashed into the one roaring down Massachusetts Avenue in the direction of the river. In this way he went to sleep and often when he dressed in the morning it was raining and the window was running with the ugly shapes of flat water.

Ruth got a letter from her brother at the farm saying that he would have to close up because the deer had destroyed whole sections of his orchard. Fred thought it was all very beautiful with the slender arched animals eating the delicate boughs and Amy put on an evening gown and came down to supper after everyone had been working all day.

There were so few guests now that they could all be seated in the dining room and Amy carved the roast at the table. Everyone talked and the meat fell away under the knife. In the dining room the curtains had not been hung yet but someone had started to put back the pictures on the yellow plaster. Amy asked Richard if he would have more meat and looked out of the window. It would be a month now and the dry snows would be coming in from the frozen harbor. Then she remembered that it was not as late as she thought it was but that the rain had driven the leaves from the trees and it was really only the beginning of the autumn.

In the middle of the meal a car came up the drive and Amy rose in her ball dress and ran to the door. A lot of people came in and she kissed them and took their coats off. Then they sat down at the table and she was busy carving the meat and keeping the coffee percolators full.

That night Amy told Richard that there were not enough beds and that he would either have to sleep with Fred or go out to the bungalow. The russian lady told him that he had better sleep in the bungalow and he said that he would sleep in the bungalow.

Amy wrote her name on the window and kept reminding herself that it really was only the beginning of autumn even if the trees were bare.

WAGER FOR WIND

Charles Henri Ford

In the time of the breath found and released
to the wind, the wind surrenders
blue of its time if the breath is blue:
it is not secret about flowers whose shattering
is understood by breath that is jagged:
if the wind chops with smoke what it is
towers are covered with, the breath flays also
what keeps them up: they come down understood:
the rhythms will be one until Sixth avenue
straddled by the elevated will be remembered
for the hearts on it that were taxis:
inside of them the tick of their beat
making an off-rhythm: the wind and breath
making a time that cannot be invaded:
breath gathered and merged asking a wager
the wind has twice won.

ALMOST A GOD

Emanuel Carnevali

I am dying under this heat
but there may be worse.

I love my wife
but I should love her more.

I love my sweetheart but her love should be more universal.
One word describes her but I do not know which word.

All shorter than something else:
All is more God-like than something else.

There is competition in the chaos,
which is very foolish.

I am in doubt as a bent willow branch
nodding to the water.

I admire the devil for he leaves things unfinished.
I admire God for he finishes everything.

Nov. 24, 1931

Dear Dick:

         's another good issue. I particularly liked Bob's
Sleepwalker, I don't know anyone who can handle his types the
way that boy is showing he can do it; full of warm detail
well differentiated, excellently observed and presented. It
is getting to be masterly work, better and better from year
to year. I don't think Bob ever did better than in this
story; very much firmer than much that he has blurted out in
the past . Really I was deeply impressed .

         Floss and I want to come in and take you up on that
drunken invitation to supper you flung out over the meadows
at us the other night . But I'll be hog swaddled if we do
before you answer at least one of the many letters I've sent
you during the past quarter year.

         The White Mule sector for your January congeries
is all down on the yellow. Want it before Christmas or will
Easter do as well? Or Yom Kippur#? 's good too, God damn good,
just as good as ever! That's how. And written only for you,
Geez how I work! and - believe it or nertz. When you say the
word I'll #### begin to white it down so you can read it .
Bout twelve - more or less - typewritten sheets.

         Who in hell told you I was editing a quarterly? I
am . No competition with you tho' but a more or less special
case . I'm at your service as long as you shall want me . Do
you want me so long? Or is it so long? For in this case I
want to narrow my choice but your virtue is that you spread
yours . You talked as tho' you felt that I had been holding
something out on you . #S a lot of crap to talk that way .
You you self told me you didn't want a thing of mine other
than White Mule so long as that was issuing . Hell, I can't
close myself down that way . Not that I have any original work
in the first issue of this new bleat; I haven't . But it gives
me paper . What a damn fool I am to have taken it up. We'll
see how you like it.

         I'm always so damnably weary these days with medicine
all day that I fall asleep before I can pick the grapes of
the evenig - evening . Shit! quarter to eleven and nothing done
but two personal letters . Have you seen Sheeler's show at the
Down Town Gallery . Take it in, it's worth a look . 13th. St.
Now, answer this one, damn you or I'll think you're never
sober . You say you work! Now what do you know about that ?
Can't believe it .

                        Yours

DESPITE THE NOTEWORTHY QUALITY of the fourth issue, Johns was impatient to begin contacting younger, lesser-known writers. Although he had no idea where to look for the undiscovered American talent of that day, he realized the urgency of giving priority to their words and ideas. This goal had become his sole mission. Maybe that Sunday in the Bronx had opened his eyes to a more meaningful purpose; perhaps he inwardly sensed that the depression was closing in around him, and that the magazine might not exist too much longer. He was reluctant to ask for additional funding from his father, who was now seriously ill with a heart condition, and Johns' moonlighting by reading manuscripts for various publishers added little to the precarious cash balance.

Such large bookstores as Brentano's in New York and Kraus' in Chicago were not selling the little magazines in the great quantities they had a few months earlier. Customers' money was tight, and the welcome checks from bookstores were getting progressively smaller.

One young writer whom Johns was very pleased to discover was Julian L. Shapiro, soon to be known to the literary world as John Sanford. During the Fall of 1931 they got to know each other well. Shapiro was a distinctly handsome young man, and in appearance seemed more a schoolboy than a graduate of law school who had forsworn practice to give full time to writing. Johns found Shapiro's "An Adirondack Narrative," which he eventually published in 1932, wholly individual, and a sign that a definite new talent could be added to *Pagany*'s roster. William Carlos Williams, in a letter to Johns early in 1932 wrote:

390-405

> I particularly like the Shapiro story. It's skillfully plotted and full of fresh observation, acute thought, courage. He has ability too in sheer use of words. I think this is one of the best things you have ever printed.

Johns had thought so, too, when he accepted it for publication, but it was good to have Williams' corroboration of his judgment. It was always a pleasure when Shapiro came over to 9 Gramercy Park, for his conversation was as original in tone as his writing. He was now living with his close friend, Nathan Wallenstein Weinstein, who was writing under the name of Nathanael West, and managing his family's hotel in New York. West's sister was the wife of humorist S. J. Perelman. Indeed, most of Shapiro's intimates were closely tied to the creative.

Despite an essential humorous naïveté, Shapiro's writing excited Johns as much as any he was publishing and his letters were filled with sound observations about the current depression, which grazed his own life only by virtue of its existence. For instance:

> Everywhere one hears the same sad slow music. The word "depression" infects from mouth to mouth as though it were the microbe of a contagious disease. The mind attitude is the worst symptom I've seen yet. The hangdog look; the supreme pessimism; the despair which has passed the stage of hysteria and has become the obstinate agony of a mouse playing dead six inches from the jaws of an alert cat in a sealed room.

Shapiro was touched as much as anyone by *Pagany*'s demise.

Although Johns was disappointed at the personal necessity of bringing *Pagany* to an end, he was assured that what he had accomplished was likely to endure through the continuing writing of its contributors. If it must come to an end, its place in American literature was secure.

Of all the contributors to *Pagany,* no one became a closer friend to Johns than William Chapman. Indeed, he was valued as such long before he considered becoming a contributor. During the first year of *Pagany,* although he had never written any fiction, Chapman had enjoyed kidding Johns that one of these days he would toss off a story and make the O'Brien Roll of Honor for the American Short Story. One of the most satisfying moments of 1931 came when Chapman laid the manuscript of "The Old Gentleman" on Johns' desk, a story Johns was proud to have submitted to *Pagany.* And sure enough, when the O'Brien Roll of Honor for 1931

289-298

was printed, William Chapman's "The Old Gentleman" was listed right along with Johns' own "Sorry Lady" and "Figure."

William Chapman had been a sports reporter for the *Brooklyn Eagle* until his wife, Louisa, became successful through her fashion art work for such important New York stores as Lord and Taylor and Macy's. What had started as a small operation became big business and Chapman had to give full time to placing his wife's work, and being assured that she was well paid.

The result was that in a depression city where many others had difficulty finding enough to eat, the Chapmans had a weekly income that gave them the status of wealthy New Yorkers. It was the Chapmans who had a penthouse apartment in New York and could afford to buy a small home in the Connecticut countryside at Bethel. Many of the exciting parties of that season were at Lou and Bill Chapman's since they had both the money and the setting to support large gatherings.

They assured Johns not only that was he always welcome at their home but that he should also feel free to bring along any contributors he might wish to talk with or entertain away from the small periphery of 9 Gramercy Park. Johns took them up on this only once when there was a dinner party for Basil Bunting. But such a small show of elegance did not seem part of the duties of editorship to Johns, who was not a man who enjoyed feeling obligated to friends.

Chapman was frankly bored by the rat race of public relations for his talented wife's commercial art. He worked diligently but still had much free time, and he started the habit of inducing Johns to knock off work on *Pagany* and head with him for the hills of Connecticut.

Always, when Chapman and Johns left the city, their goal was the same place, the small old house in the town of Bethel which the Chapmans had bought. Now they were rebuilding it, and since Louisa Chapman had a great deal of work on her drawing board in New York, it was Chapman and Johns who worked together on the house.

This exodus from the city to the countryside was becoming more and more common. Josephine Herbst and her husband John Herrmann had set up their retreat at Erwinna, in the rolling country of

Pennsylvania. Malcolm Cowley had made his exile's return to the Connecticut countryside at Sherman and was already scribbling notes for a novel about this community of creative individuals which included e. e. cummings. Stuart Chase and his wife Marian Tyler were pleasantly established in Redding, Connecticut, as were Joseph Wood Krutch and his French wife Marcelle.

By the end of 1931 Johns was positive that eventually he would move to Connecticut, where property was reasonable. His second year as editor of *Pagany* was one rich in activity and personal reward. Yet he knew that *Pagany*'s third year, and quite possibly its last, was going to be difficult.

Erwinna, Pennsylvania

Nov. 3, 1931

Dear Mr. Johns;

I enclose a section of my book to use in place
of the story. In case you don't like it, please send it back to me
together with the story. I really like this and ~~xxxxxx~~ will send
it somewhere else in case you do not care for it. Although it is
part of my novel, its meaning is perfectly clear and complete asit
stands. I looked up your original letter of a year ago about the
other story and you did not say a word about not liking it. It was
a story of John's you sent back with the comment it was not up to
his best stuff and he agreed with you. If you don't care for
A Mule's No good for Breeding, send it back please and I-ll send
something else another time when I have finished my novel and begin
doing shorter things again .

Yours sincerely,

Josephine Herbst

So far as I know, Bill Williams never cared
for anything I wrote. He likes a different sort of
thing, which is quite all right. There is room
for many kinds of writing in this country, or
there ought to be.

Casa „Son Palerm"
[Camino Vecinal de]
[Genova á Porto-Pi]
Palma- de- Mallorca
I. B. ← Spain

Dear Dick:

We finally have an address, and what an address. Cagnes was reported overrun with awful English Montparnassians, so we came here to join the Daniels. We have an enormous house for $15 a month, a maid for $1.50 a week; all else in proportion; so that if we can raise any money at all we shall be able to stay here in complete comfort. If you really do sail for Europe, come stay with us a while here to rest up after Paris. The climate is gentle and balmy, the natives agreeable, and we know practically nobody.

I judge from my progress through Europe that I am a favored correspondent, for everyone I met, while testifying the highest opinion of Pagany and of you, was clamoring that you had on your desk three unanswered letters of his, asking for copies, money, information, or what not. I accordingly protest myself highly honored.

I suppose the Fall number is out some time since, and will, after its devious forwardings, reach me here. I am very interested to see how comes on. For the next I am submitting a poem, *Very Well Thank You,* which I enclose. Customary non-obligation. I've been spending most of my time since arrival in revising that God damned youthful error *Cinderella* for press. That will be finished within two weeks, after which I can really get going on new stuff, what I most want to do.

Don't banish me into the exterior Darkness with your other correspondents, but let me have of your news.

          Affectionately ever...

Dec# 30, 1931

Dear Dick :

Helloooo!   (Echo) Hell o   o . . !

Before I forget it : Bob says he has not received the last three issues of ### Pagany . Won't you send them to him ? c/o The American Express, Munich, Germany . Or shall I ? (Echo) Or shall I ?

Floss had a note from Eleanor who said that she would not#be able to come down this year. We both agree with her that the last issue of P. is the best so far; solid, excellent reading. With a good upthrust to it. The scene in Florence was very enjoyable - except perhaps toward the very beginning where it was a little wordy .

Contact is coming along slowly. I see nobody . All my news is by mail. (Echo) - by mail. Oh yes, Kamin says I am to talk over the radio . When and where I dunno .

The Dragon Press, Ithaca is looking over stuff of mine with a view to publication, the short stories etc.

Oppen is bringing out a book of mine in France some- where : the novelette and assorted prose bits * about 100 pages. To sell cheap : 35¢ !

Guess that's all . Did you receive the last installment of White Mule? (Echo) - mule?

Prince, though your letters are so sweet to imagine sweeter would they be were I get ketch um.

Yours as ever ####

[signature]

P. S.   Pound writes (as he may have written to you) Eliot has been appointed Prof. of Poetry at Harvard - and P. wants us to give him sweet welcome : Sweet Thames run softly till I end my song .   Shall we ? But if so, why? I can't for the life of me understand why we should . For of all the beshitten - he is the beshattest . But we must be generous and decorous - and everything but phosphosous - or sulphurus . We must lick his shit - and like it - for the sake of good manners . Well, I'll be damned if I will . And why inflict it on us ? We neither need him or want him .

3.

*Down and Out
in Bethel and Redding*

VOLUME III

1932 – 1933

Johns felt optimistic about the content of *Pagany*'s first issue for 1932, but also realized that smooth sailing was definitely a thing of the past. The first issue of the new year was published on time by a printer he found whose prices were reasonable, and who was entirely disinterested in the content of the quarterly except to see that it was printed correctly.

William Carlos Williams was going into this new year in an expansive, optimistic mood. He was happy with the way *White Mule* was developing and said in a letter:

> I have never enjoyed writing anything more. It's a real pleasure to me that you are pleased because I am writing it for you.

At the same time Williams was deeply immersed with Nathanael West in editing the first issue of the reborn little magazine *Contact*. West had just completed his first novel, *Miss Lonelyhearts,* and although he had offered a section to Johns for *Pagany,* he requested its return for rewriting. The section was never resubmitted to Johns, but published with the complete novel that year.

Johns, however, got a lift from Williams' words:

> The last *Pagany* shows the results of your experience in publication during the last two years, it is uniformly excellent reading from beginning to end.

He then went on to say:

> I want to speak of *Pagany* (in *Contact*) as the results of effective good taste in selecting material the hide bound minds of present day publishers have muffed.

Indeed almost all comments on the first issue of the new year were satisfying.

When Katherine Anne Porter submitted her poem "Bouquet for October," Johns, who had admired her recent first book of short stories, *Flowering Judas,* was undecided about printing it. He liked

384,385

this poem but it seemed less crafted than her stories; also it was expatriate in tone and by this time Johns was fed up with expatriate writing. This was, however, the work of a young American woman who was now living in Germany, and what she was saying was from the heart of a transplanted individual reacting sensitively to the natives of a strange land.

Jean Toomer's *Cane,* with a Foreword by Waldo Frank, had made a lasting impression on a younger Johns when he first read it in 1923 because a Negro was writing with understanding of and pride in his color. Now here was his poem, "Brown River, Smile." As Waldo Frank had noted of Toomer's writing, this poem showed his "complete freedom from the sense of persecution," and despite being a little crude around the edges, it was included in *Pagany* with pride.

386-389

Above all other contributors printed for the first time in *Pagany,* Volume III, Number One, Johns' enthusiasm was kindled by the writing of Julian L. Shapiro. Shapiro had already shown Johns sections of a novel he was writing entitled *The Water Wheel,* centering around a character named John Sanford. Shapiro would eventually adopt the name John Sanford as his literary *nom de guerre.* The story Shapiro submitted to *Pagany,* "An Adirondack Narrative," had a rich simplicity which Johns felt a truly fine achievement by one so young. Caught up in his desire to be a writer, Shapiro had given up his practice of law until he finished *The Water Wheel.*

390-405

The last months of 1931 and the early days of 1932 had been largely spent at the family home in Lynn. The first issue of *Pagany*'s third volume was organized and planned there, and it reflected Johns' clarifying design for the contents. From the inception of the magazine, there had always been space available for the unknown writer whose quality seemed individual and distinctive, as well as those authors already well established in the literary frame of the little magazine. While at Lynn, Johns also went over the correspondence from those contributors who took the time to evaluate the quality of individual pieces in their letters.

It was interesting to note that one or more would write disparagingly of a certain contribution, while others might find that same piece one of the best in that particular issue. *Pagany* had never succumbed to any one particular literary clique, and Johns knew he was most content when he printed those writings which he himself thought of pertinent value to the understanding of humanity in the Thirties, when everyone was affected by the perilous national insufficiency of cash.

Thus, in this first issue of the new year, Johns looked more closely for the new voice, the freshness of impact in the words of youth. He was proud to offer O. E. Rudge's translation of Jean Cocteau's essay in indirect criticism, "The Laic Mystery," which he received from Ezra Pound only after it was rejected by Lincoln Kirstein. This essay exemplified a major facet in the writing of an erratic genius, certain to obtain an important place in the writing, art, and cinema of his generation. It was also rewarding to include a poem by John Gould Fletcher, so long a resident of Sydenham, England, that many thought of him as British although he had grown up in Little Rock, Arkansas, and been educated at Phillips Andover and Harvard. *406-408*

Now that the expatriates along with their continental English cousins had been published in *Pagany,* it seemed of prime importance to print the poetry of Etta Blum, a schoolteacher from Sunnyside, Long Island, and also the harshly immediate words of Josephine Herbst in "A Dreadful Night." William Carlos Williams stated: *415*

409-414

> I have never been able to praise, as I should like to, Jo's devoted work. But to Jo herself I constantly have my hat off.

Her first novel, *Nothing Is Sacred,* had been unsuccessful, true; but there was a drive and power in her words which Johns respected.

Tess Slesinger from Brooklyn was another woman whose writing Johns admired. She had been printed in *This Quarter* and *The Menorah Journal* and was now busily engaged in writing a novel, *The Unpossessed,* which promised to reveal the urban American temperament in a far more searching manner than the plush decadence of Mary Butts' characters, as richly presented as they had been in their self-centered eroticism. Miss Slesinger wrote with stinging frankness of the texture of family life, and her story, "Brother to the Happy," was both sophisticated and sound in its approach.

Jan. 6, 1932

Dear Dick:

About Eliot, I'm perfectly willing to read and
to admire his verse but I see no reason for welcoming him
to America. I resent his intrusion here and wish that he
might stay in England till he shall be dead and buried. I
dislike his mind and all that it connotes - or almost all.

Yes, Angel Flores and his Dragon Press may
prove the solution to many of my difficulties with publication. It comes so perfectly to my wishes that as yet I
do not count too heavily upon it . But I have seen Flores
and I liked him at once . Anyhow, they have announced a
book, I presume it is Old Doc Rivers . Here's hoping.

And I sent them the collected short stories last
week, fifteen in all - after careful revision.

I wish I could sit down and finish White Mule. I
have never enjoyed writing anything more . But since you
are willing to go on taking the bits as they come I'm not
going to rush it . It is a real pleasure to me that you are
pleased because I am writing it for you.

The last Pagany shows the results of your experience
in publication during the last two years, it is uniformly
excellent reading from beginning to end . I have read the
last issue particularly carefully inasmuch as I want all
the help I can get in making up Contact . The only result
of my cogitations so far has been an appreciation of your
work . But/will not have the general reading appeal that
you have sought. In the first place I will not be able to use
so much material and in the second I want to bear down more
than you have cared to on the significance of the word, as
material . One feature of C. will be my own Comments. Perhaps
this is sheer vanity. I dunno. But it is my purpose for all
that and the thing that has made me want to take the trouble
to go on - and to give up the time . I want to speak of
Pagany (sooner or later) as the result of effective good
taste in selecting material the hide bound minds of present
day publishers have muffed . But Contact, rightly or wrongly,
is more narrowly aimed . Perhaps that will be what's the
matter with it . Anyhow it is half printed and will be out
by the end of the month - as it looks now.

Paul swims Sunday afternoons at the N.Y.A.C. Floss
is well . May we call you up - well, next Tuesday or Friday
for a supper date? No special news, just the January thaw.

Yours

Bill

112 E 11 St
Jan 11 1932
N Y C

Dear Johns,

I am sending you a short short story : Winter In
My Heart.

I signed up recently with the Viking Press for two
novels, the first which has been rejected by 18 leading publishing houses. But Viking Press, although they tell me it is
a major book, in their opinion, are not willing to publish it
until they see a hunk of my new book which I am just starting.
They have already given me an advance, so I can't kick very
much and the contract I have signed is very good, I think.
This means about another year of work and sweat before I break
through. "ell, it's all in the racket, as Tolstoi said.

Otherwise not much new. I landed a pretty fair story in
the American Mercury last week, which ought to see print this
spring or so.

How are things going with you? I would like very much to check
out of this goddamed town, but I guess I'm stuck here for another
year or so. Frankly, I was disappointed in John Dos Passos Eveline
Hutchins and Dahlberg leaves me cold. It seems that Dahlberg, running
dry, has abandoned straight realism of Bottom Dogs and now is acrobating
with words and snap-shots. Maybe I'm wrong. Carl Rakosi in his
Three Poems in the Autumn number is swell; I can think of no other young
fellow with as much promise as Rakosi; he has humor, wit, bitterness
and a light, agile touch. Also Horace Gregory; he's fine. Regards,

HALPER

E. POUND   **RAPALLO**

23 Feb.

VIA MARSALA 12-5

Dear Johns

      I am relieved to hear that Pagany still exists. As the cheque you sent me was bad , and as my letter informing XXX you of the fact came back marked "second notice " unknown , I was rather uncertain as to yr/ continued welfare.

      Cocteau's address is

          9 rue Vignon , Paris I re.

Rudge chq/ better come via me , as address varies from week to week.

Please do not send either of them cheques unless there is money in your bank to meet same , as it will unduly complicate foreign relations.

NUMBER 1 *January–March*

Contents

PAGANY

To G . . .

BOUQUET FOR OCTOBER
Katherine Anne Porter

This is not our season, the spring-born
Put on winter like a hair shirt, remember death and wait
For the turn of the year.

It is not timely to say once for all
What love is. (Once for all words are engraved
On monuments celebrating potbellied kings, high bosomed ladies,
Philosophers, clowns, slender pages with crossed ankles,
Knights clasping with smooth knuckles
Blunted answerable arguments of heroics;
Above all, on the tombs of Statesmen.)

Streets of burnished iron, tender grass
Neatly shaven to the grey lips of water,
Hotels, cinemas, the loud cold shudders of ships,
The spouting of whales, the pocked jaws of friars, the orchestra of
    machinery,
All all such memories are rayed metal, each shears off in turn
One minute from another, I must lose them all
Unless we make a sheaf of them together.

Landscapes such as the Flemish painted are justly
Asleep among windmills, thick with the smell
Of warm milk-soaked hides, ruminant breathings, clean orderly hoofs,
Minute proprieties of doorways curtained with wood smoke,
Shaded away from clotted sky, winter thick water,
Numbed with certainties, snoring in a snowdrift.

If the frost stiffens our hair, we have still the taste
Of sun in our teeth.
The sea has hauled us by the shoulders over and under.
We have stretched our muscles and yawned in the smell of cedar.

Catalogues of defeat, advantages stratagems, successes, anticipations,
Dried glories under glass, honors, a point of view petrified on its feet,
I would leave in my will to those for whom such things are substance.
We will walk in the Tiergarten: invisible
To the little eyes buttoned up against the frail sunlight:
Observe the dubious riches of decay, pity
The bereaved branches, the exhausted leaves dropping
Like tears which nobody notices.

This is not our season, the spring-born
Wear winter like a thorn wreath, sniff the wind
For the earliest rumor of sap, the singing
Thaw of rivers, feel under their ribs
The snap of locks when the earth turns
The key to her wine vaults and the wines flow upwards.

Here on a marble bench we are at peace to mingle the ashes
Of our cigarettes, and to exchange our tokens:
A peach stone for a pigeon feather, a grasshopper wing for a sea shell.

BROWN RIVER, SMILE

Jean Toomer

It is a new America,
To be spiritualized by each new American.

Lift, lift, thou waking forces!
Let us feel the energy of animals,
The energy of rumps and bull-bent heads
Crashing the barrier to man.
It must spiral on!
A million million men, or twelve men,
Must crash the barrier to the next higher form.

    Beyond plants are animals,
    Beyond animals is man,
    Beyond man is the universe.

    The Big Light,
    Let the Big Light in!

O thou, Radiant Incorporeal,
The I of earth and of mankind, hurl
Down these seaboards, across this continent,
The thousand-rayed discus of thy mind,
And, above our walking limbs unfurl
Spirit-torsos of exquisite strength!

The Mississippi, sister of the Ganges,
Main artery of earth in the western world,
Is waiting to become
In the spirit of America, a sacred river.
Whoever lifts the Mississippi
Lifts himself and all America;
Whoever lifts himself
Makes that great brown river smile.
The blood of earth and the blood of man
Course swifter and rejoice when we spiritualize.

The old gods, led by an inverted Christ,
A shaved Moses, a blanched Lemur,
And a moulting thunderbird,
Withdrew into the distance and soon died,

Their dust and seed falling down
To fertilize the five regions of America.

We are waiting for a new God.

The old peoples—
The great European races sent wave after wave
That washed the forests, the earth's rich loam,
Grew towns with the seeds of giant cities,
Made roads, laid golden rails,
Sang once of its swift achievement,
And died congested in machinery.
They say that near the end
It was a world of crying men and hard women,
A city of goddam and Jehovah
Baptised in industry
Without benefit of saints,
Of dear defectives
Winnowing their likenesses from weathered rock
Sold by national organizations of undertakers.

Someone said:
      Suffering is impossible
      On cement sidewalks, in skyscrapers,
      In motor-cars;
      Steel cannot suffer—
      We die unconsciously
      Because possessed by a nonhuman symbol.
Another cried:
      It is because of thee, O Life,
      That the first prayer ends in the last curse.
Another sang:
      Late minstrels of the restless earth,
      No muteness can be granted thee,
      Lift thy laughing energies
      To that white point which is a star.

The great African races sent a single wave
And singing riplets to sorrow in red fields,
Sing a swan song, to break rocks
And immortalize a hiding water boy.

      I'm leaving the shining ground, brothers,
      I sing because I ache,
      I go because I must,

Brothers, I am leaving the shining ground;
Don't ask me where,
I'll meet you there,
I'm leaving the shining ground.

The great red race was here.
In a land of flaming earth and torrent-rains,
Of red sea-plains and majestic mesas,
At sunset from a purple hill
The Gods came down;
They serpentined into pueblo,
And a white-robed priest
Danced with them five days and nights;
But pueblo, priest, and Shalicos
Sank into the sacred earth
To fertilize the five regions of America.

Hi-ye, hi-yo, hi-yo,
Hi-ye, hi-yo, hi-yo,
A lone eagle feather,
An untamed Navaho,
The ghosts of buffaloes,
Hi-ye, hi-yo, hi-yo,
Hi-ye, hi-yo, hi-yo.

We are waiting for a new people.

O thou, Radiant Incorporeal,
The I of earth and of mankind, hurl
Down these seaboards, across this continent,
The thousand-rayed discus of thy mind,
And, above our walking limbs unfurl
Spirit-torsos of exquisite strength!

The east coast is masculine,
The west coast is feminine,
The middle region is the child—
Force of reconciling
And generator of symbols.

Thou, great fields, waving thy growths
    across the world,
Couldest thou find the seed which started thee?
Can you remember the first great hand to sow?
Have you memory of His intention?
Great plains, and thou, mountains,
And thou, stately trees, and thou,
America, sleeping and producing with the seasons,
No clever dealer can divide,
No machine can undermine thee.

The prairie's sweep is flat infinity,
The city's rise is perpendicular to farthest star,
I stand where the two directions intersect,
At Michigan Avenue and Walton Place,
Parallel to my countrymen,
Right-angled to the universe.

It is a new America,
To be spiritualized by each new American.

AN ADIRONDACK NARRATIVE
Julian L Shapiro

Back of him a branch snapped and when he turned he saw a girl coming out of a clump of bushes with her body twisted so she could get her dress off a thorn that caught it up. She didnt know he was there till he called to ask if he could help her but she told him no without looking his way.

The dress was heavy draping stuff and it was pulled so tight against her body he thought she didnt have anything on underneath it. He could see her legs halfway up her thighs. The backs of her knees were straight and without bulges. Her arms and neck were browned and her shape was good.

He said she was having a tough time of it. As he spoke he heard her say something angry and her arm came down quick and there was a sound of ripping goods. She turned and came out of the bushes and when she walked up to him he saw a hole in her skirt and a piece of cloth hanging down in a thin strip. He laughed and said she should have let him help her. She said it didnt make any difference and asked him what he was doing there. He said he was up from New York on a vacation. She asked him if he was staying at Bennetts up the road and he said yes it was a nice place. Then she asked him what he did in New York and he said he worked in a furnishing store and she said what kind of furnishing. Mens. He sold shirts and socks and hats. Neckties too. The girl asked him how long hed been doing that and he said six or seven years. Then she wanted to know how old he was. 29. She asked him if it was fun selling things in a store and he said no it wasnt much fun and it was hard work in hot weather. He said this was the first time hed ever been in the Adirondacks and hed gotten sick the month before and the doctor told him he should go to the mountains for a couple of weeks. So he came here. She asked him how he came to be at Bennetts and he said he read in a vacationguide that Warrensburg was over a thousand feet up and that was just about right for him so he borrowed a Ford and drove up from the city. When he got to Warrensburg he asked the man in the drugstore Bertrand for a good farmhouse and Bertrand said Bennetts was as good a place as hed be like to find around those parts.

The girl asked him what he did all day and he said *I walk around up and down. Sometimes I go off across the fields and do like Im doing now. Sit on a stone. Its good to sit still for a while.* When she wanted to know if he ever went in the woods he said he didnt know his way around and hed read it was easy to get lost in the woods and he wasnt much of a mountaineer he guessed. She said the woods were pretty good fun and she knew a nice place to swim. Viele Pond was only five miles up the road and nobody was living at the lodge. Sometimes she went up there alone and took a swim. The water was pretty cold around that season but when you came out again in the sun it was good. He said it sounded all right and maybe they could go sometime. She said it was too far to go that afternoon but they still had plenty of time for a walk if he wanted to. Shed show him the woods.

He said hed go but first hed have to take the Ford back to Bennetts. They both got in and it was only a minute or two before they drove in the barn. Mrs Bennett was just coming out with a hatful of eggs. When she saw the girl she called out hello Hattie what you doing down this way. Hattie said she was just walking around. Mrs Bennett said she hadnt ought to be so strange and when she took an afternoon off she might come down and be sociable. Then Hattie said she was going to show the boarder around Harrington Hill and Mrs Bennett said that was a good idea and went down to the house. Hattie said everybody liked Mrs Bennett she was so nice. Hattie got out then and he drove the car in a corner next to a rusty tractor. When he came out of the barn Hattie was fooling around with a kitten she found under the runway. The kitten was gray as a mouse and not much bigger.

He said he was going in the house to get a sweater. Hattie said shed wait for him on the porch. When he got up to his room he opened a fibre suitcase that was on the bed and took out a navyblue bathingsuit. It still had the pricetags on it. Then he sat down on the bed. There was a box of candy on the dresser. *My sister gave it to me before I went away. The wrappings on the candybox. She was wrong to waste the money. It was nice of her to think of me though. A toothbrush sticking out of a celluloid case. Cheap militarybrushes one up one down. A thin comb cutting the sides. A razor in a cardboard box. A shavingbrush that slides back in its own handle when you pull down a little button. A tube of shavingcream. A tube of toothpaste. Round and new by bent and twisted. A roadmap of New York. Two pencils. Three books. The names. A bottle of witch hazel. A bottle of fastener for my hair.* He looked in the mirror and described himself. *My face is oval. My ears dont stick out. My hair is black. My teeth are white. My lips are medium thin and plain red. My hair is flat against my head. Im not handsome. Im not homely. Im in between. Im thinking of messing up my hair. My hands are hands. My face is a face. Im in the country. The countrys different from the city. Im thinking maybe I shouldnt go walking with her.* He took the tags off his bathingsuit and threw it back in the suitcase. He combed his hair and got a sweater and went downstairs. Hattie was sitting on the porch steps. She still had the kitten and it was climbing all over her. The door slammed as he came out and the kitten was off the girl and under the steps like a shot.

They went around the barn and he followed her through a groove in the field. For a way the path edged the woods but when it began to slope up it bent and got lost in bushes and dried leaves. Greenspeckled rocks spotted like they were corroded humped up from clusters of precise ferns. Leaves that were lightbrown and lastyears powdered and gave under their feet. Small dead branches cracked. Those broke the quiet in the woods and so did squirrels sounding longsucked kisses and birds making five or six quick clear notes like a flute coming from a distance.

He didnt enjoy the climb because at every step he was ready to be afraid. He liked the sounds that came from back of the trunks of trees and bushes and piles of rock but he couldnt get used to their suddenness and their quick dyingout. He couldnt help getting himself ready for his next nervousness. There were spiders that were quick and ugly and without expression. A web came around his face and hair and he shivered when he brought up his hand to brush it away. There were snakes too. When he was a boy hed killed one with a rock and carried the thing away on the end of a long stick. He dropped it in a hole along the road and then he ran home and went up to his room and he was sick for a couple of days. Hed heard of boys that liked to hunt for snakes and pick them up by their tails and snap them away quick so the back made a cracking sound. The boys said they enjoyed that. They said it was good fun but he never went with them.

Hattie was leading the way up a steep slope and he tripped and almost fell over a twisted root that looked like a thick snake. After that he was more careful. Then the ground got level and the trees opened out. From the clearing he looked down and saw Bennetts several hundred feet below. The view was very good. The day was clear and off to the north he could see seven ridges of mountains and not two ridges were the same color. About five miles away the nearest was dark green and from that to the last ridge he could see the colors went all the way from blue to lavender and purple. Each ridge waved up high peaks so when you half-closed your eyes you saw a long scalloped wall. Hattie pointed and said the peak way off there was Mount Marcy and it was the highest in the Adirondacks more than five thousand feet. He looked down along her arm and saw the peak she meant. Then she showed him White Face and a couple of others.

Hattie said if they kept on a little theyd soon come out on the dirt road again. They climbed down and then they were standing right on a shoulder of Harrington Hill where the road was carved out. He asked Hattie where it went to and she said the first place up from the bend was her fathers farm and it was plumb on top of the hill. About three miles on along the ridge was the Viele Pond property. After that the road got very bad and you could hardly get through even with a horse. Stewart Brook ran out of the pond over a rotten beaver dam and the road followed the brook downhill. Almost always at that season the brook ran over the road in a dozen places and there was a hole down there where a car got bogged down and theyd never been able to haul it out. It was there yet rusty and torn apart and that was all of ten years now.

While they were standing there talking in the middle of the road a rabbit stuck its head up from back of a mound and sat very still for a few seconds. The first move they made it was back down its hole so fast it looked like someoned grabbed it down by its tail. A small automobile came around a turn and when it got near them it stopped and two men got out. They said hello to Hattie and seemed pretty friendly with her.

When she tried to make an introduction she found out she didnt know the name of the person she was with. He said his name was Gibson Alfred Gibson and then the men told him their names. Robbins and Lemmon they said and they were game wardens. They said they were on their way up to Viele Pond to keep an eye open for some poachers theyd heard were up that way. Thered been some shooting near the pond for three or four nights and it was likely there was a foreign bunch in there jacking deer. Gibson asked what jacking meant and Robbins said it was hunting deer at night with a light a searchlight. You had a boat and you paddled near the shore keeping quiet and flashing your torch into the brush. The deer came down at night to feed on the lilypads and once you got the deer in the light they just stood there and looked at it and it was nothing to bring them down. The wardens said deer were out of season anyway and if they caught a poaching outfit theyd give them plenty.

Robbins and Lemmon had a lot of time to spare. They said they didnt want to get up to the pond much before dark so they took Hattie and Gibson back to their car and showed them what they called their arsenal. Lemmon opened the back of the car and brought out two heavy rifles. He explained they were leveraction 25.30 Savage repeaters and each held seven long brass shells. To show the power of the rifles Robbins put one up and fired a slug through a foot of pine tree. Then he asked Gibson if he wanted to try a few shots. Gibson said hed never fired a rifle in his life not even in a shooting gallery but he thought Hattie might laugh if he refused so he took the gun and tried to make a shot like Robbins. He didnt know the piece had an awful kick in it and held it loose against his shoulder. When he pulled the trigger he thought the rifle went to pieces in his hands. The butt jumped back in his shoulder and came near knocking him down. Of course the muzzle went off line and Robbins smiled when he said the bullet was likely still up in the air.

Lemmon said the rifles werent all they had with them. They opened their coats and each showed a .38 revolver under his left arm. Robbins took a .22 target pistol out of his pocket. Hattie got excited when she saw that and said she knew how to shoot pretty fair so Robbins handed over the pistol after he loaded it. Hattie called two hard shots and made them both. Gibson didnt want any more shooting for himself but it was sport to watch a woman handle a gun. Just then a red squirrel came out on a branch of a tall beech and froze when it saw the people below. Hattie lifted the pistol and the squirrel made a dash for cover. The girl knocked it out of the tree with two fast shots and when she went over to pick it up it was still kicking. She held it head down by its hind legs and gave it a good cut back of the head with the side of her palm and after that it didnt kick any more. She brought it over to show Gibson. Both shots were hits one in the head and the other in the side. The wardens said Hattie had a good eye and after talking a little more they had to go away.

Then Hattie said shed have to go home. She offered Gibson the squirrel and said it was good eating especially the saddle and hind quarters and Mrs Bennett knew how to fry it so it tasted like chicken but Gibson said he thought the squirrel looked like a rat and he knew he wouldnt be able to eat it. Hattie said he didnt have to eat it if he didnt want to but she was sure Mrs Bennett would like it and would he take it back for her. Gibson said he didnt like to touch the squirrel. Hattie laughed and said it wouldnt bite him but she couldnt make him touch it.

Before she started up the hill she said there was going to be a dance that night for the benefit of the County Poor Home. The dance was at the Home and if hed call for her after supper they could have a fine time. The band was coming all the way from Glens Falls. Everybody was going to be there and he could meet all her friends. Gibson said he had nothing to do that night and hed be glad to go with her. Then Hattie thanked him for the walk and said shed look out for him after supper.

* * *

It was much cooler on the way back to Bennetts. The sun was throwing long shadows over his shoulder but it was still high enough up over Harrington Hill to show up against the seven ridges only now all of them were different shades of purple and seemed to make one mountain of terraces. Down in the valley where the Schroon ran through Warrensburg lights were on in the houses and streets and made a nice sight from way up there. The woods were thick and dark now and came to the edge of the road as it bent down the hill. In the brush there were all kinds of sounds and in some places where the road took a dip a wet smell came out of the trees. The road was made of clay and sand and didnt have any grooves in it so he hardly had to watch where he was walking and he wasnt ready for a beating and flapping of wings so close he could have reached out and touched the spot where it came from. Then a large bird floated off a stump and sailed down the road. It lighted on a tree and when Gibson got near again he saw it was an owl. He stopped about ten yards away because hed heard owls could be pretty bad with their beaks and claws. He picked up a couple of stones and let the bird have it. At the first pitch the owl flew in the woods and Gibson heard the sounds it made get smaller and smaller as it beat its way through the leaves.

By the time he got to Bennetts it was near dark and they were waiting supper for him. He washed his hands and face at the kitchen sink and sat down at the big table set over near the stove. Old man Bennett kept cracking jokes all through the meal. Mrs Bennett was there of course and so were three farmhands. They all liked Gibson and called him Mr. When Mrs Bennett got all the things off the stove she sat down and had something to eat with the men. She listened to the talk for a while and then she started to josh Gibson about making a hit with one of the nicest gals in Warren County and that was a fact. Gibson laughed and didnt mind what she said. When she asked him if he was going to the high life down at the Home that night he said yes he was taking Hattie and then they all had a laugh. Gibson felt something clawing the cuff of his pants and then the gray kitten came up his leg and in his lap. It put its fore-paws on the table and took a look around like it had its pick of everything there. Mrs Bennett poured some cream in a saucer and pushed it across the table. When Gibson put it near the kitten he heard its insides start working and then the whole animal was shaking. Its pink tongue shot in and out and the cream didnt last very long. After the kitten finished it sat back and washed its mouth and whiskers and wanted to go to sleep with its head inside Gibsons sweater but he said hed have to hurry if he wanted to be on time so he gave the kitten to Mrs Bennett and went up-stairs. After about ten minutes he came down again wearing a gray suit and a blue soft shirt. Mrs Bennett told him he better take a coat if he didnt want to catch his death of cold. He got the coat and said goodnight to everybody and went out to the barn to get the Ford.

At first it was so cold it didnt turn over but he got the thing running and it warmed up on the way to Hatties farm. By car it was only about ten minutes up the hill to her place. When he got there he honked his horn and Hattie came out of the house. She had on a long coat and he couldnt see what she was wearing under it but her hair was done up very tight around her head. From what Gibson could see she looked pretty good and he said so. Then she climbed in and they started down the hill.

In the valley and out along the river road they passed haywagons loaded with fellows and girls all bundled up in blankets and scarves and everybody in the wagons let out a yell when the Ford went by. In one wagon there was a girl that recognized Hattie and then they all yelled out something about Hattie and her new beau from the city.

The Home was at a place where the road crossed the Schroon and made a long climb over the ridge to Boltons Landing. When they got to the Home Gibson saw one big wing of it was lit up bright and there were lanterns strung up on wires from the porch to a bunch of trees on the lawn. A lot of people were outside saying hello to each other and still more were sitting at tables where the porch was closed in. After Sanford parked the car in an open space back of the building they got out and he helped Hattie take off her coat. She was wearing a thin creamcolored muslin dress and the top of it had stitched designs of yellow crossed by light green but there wasnt so much design that it took your eye off the plain lines of the dress. Many washings had run some of the dye off the threads and onto the muslin making little blurs around the crosses but the dress was clean and it looked good on Hattie. She wore light shoes with high heels and with straps that buttoned around her ankles.

Gibson bought tickets from an old man sitting back of a table at the door. The man knew Hattie and asked after her Pa when they went by. Inside the music was going and there were about a hundred couples on the floor. Gibson was for watching the dancers a while but Hattie wouldnt have any of that and he must dance right away. He wasnt such a bad dancer so he didnt care and they went out to the floor. Hatties waist was thin and he could put his palm far around her. He kept it against her side and sometimes he felt her breast come down and touch it. Hattie liked to dance close and they went on dancing that way for a long time without having much to say. Her body was pretty light and he thought it was a pleasure to move with her near him.

In between dances she introduced him to dozens of fellows and girls and most of them looked nice. All the fellows were strong and sharp and when they smiled they showed they were glad to know you. Some of them even said they hoped Gibson stayed in Warrensburg for a time so they could get around to meeting him again. The girls were pleasant and carried on a lot and kidded Hattie when Gibson couldnt hear but he knew they were talking about him because they looked over his way once in a while and laughed when they saw he was watching.

The band started to play *Fiesta* and while they were dancing Gibson told Hattie she must be getting sick of dancing with him all evening and it was funny none of her friends asked her for a cutin or an encore. Hattie said she guessed she wasnt so popular but if he was tired of dancing with her they could trade with another couple so if there was anybody else he felt like dancing with shed arrange it for him. But Gibson said he meant it must be tiresome for her not him and he was perfectly satisfied to dance with her till his shoes wore out. That made Hattie smile with pleasure and she held him tighter than before. They both thought it was the best dance of the evening.

After it was over they went out on the porch to one of the tables. Bertrand came along with a fellow he introduced as Doc Cunningham and they sat down. Bertrand said he hoped Gibson liked the Bennett farm and Gibson said it couldnt be beat and he was glad hed spoken to Bertrand that day he drove up from the city. A tall blondhaired fellow took Hattie out for *Sweet and Lovely* and Gibson watched her through a window. He thought she was a fine dancer. There wasnt anything flashy about her steps. She could do anything her partner tried but she didnt put on any trimmings of her own. She didnt jerk around and Gibson admired the way her feet went from one step to the next like the whole dance was one movement. She kept up a conversation with the fellow leading her but she knew Gibson was watching her because she gave him a smile whenever she went by the window.

Bertrand waved to a man and woman and they joined the party. They were Mr and Mrs Reoux and they owned the Viele Pond property where the hunting lodge was. If he got time Gibson wasnt to miss it because there werent any better woods in all those parts. Hattie came back in time to hear the talk about the pond and asked Mrs Reoux if she could show Gibson around the place. Mrs Reoux said she could go up any time permission or no permission. Then the older people began to talk about a rumor that the D & H was going to put through a single track from Lake George to Ticonderoga.

Hattie and Gibson werent much interested in that so they talked about other things but they were at it only a couple of minutes before the band started *Dein Ist Mein Ganzes Herz* and Gibson wanted that one with Hattie. She said all right and they went out on the floor again. When Gibson found out it was the last dance he said he was glad nobody else took her out for it.

Gibson gave two couples a ride to Warrensburg. It was very cold going through the valley but Hattie looked warm enough in the coat she was wearing and Gibson was glad hed listened to Mrs Bennett about his own coat. The couples in back were singing all the way in and having a fine time and when they got onto the main street of the town they offered to stand treat to coffee at Halls because Gibson helped them with the ride but Hattie said she thought it was kind of late so they drove the other four up to Halls and left them there.

On the way up the hill neither of them said much because there was a heavy mist on the mountain and the lights of the car went against it like it was a blank wall. Gibson had to go very slow and the only talking they did till after they got past Bennetts was about the road and where the turns were. After Bennetts there was no more fog. The sky looked a cold blue and many stars were in it especially over to the west where they were sprinkled like sand. When they got to the shoulder of the hill where theyd been that afternoon Hattie told him to stop and have a look down at Warrensburg. He did and looked where hed seen the lights in the evening. There wasnt one. The whole valley was filled with gray fog and they were a couple of hundred feet above the top of it. If the fog didnt stay down there so still it would have looked like smoke it was so thick.

Hattie said she thought he should stay in the mountains for a while and he asked her why. She said hed get better. He said he wasnt sick exactly and she said no but hed get better in the mountains than hed ever get in the city. Anybody would. He said *Its nice up here all right and the people are fine to me. The airs good and sometimes the views like nothing Ive ever seen before but I guess Id get tired of trees and dust and hills after a while.* Wasnt it better than the city. He didnt answer that but asked her if shed ever been in New York and she said yes once a couple of years ago for about three months. Then he wanted to know why she didnt stay. She was pretty and smart and likely she could make a good living there instead of slaving around on a farm four or five miles from the nearest town. Hattie said she knew she wasnt badlooking and she even thought she might have it pretty good in New York because she had an uncle there that had some kind of business and hed give her a job if she wanted one but she didnt like the city. Or it wasnt so much that. She just liked it better in the country. Then Gibson said it was the old argument city and country and hed heard it before so he was a little tired of it. You didnt get anywhere arguing like that. He guessed your taste settled it. For her the country was better. For his part give him the city every time. She said he should let her show him a thing or two now he was up in the mountains and they might open his eyes because after all you really had to stay in a place if you wanted to know about it. You maybe didnt get to like the mountains if you only stayed a few days so would he like to go up to Viele Pond with her next day. Bertrand was right when he said there was nothing like it around those parts.

She was pleased when Gibson said hed go with her. She told him shed make some sandwiches and get some fruit and they could take it along in the Ford. He wasnt to forget to bring his bathingsuit and a towel and she said he could call for her around ten in the morning. All the way up from there to Hatties farm she was talking about what shed show him and how hed like it better than any place hed ever seen. She was sure of it.

When he stopped the Ford in front of her house Hattie put her arms around him and kissed him a few times. Then she let go and he helped her get out of the car. He had his arm around her waist and they walked in the grass back of the house where it was wet like itd been raining. The fog was spreading up from the valley and all the trees had it in their upper branches like smoke and most of the branches were hidden so that they were walking in an orchard of poles. When they got near the barn Hattie said if he wanted to talk some more it was warmer in there and they could sit on the haypile. He said all right so they went in. When they sat down in the hay she put her arms around him again and kissed him many times. She had a good mouth and he liked the taste.

He could hear the cattle clumping on the wooden floor and every once in a while a horse kicked out a hoof and it hit the side of a stall. Over to one side was the henhouse and from it there came a low clucking of birds. Outside the barn there wasnt a sound. Gibson lay back in the hay. Hattie was right next to him and her face was only a couple of inches from his when she leaned over him. He tried to put his arms around her but one of his hands touched her breast and stayed there. Then he got excited when he found out shed let him do anything to her so he sat up and said he thought itd be better if he went back to Bennetts. It was late. They walked out to the car and before he got in they kissed each other again. After that she said she still wanted him to see Viele Pond and was he coming for her at ten. He said yes.

* * *

At ten oclock he was back there for her. Hattie came out of the house with a paper bundle and her bathingsuit wrapped up in a towel. She was wearing a gray dress and low shoes without stockings. They were glad to see each other and when they got a little up the road out of sight of the farmhouse she moved over close and kissed him. The road was bad and in hollows there were deep ruts filled with water where itd drained off the slopes on both sides. Almost all the way the trees came together over the road but in the clear spaces the road was firm and Gibson could go over it at a good clip. Chipmunks and rabbits ran across the road in lots of places and once they saw a grousehawk coasting low over a small marsh where the trees had no leaves and a brook came out and ran under the road. Hattie asked him to stop just before they came to the planks over the brook and not to make any noise but follow her. She walked up to the bridge and lay on it belly down with her head over the side looking at the water. Gibson did the same thing and his face wasnt more than a foot from the water. Soon a bunch of small fish came swmming out from under the boards. They stood out clear against the tan bottom with their fins and tails moving very slow to keep them from going down with the current. The fish had little round designs on their sides and backs. Hattie whispered they were brooktrout and then she dropped a pebble in the water and the trout disappeared so quick it was hard to believe theyd ever been there.

They went back to the car and drove on. The road was sloping down a little in front of them now and there was no more brush in the woods but the trees were still so thick no sun came through anywhere to light up the piles of brown leaves that covered the ground. Sometimes right in the middle of the woods there was a boulder as big as a barn and all greened over with moss. Once Gibson got his eye on a big gray squirrel as it made a long jump from one tree to another. Hattie showed him a lot of different kinds of trees birch beech walnut black spruce.

A long slab of rock made up the next fifty feet of road and at the end of it there was a deep hole that almost tore the car in half. After that there was a clearing and a very small frame house without a porch. Over the door was the word *Buckhorn*. Above that and right under the eaves were nailed the bleached antlers and skull of a deer. Hattie said the house belonged to some people from Utica but no oned been up to use it for years. A little while later the slope on the left side of the road went down instead of up and then through the leaves on that side Hattie pointed to the water of Viele Pond. They went around a bend and came to the hunting lodge belonging to the Reoux. It was a goodsized house made of timber and with a wide low porch that was only ten feet from the road. Gibson pulled the car in alongside the house in the grass of a clearing on the right of it. From there on down past the back of the house the clearing sloped away till it met the woods again in a dark grove of pines.

They took the stuff out of the car and went down to the grove. The needles were so thick their feet sank in up to the ankles. On the other side of the grove the pond came in again. They put their things under a tree and went out on a small dock for a look around. You couldnt see the house from there but the pond was spread out all around you. Except for a large open space in the middle of it the pond was choked with waterlilies that dotted the surface everywhere.

Hattie said she was going in for a swim while the sun was high. Was he going in. No. Why not. He said he didnt feel like it. Itd be fun watching her though and she shouldnt stay out just on account of him. She didnt ask him again but got her suit and went back of a pine. Gibson stayed on the dock and looked around the pond. On the far side it was pretty wild. From where he was it looked like a marsh with the stumps of rotted trees coming up out of the water. Among the stumps were longstemmed green and brown cattails and back of those where the water ended was a broad stretch of leafless brush that went back up the slope through dead trees till the green ones of the woods started again. Everywhere else the trees grew thick right down to the edge of the pond and white clumps of birch leaned out over the water. From around a small point Gibson heard water spilling away and he guessed that must be the dam Hattie spoke about the day before.

Then she came out from back of the tree and walked down to the dock holding the towel and her bathingcap in her hand. He thought her shape was very good. Her body was brown wherever he could see and pretty well rounded off especially at the waist and thighs. He helped her get in a flatbottomed boat that was at the dock and then with a broken oar he paddled through the thick mass of lilypads out to the clear water. When he got to the middle she anchored the scow by dumping out a large rock that was tied to a ring in the seat with a long length of clothesline. Hattie put her cap on and then she stood up and went over the side. In a couple of seconds she was up squirting a jet of water out of her mouth and blowing and puffing while she tried to tell him how cold the water was. She swam around the boat in a wide circle three or four times and finally got warm enough to turn over and float on her back. Gibson thought about his body. *Just as my face is only a face so my body is only a body. Theres nothing about it to make it different. Its the same as almost every other body. It has no large clusters of muscle and no unusual abilities. In some places its too thin and in others too large. Its toes are a bit twisted. Its feet are too much like planks. Its white all over except in the face where its a yellowy brown. Ive too much hair on my face and not enough under my arms and under my belly.*

Hattie swam over to the boat and hung on the side. Gibson touched her face and arms and liked the feel of the cold drying water on them. Then she climbed in and stretched herself out along a seat to get some sun and dry off. A lazy blue and gray bird came over a hill and Hattie said it was a heron. It flew to the marshy end of the pond and came down standing in shallow water looking like one of the dead stumps. Hattie shouted across the water and the heron went up in the air again and over to a bare tree way up the hill. Hattie asked Gibson to keep his eyes on a certain clump of birch. He did and after a minute or two a blue and white bird dived out of it fast down to the water. It was a kingfisher

Hattie said and when it came out of the water again it had a small fish in its bill and had to work hard to get up in the air again.

Hattie said they should go back to shore and eat the stuff shed brought so Gibson paddled in to the dock. Hattie said to lay out the food under a tree and get some water from the well back of the house and shed get dressed in the meantime. Itd only take her a minute. First he went up to the well and found a bucket hanging on a nail in a tree. He filled the bucket and took it back to the grove. On the way he got a look at Hattie. She didnt have anything on and she was drying herself with the towel. She looked up and saw him but she didnt yell or try to cover up or anything like that. Then he went closer and leaned against a tree a few feet away. Where the sun hadnt hit her she was very white and the spots of red on her breasts were small as pennies.

He said hed wait while she dressed and she kept on like there was no one there. All the time he didnt take his eyes off her but she wasnt ashamed. She put on her dress and then sat down to get the pine needles off her feet before she put on her shoes. Gibson didnt move till she finished and when she did after running a comb through her hair a few times they went out to where the food was. Shed brought some ham and cheese sandwiches and several pieces of fruit. They ate that and washed it down with drinks out of the bucket.

Then they went over to the other side of the grove where the dam was and lay down in the needles. Gibson had his head on Hatties shoulder and smoked a cigarette while they listened to the noise the water made falling from the pond to the rocks. Hattie asked him if hed ever heard a thrush and he said no so she told him to be quiet and listen. Gibson listened and the only sound came from the water in Stewart Brook but when he got used to that he heard the same string of fast notes that hed listened to the afternoon before. Hattie said that was a thrush a woodthrush. She said it had a fine voice and he said yes and asked her if she liked the music of birds. She said she did and she listened to it a long time whenever she was in the woods and to thrushes so much she could even make their call. Gibson said can you and he wanted to hear so she made her lips in an odd shape and twisted her fingers in front of them. Then he heard some clear high notes that sounded like they came out of a reed. She did it two or three times and he said it was pretty good. She told him a thrush made its notes so fast she had to hang around for weeks before she got them. Shed teach him if he wanted. He said it wouldnt do any good because if he whistled like that in front of his friends in the city theyd say he was a fairy but it was nice to hear her though. Hattie wanted to know why theyd say he was a fairy if he did that and he said theyd all want to know what kind of music he was whistling and hed have to tell them he was imitating a thrush. When he told them that theyd laugh out loud at him. A thrush theyd say. Thats a hot one and when you going to take to leaping around woodland dells in a pair of pink drawers. Hattie said she didnt exactly see the connection between imitating a thrush and dancing in pink drawers. Gibson said he went around with fellows that were kind of critical and they had expressions that meant a lot more than they seemed to. It was hard to explain.

Hattie said she could see he didnt like the country much but she couldnt understand why and asked him to tell her. Gibson said *while you were getting undressed and I was on the dock I pulled a waterlily out of the pond. I took a smell of it and my stomach almost turned it was so sweet. Then I looked out on the pond and saw all those thousands of open waterlilies and I knew that right after the sun went down all the flowers would close up and stay that way till tomorrow. The rest of the countrys just like that. The lilies open and close all the time. Everything comes out and goes away in its season. You cant say much for that. You cant keep on describing it and liking it as much the hundredth time as the first. In the country the big things the season but in the city there arent any seasons and you dont know what to expect. Here the corn comes up and you know what corn looks like and the trees and hills and sky are always the same. As far as Im concerned one ear of corns the same as every ear of corn and one trees like all the other trees. Where I live in the city theres a tree in our backyard. From here right now I can see ten thousand trees but you cant expect me to get that many times as excited.* Hattie said she guessed it wasnt so exciting selling neckties either and Gibson said *When you come right down to it it isnt any worse selling neckties than it is hoeing potatoes all day or walking five miles to school.* Gibson waited a while and then he said he was going to drive back to New York the next day. Hattie said she had no idea he was going away so soon she thought hed be there a couple of weeks. He said yes he thought so too but hed changed his mind. Hattie said she was sorry he was going because they could be good friends and have good times if he stayed. Gibson said if she ever went to New York she should look him up and he wrote out his address on a card and gave it to her. She said she didnt think shed get down to the city. Gibson said sure she would.

Lemmon came up along Stewart Brook then and sat down when Hattie asked him to. He told them theyd had some luck with the poachers. Late the night before thered been some firing over by Black Spruce

Mountain. That wasnt near water so they guessed the poachers had got
scared of shooting too much around Viele Pond. They started out across
country in the dark and caught three of the poachers in the act of lugging
away a big buck. Robbins had them covered and they couldnt see where
he was but even so one of the fellows wanted to fight it out and put his
gun up to let the wardens have it. Robbins figured there wasnt any
other way so he let fly with his .38 and got the man in the leg. All three
were from Albany and worked for a hotel outfit. The wounded man was
carried off by his two friends and Robbins was with them in the car on
the way back to the Lake George lockup. Lemmon said he was staying
behind to pick up others of the party if there were any. He said it would
go pretty hard with the fellows they arrested and also the hotel people.
It wasnt often now anybody tried to pick off a warden but there were a
lot of folk that didnt give a damn what the woods were like as long as
they managed to get some meat out of it. Lemmon said hed always liked
the woods and wanted to keep them like they were and strangers never
did a place any good. He didnt mean Gibson he said. They always took
what they could get and to hell with the man that came along next. Well
hed have to move on Lemmon said. He was glad hed seen Gibson again.
The warden nodded to Hattie and went away through the grove toward
the road.

Gibson and Hattie drove back to Hatties farm and he said goodbye
to her there.

ELEGY ON AN EMPTY SKYSCRAPER

John Gould Fletcher

I

Against the wall of this sky
Leaden pall threaded with cardboard boxes, the pale light of the towers
Flickers unearthly still,
Long leaden streets between them:
Against the wall of this sky, the cream-white face
Of stone blocks bound in glittering steel gleams high;
Juts to the sky, and breaks
Packed huddled ranks of clouds and roofs apart
Thrusting its own horizon yet a little higher.

Beauty is spread
Here over hollow voids; beneath these walls
Clamour of traffic slides through corridors,
Long elevator-shafts shoot mountainously upwards.
Steel on the surface repels
This drizzling daylight; through the inner core
Vertical darkness spreads,
Extends its empire upwards,
Forces the tower to tremble with dull sound.

Noise of wheels tuned to wheels,
Spinning the darkness skyward,
Forcing the human darkness that should hide
The earth in fruitfulness, still bleakly upwards
In a stark affirmation,
Stone flanged to steel here to repel the daylight,
Void affirmation, since the sky goes higher
And men drift past, unseeing,
Bowed deeper by the weight of locked-in stone:—

Balancing bodies against the heat that holds
Its swift course vertically downwards;
Dragging their heavy feet into its molten pavements,
Swaying their shrinking flesh against its reverberant walls;
Noise of wheels tuned to wheels,
Bewildered with the men that move amid them;
While still the tower lurches
Upwards with its long shadow,
Flight of white ripples four-square on the sky.

Here in this drift against the wall of the sky,
Steel arms that lift,
Tackle that rattles,
Torches that sputter,
Chattering hammers that shake the empty brain,
The roar and the mutter
Of the swift elevated train
And the ships at the dockside,
The pencilled lines of the bridges
The dull green carpet of park,
The wide grey floor of the bay—
Is all this living to-day?
The fuming and looping line of the surly river to westward,
Stained by the sunset to red—
Is all this living, or dead?
Dead are twinkling lights and the sombre reflections
Of the earth-dwellers stretched heavenwards here from below?
Who is there living to know?
Only the wide hollow offices, the corridors empty of light,
Tier after tier going downwards here into night.

II

Thick pencil of shadow stretched across the street,
If I could lift
Your weight and make you write;
Or if at night
I could make move that fixed and arrogant light
That stands there emptily glaring to repeat,
In higher guise, the street lamp's signal-flight;
What against all the words that we repeat

In vain to-day,
What is the one word I would make you say?

"Here where once stared in dumb hope to the sky
Man by his naked blaze, and saw smoke take away
In folds of undulating grey
His prayer, not knowing walls however high:
Here wall on wall is heaped, steel thread to thread
Is riveted to extend the ever-dead:
Vain flight of shadow where the chasms cry."

And yet we pray and mind our own affairs:
And sky-signs echo back unanswered prayers.

III

Could I but strip you down,
Tear steel from steel in long peeled strips, and break
The interlocking blocks of cream-white stone,
Send them like autumn leaves swift spinning down,

Or level, near and far,
This city, spread about you greening fields,
Leave you alone, all empty as you are,
Gleaming-nerved flower that no grass reveals,

Either I'd do:
But it is vain within your walls to go,
To feel in your dead heart the beat and strain
Of hopes grown panic-smitten, to and fro
Millions of meaningless lights,
When all about you is the soundless night's.

There is wide space between
Man's topmast and his keel, and in it death
Comes without sign or sound or stir of breath.
No one shall fill that room, or take his place
In it, as stowaway or come-aboard;
Nor shall the meagre window-blind be lowered,
Nor shall the dark be levelled by a face.

A DREADFUL NIGHT

Josephine Herbst

A light was on in the kitchen and Georgia tiptoed in so as not to wake the family. She took her slippers off and her party dress and hung the dress over the back of a chair so it wouldn't get mussed. It was dark and quiet in the house and the old floor boards creaked as she went to hook the screen doors for the night and standing there, looking out, all the insects in the empty lot next the house singsonged a note higher and then died down again and she was a little scared to be all alone. Not many girls her age would be brave enough to walk home from a party all alone and she was proud of herself and knew that the next day she would tell the girls about coming up the hill and how she thought she saw a man hiding in the weeds and when she walked faster, he walked faster, right behind her, and she was afraid to run. She just walked on and swung her arms and picked a tall white clover to put in her teeth to show she didn't care and when she came to the corner, she looked back, and he wasn't there.

When the doors were hooked she started toward the hall and heard a thud in her mother's room and then someone coming down the stairs. Georgia moved toward the dining room as her mother came in from the hall. She was in her nightgown and sat down on the nearest chair. "Get me a towel from the kitchen," she said. "That vein in my leg broke."

Georgia hurried to the kitchen and snatched at the first towel she saw. She brought it back and her mother looked at it and said, "Not a dish towel. A clean one, out of the pantry." The diningroom was dark and neither of them thought of turning on the light. The kitchen light was strong and Georgia got a clean towel and handed it to her mother. "I'll call Papa," she said and hurried to the hall. A drop of blood had fallen to the dining room linoleum with a thin splash like rain water. "Do you remember, should you tie above or below?"

"Above, not below," said Georgia. She kneeled by her mother and tried to remember the page from her Physiology book. She could see the picture of the heart with the blue and red, and the broken ends of the artery but she wasn't sure if it was above or below you tied. When she had studied that page she said she would always remember on account of her mother who had varicose veins and the doctor said she should wear a rubber stocking or it might burst some day. She wound the towel around and held it tight and the blood soaked through. Georgia got up and ran to the hall and called, "Papa."

Her voice sounded high and scared her. She came back and looked at her mother. "Are you sure it's below," said Mrs. Strawbridge. "No," said Georgia. "I'll phone for a doctor." Mr. Strawbridge came down the stairs in his nightshirt and bare feet. His hair was mussed on his forehead. "What's wrong?" he said.

"Nothing," said Mrs Strawbridge. "That vein in my leg broke. Don't get excited." Georgia's yonger sister came down the stairs. She stood in her little nightgown looking scared. The blood soaked right through the towel. Mr Strawbridge hurried up the stairs and put his trousers on. He came back and said, "Has it stopped?"

"No," said Mrs Strawbridge. "Get me more towels." Charlotte stood on a chair to get the towels down from the pantry shelf. Mr Strawbridge came in with a basin of water. Georgia was trying to get the nearest doctor on the phone. It was a dial phone and she got a busy number. Then no answer. She said, "I'll run and get Mary."

"Don't get her," said Mrs Strawbridge. "It'll just frighten her." Charlotte tried to get the doctor again. No answer. "Perhaps the phone's busted," said Georgia. The others paid no attention to her.

"Someone get me something to put around me," said Mrs Strawbridge. Her voice sounded faint. "And get the camphor."

"Get the camphor," said Mr Strawbridge and his voice sounded shaky as if he were going to cry. Charlotte got a coat from the hall and wrapped it around her mother. Georgia felt sick at her stomach. "I think the phone's busted. I better run for the doctor," she said. Charlotte brought the camphor to her mother and Mrs Strawbridge said, "Bring a chair so I can put my leg up." Mr Strawbridge brought a chair. "I'm going," said Georgia. No one heard her. She rushed out the back door and down the street. It was after twelve and a still moonlight night. The houses were all dark. Her feet made hollow flapping sounds against the cement walk as she ran. "Don't let her die, don't let her die, don't let her die." Her mother has been sewing on her new clothes so she could enter highschool in the fall. Working the machine had done it, if her mother died, she was a murderer and done for. She ran for the doctor to save her mother. Her sister Mary lived on a side street and she ran up under the trees. On the front porch, she called, "Mary." Mary's voice answered, "What is it? is something wrong?"

"Mother. That vein in her leg broke. I'm going for the doctor." She listened and heard Mary speak to Bill. "Turn on the light, can't you find it?" Mary was up moving around in the dark and Georgia called, "I'm going for the doctor" and she ran down the street toward the hill and at the bottom of the hill five blocks away was the nearest doctor. She clattered up to the doctor's porch and punched the bell and no one came. She kept her finger on the bell and at last she saw a light and behind the stained glass square of the front door a woman came slowly down the stairs, and then she stuck her head out. "The doctor's not in," she said. "Oh," said Georgia, wringing her hands. "Oh," and she stood a minute and the woman said she'd have him come as soon as he came home. Georgia told where they lived and said her mother had broken a vein in her leg.

Then she rushed down the street toward the drug store. She decided to ask the drug clerk what to do. She couldn't go home. The drug store was open and the clerk was talking to a young fellow with a cigar. They both stared at Georgia. She saw she was in her underslip with only a sweater. "Should you tie below or above for a broken vein," said Georgia. "Below," said the clerk. "That's what I thought," said Georgia. "Can I use the phone?" She got the house and her father answered. "It's still bleeding and the doctor hasn't come, I don't know what to do, " he said.

"Don't get excited," said Georgia. "The drug store clerk says you tie below, just tie tight, and I'll bring a doctor." She hung up and saw the clerk and young fellow watching her and wondered if they weren't considering her pretty brave. But only for a minute, the next minute she asked, "Do you know the nearest doctor?"

"Doc Small up Rebecca Street."

"That's right," said Georgia. "I'll go there."

"Why don't you phone. Here, use the phone. Wait a minute. I'll get it for you." He twirled the dial and after a wait handed the phone to Georgia. She took it and said to please come right away. "Is it a vein or an artery?" Georgia's hands were shaking and she looked at the clerk and said, "Is it a vein or an artery?"

"You said it was a vein, here a while ago," said the clerk.

"It's a vein," said Georgia in the phone. "I'll be there, don't get excited," said the doctor. Georgia hung up. She called the house again to tell them the doctor was on the way but got no answer. Her teeth chattered and she hung up.

"You better run along home," said the clerk. A woman had come in and stood looking at her. The fellow who had been talking to the clerk said something in a low tone to the clerk. "Want a sniff of ammonia or something," said the clerk.

"I'm all right," said Georgia. She said "thankyou" to the clerk and the three people in the store stared at her. She started back toward home, running a little. When she came to the street where her sister lived, she turned toward the house. If her sister was still there, she would wait and go on home with her. The house was dark and Georgia called and there was no answer. She knew she would have to go home now. She started and thought, "Save her and I'll give up highschool, I'll give up college." Her legs felt stiff and her hands were all swollen and stiff from hanging down as she ran. She pinched her fingers and wondered if she would have to give up highschool and college if everything turned out all right. She had just said she would, perhaps it would work out like that. But her mother wouldn't let her give them up.

When she came to the corner, she could see the house lighted from top to bottom. She stood in the grass and tried to see the living room window. A lot of people were standing around, like a party. Then she heard a moan, like nothing she had ever heard. Like an animal. The people stood without moving under the light looking down. She couldn't sort the people out in her head but at last she saw a woman down the street who was the wife of a conductor. This woman had never stepped a foot in their house before and how she ever got there Georgia didn't see. There was another dreadful sound and then the people looked up and seemed to be listening to someone who was out of range of the window. They all turned and began going out the side door. Georgia sat down on the back step. She was limp as a rag but nobody was crying and her mother must be saved. Georgia could go on with her education and amount to something and be worthy. She leaned her head on her knees, she was so tired out. Someone came to the back door and said, "For pity's sake. Here she is." It was Mary, Georgia got up and opened the screen door. "Where on earth were you?" said Mary.

"Why I went for the doctor and just got back," said Georgia.

"Yes, that was a senseless thing to do. Why we phoned for Dr Ellsworth and he had begun to take the stitches before that fellow you ran after showed up. And much good he would have done, smoking a cigar. A doctor, smoking."

Georgia followed Mary into the house. Her mother was on the couch, very pale but she smiled. "Where were you, poor child."

"For the doctor," said Georgia. She looked around. Patches of white flour were all over the carpet. "What's this stuff," said Georgia.

"Oh those people," said Mrs Strawbridge. "Their crazy ideas, and I guess we all lost our heads. One said to throw flour on it and it just gummed everything up."

"Little Charlotte didn't lose her head," said Mary, putting her arm around Charlotte who stood there in her nightgown with a kimona on top of it. "She was as brave as could be."

"You go to bed, baby," said Mrs Strawbridge. Charlotte kissed her mother and walked out of the room as if she were sleep-walking. "The little thing," said Mrs Strawbridge, "she called all the neighbors."

"Guess we'd better let mother rest," said Mr Strawbridge. He and Bill had been getting the bed from upstairs down and setting it up in the living room. "You'll get a good sleep and be fit as a fiddle tomorrow," he said. Now that it was over he was ready to boss the show and he capered around and said that in a day or so mamma would be dancing.

Georgia was uneasy about the part she had played. "I ran for the doctor because I thought the phone was busted," she said.

"You," said Mary. "You ran away, you mean. We know you. That's what she always does, mother. Don't you remember that time I was sick and the blanket caught fire. She skipped over the bed and ran out of the house and all around the block. We could have burned to a crisp."

"Now she did the best she could," said Mrs Strawbridge raising her head and looking warningly at Mary.

"Yes, and that other time when Charlotte swallowed the alcohol and we thought it was poison. She ran around the block then."

"She was all right," said Mrs Strawbridge. "You better run along Mary, it's late." Georgia looked daggers at Mary. Mr Strawbridge came over and put his arm around Georgia. "You're a good girl," he said. "You're papa's girl, don't you worry."

It was very late and no use trying to clean up the flour. Georgia felt sick but she got a pail and started in on the dining room linoleum where her mother had been sitting. The rag soaked around on the floor and she rinsed it and the water colored and she got a fresh pail of water. Big dark spots led from the linoleum into the hall and up the stairs. Mrs Strawbridge called, "Don't do that, it will wait until morning." Mr Strawbridge was going to sleep on a sofa near his wife and he had taken off his shoes and waited for Georgia to finish so he could undress and turn off the lights. Georgia called, "I'm just going to do the hall a little, you go on to sleep."

The hall was full of moonlight and the shadows of the grapevine on the front porch sprawled over the floor. Georgia took the rag and moved it along the hall. Every two feet she scrubbed and then moved on, on her knees. She moved up the stairs and into her mother's room and beside her mother's bed. Then she took the pail down and emptied it and rinsed it and rinsed the rag and stood the pail on the back porch and hung the rag on a nail. She scrubbed her hands good in the kitchen with yellow soap and then she scrubbed them with white soap and put some nice lotion on. She felt sick at her stomach all the time and she went into the washroom and tried to be sick over the bowl. Her face was very white in the mirror. She looked sick. When the lights were out, she tiptoed back through the dining room to the hall. Her mother called, "Goodnight," and she answered and went up the stairs. Charlotte was in bed and pretending to sleep. The bedroom windows looked out on a great field spiked with long shadows of cotton wood trees. It was a close night. The insects had suddenly stopped singing. With every breath you could smell blood. It was like strong rainwater full of rotting leaves. Early that evening Georgia had gone to a party and everyone had laughed. She put her hands over her face but the smell of blood was stronger than the smell of lotion.

The two girls lay flat in bed and had nightmares and woke up again and again sweating. The smell was always there and Georgia longed for morning. She was grateful for the way things had turned out and wondered how long it would be before her mother could use the sewing machine again.

IF SLEEPING

Etta Blum

If sleeping I have seen a face arise
with eyelids greened by surge of constant water
and mouth a twisted oblong rising toward
the empty eyes that sideways search and peer

if this face I have seen then too beyond
three lonely trees in flame that set a sun
upon the cold corruption of that cheek
the marbled dying and the breathless beat

So do I walk upon the quaverous edge
of curveless shores where hollowly the shells
suck in the trilling vastness of the night
to shrilly sob thru frightened slits of space

2/15/32

Dear Dick :

While I'm waiting for this baby to be born : It's another first class issue. If Pagany can't see then no magazine can see, there are no readers and there's not much taste and little good sense in the land.

I particularly like the Shapiro story. It's skillfully plotted and full of fresh observation, acute thought, courage. He has ability too in sheer use of the word. I think this one of the best things you have ever printed.

I read this story first, in fact it's the only one I have carefully gone over so far. I'm doing yours now. I like it the best of anything of yours so far. More another time.

You told me I might look over the material you have with a view to finding something for Contact — something which you cannot use. How about it? Maybe you could select a batch of stuff which I can look over. I'd come in if you will name the day or evening.

While I have goes on. You can have the next chapter any time you want.

S.

I dropped in at your place last week but there was no answer to the bell.

Is there any chance of getting work from Caldwell through you?

Contact should be out this week. I'd greatly appreciate a frank criticism of it from you. Please do this. Let's hear what you have to say — as to the format and contents also. If there are any suggestions to make, make them — no matter how damaging they may be.

The book of mine Zukofsky is interesting in should be out any day. I'm curious to see if anyone buys it at seventy five cents. The Dragon press (Ithaca) promises a book of my short stories including <u>Old Doc Rivers</u> — about half the stories have never been seen by anyone. A publisher in N. Y. is showing some interest in the collected poems. All of which sounds as if I might get my deck cleaned by spring. That has been my object this year — to clean up. I can't do any major work (other than the chapters of White Mule — 4 a year) until then. Once I have wiped out my past by printing it I'm going to — do whatever I succeed in getting done.

Please write.

yours

Bill.

Dear Bill:

Up in Boston due to the very critical illness of my father. Will let you know as soon as I get back to town as I am eager to see you all. Contact sounds most fascinating, both from you and from Kamin. Trust I shall be able to hear you interviewed over radio. Do go ahead with White Mule just the way you want to, fast or slowly. Don't let me down on it though. You know I count on it. Next part due at the latest by the middle of March. My best to whom you will.

Affectionately,
Dick

The death of Benjamin N. Johnson, Boston attorney, was duly noted in the press of the large cities of America in early February without knowledge that it might well be considered the point when *Pagany* entered its terminal phase. It meant a great deal to Johns to have so many contributors, who over the years had become personal friends, write to him to convey their sympathy for the loss of his father.

419-422

Casa „Son Palou"
Camino Vecinal de
Genova á Porto Pi
Palma-de-Mallorca

Dear Dick:

By the vagaries of the transatlantic mails I received simultaneously your letter announcing your father's illness and one from my mother announcing his death.

I know very little of your personal life, Dick, and accordingly have no idea how intimate or sympatique you may have been, but to whatever extent it is suitable and fitting I offer you my sympathy and condolences, and regret that I was not in Lynn in case I could have been of any practical use to you in what must have been a busy and trying time.

~~Doubtless editorial details~~ will not much interest you at the moment: I'll defer for a week or so answering your letter.

With much sympathy and affection, Dick..

[signature]

11 March
1932

Wrens, Georgia
March 7th 1932

Dear Johns:

I am not worth a damn as one
who offers sympathy, but I just want you to
know that I am sorry that you have lost your
father.

Many thanks for the twenty; it
changes my outlook entirely. I wish I could
get along without having to exist on what I
can make by writing.

I haven't seen Watkins yet, but
I have sent him word that you are accepting his
story. If he has anything at all in him, he
will get down and do something. I hope so.

A new story is enclosed. I am
sending it now because I may not be able to do
another story for six months. I can't do anything
until this new novel is satisfactorly disposed
of. Scribners have made no decision yet.

-Best wishes. Hope to see you by the 1st of April.
Sincerely,
Caldwell

Yes, I received Williams' note all right. I sent him a
story which he wrote that he was taking. Thanks for giving that
him my address. --I have busted up with CLAY. It developed
he wants only a certain kind of writing. Tragedy and tears, for God's
sake!

February 24th, 1932
265, Riverside Drive.

Dear Johns,

Thanks for your kind letter about my
stories. Im glad you like the new ones and
glad, too, that Williams thought the Narrative was all right.

Ill be looking forward to seeing you
when you get back to town. Give me a ring
and say when its convenient and we can have
dinner some place, if you wish.

I saw an announcement in the Times of
the death of a Benjamin Johnson, of Lynn.
When I read the name Richard V. Johnson as
one of the sons, I recalled your having told
me some time ago of the illness of your
father. If the person mentioned in the paper
was your relative, wont you please accept
my sympathy and an offer to be of service
to you here while you are compelled to remain at home. If there is anything I can
do, all you have to do is let me know about
it.

Yours sincerely,

J. L. Shapiro

January 28, 1932.

Dear Dick:

Thanks much for the Paganys and your note. I'm glad
you!re using <u>An American's London</u>, and the other, which you have,
<u>When it rains</u>. Will you please title that one, <u>Mausoleum London</u>.

As I've been working on a novelette, and still am, haven't
gotten around to the article yet. Saw Dudley Fitts's pinpricks. I
don't know how one who writes as badly as Fitts can set himself up
as a critic of prose. As for all that nonsense about waging a
losing battle with Calliope, what can one say about that kind of
uncritical stuff. Nothing, and I think that's what my answer is.
Fitts in the past has viciously attacked both D.H.Lawrence and
Sherwood Anderson. Well anyway, in conclusion, I think Dudley Fitts's
preparatory school turgidities are highly narcisstic.

Was sorry to hear you had to clear out because of your
father's illness. Sara and I want you to come over and have dinner
with us as soon as you come back. Another thing, I'm trying now to
scrape together some money to get to London, where I think I'll have
a better chance of placing my book. For the past five years New York
has been an impasse for me-a kind of unremitting defeat out of which
I've got nothing but blankness and a disheartening emptiness. So I
may be off some time next month.

Sara and I send our very best to you.

Edward Dahlberg.

4716-39th Avenue,
Long Island City, New York.

JOHNS RETURNED TO NEW YORK to get the second issue of Volume III on the press. Although he found it difficult to admit, he knew this must be the final year of *Pagany*. His father's estate was nowhere near settlement, but the administrators felt it only fair to give Johns a clear picture of the financial situation. Prior to the collapse of the market, Mr. Johnson had been a nominally wealthy man and at that time had willed large donations to Harvard and Radcliffe, the Lynn Public Library, and a number of other charities. These had to be paid out in cash before the balance of the estate could be estimated, and the conversion of investments into cash on hand at this period in the depression would draw heavily on the balance. Johns was told quite frankly that his share of income from the estate would be very small, and that he should expect to earn his own living to supplement what would be only a subsistence annual amount.

Johns had already purchased a home in Redding, Connecticut, and had begun to recondition it to be comfortably habitable. He had built stalls in the barn for his father's two riding horses and since this carpentering was already finished, there was no countermanding it. Johns sold the two horses at once. Plans on the house were simplified, making it at best a rural retreat for a man who must earn his living elsewhere, one ill-equipped educationally to expect those earnings to be large. But Johns put·that worry aside for future consideration. *Pagany* would see its third year through somehow.

At this time Johns was much in need of an emotional lift and was indeed glad to read Dudley Fitts' comments on *Pagany* in his little magazine review printed in the January–March, 1932, issue of *Hound and Horn*. *425-430*

The second issue for 1932 had several new names to introduce. Johns was most pleased with the work of Benjamin Appel and Harry Roskolenkier along with the fact that H. D., wife of poet and critic Richard Aldington, had sent from Switzerland one of her finest poems, "Electra-Orestes." It was an impeccable piece of work, worthy *441-443* of this recognized Imagist poet, who had been considered one of the finest American poets since her graduation from Bryn Mawr as Hilda Doolittle of Bethlehem, Pennsylvania.

Benjamin Appel came from a very different background. Johns had met him a number of times and was warmed by listening to this dedicated young man, only twenty-four years old but positive of what he would do with his life. Appel had been born in the Hell's Kitchen area of New York, a district of tenements sandwiched between the lights of Broadway and the docks of the Hudson River. Both his mother and father had emigrated from Poland out of cultured families with the determination that their eldest son, Benjamin, would graduate from an American college. Although they did their best to protect the boy from the bad influences of the neighborhood, the sturdy but sensitive son could not help but learn about the hard facts of life from the other children in this environment. Appel studied at the University of Pennsylvania, New York University, and at Lafayette College, from which he graduated in 1929. Right now, in the heart of the depression, he was working as a tenement inspector for the City of New York.

436-440

In "The Summer Witches," Appel crammed all the sensuous quality of the Summer season into a very few words, making the story richer by allowing the reader to sense the relieved escape of the narrator from the grim pattern of urban streets. Johns had a great deal of personal affection for this particular story.

Harry Roskolenkier's poetry was an amazing manifestation from a young man who had been a sailor and an oiler on drawbridges, and who had been gathered in under the revolutionary blanket of the proletarian writers. His poems had a rich individuality and sensitivity of feeling. They rounded out the contours of this Spring issue.

MAGAZINE REVIEWS

"LONELY HEARTS COLUMN"

> FRONT. *Trilingual quarterly. Editors: Sonja Prins, Norman MacLeod, Xavier Abril, &c. Den Haag, Holland.*
>
> THE LEFT. *A Quarterly Review of Radical and Experimental Art. Editors: George Redfield, Jay du Von. Davenport, Iowa.*
>
> HESPERIAN. *'Issued occasionally'. Editor: James D. Hart. San Francisco, California.*
>
> NATIVITY. *Quarterly. Editors: Boris J. Israel, Norman MacLeod, &c. Delaware, Ohio.*
>
> PAGANY. *Quarterly. Editor: Richard Johns. New York.*
>
> PROCESSION. *Quarterly. Editors: Derek Fox, Peter Ruthven, &c. Ann Arbor, Michigan.*
>
> THE NEW REVIEW. *Bi-monthly. Editor: Samuel Putnam. Paris.*

Front and *The Left* represent the sociological Left Wing. Of the former, four numbers have appeared, with work in French, English, and German. Of the latter, only one number has been published; a second is long overdue. Both magazines are animated by an uncompromising sincerity; both are vitiated by an inability to achieve a balance between art and propaganda. In the opening article of *Left*, V F Calverton worries out a platitude to unnecessary length,

concluding that 'the revolutionary critic does not aim to underestimate literary craftsmanship. What he contends is simply that
literary craftsmanship is not enough. The craftsmanship must be
utilized to create objects of revolutionary meaning. . . . In a
word, the revolutionary critic does not believe that we can have
art without craftsmanship; what he does believe is that, granted
the craftsmanship, our aim should be to make art serve man as a
thing of action and not man serve art as a thing of escape'. I do not
know what Mr Calverton means by 'objects of revolutionary
meaning'; and I feel that a bit more prose craftsmanship would
have avoided the hocuspocus of that final cadence; but the simple
conflict is there, 'in a word'. What is the duty of an artist who must
also propagandize? Can a poem be a sociological tract? Given a
propagandist who happens also to be a true poet; given documen-
tary phenomena as material for a poem: is the artist to bend,
arrange his material to suit his poetic theory, or is he to suppress
his poetic theory better to serve the ends of his propaganda? I
believe that Norman MacLeod, for instance, is one of the few
thorough artists writing to-day. If certain of his poems are not the
final expression of the Southwest, of industrial tragedy, of the
proletarian consciousness, these things will never be said. Yet,
consider this passage, from a long poem in *Nativity:*

> The barren land.
> Rigs like penitent crosses black against the pale New Mexican dawns.
> Let a stronger, brawnier poet come from the heart of a people
> singing the war against mankind
> before the song can die in his throat
> fearful of capitalism.

Here it is in a nutshell. The first two verses, evoking the mesas and
the crag-based crosses of the *Penitentes*, are legitimate, although
too imprecise to partake of MacLeod's best vein. Thereafter the
'social note' breaks through,[1] first in a verse of commonplace
Whitman, then quickly degenerating into a series of prosaic clichés,
to end with that ghastly (from an artistic point of view) 'fearful of
capitalism' — for all the world like a limping adonic at the end of a
bad Sapphic. The synthesis of medium and direction is unaccom-
plished; the poet is lost in the pamphleteer. Now MacLeod, like

---

[1] I would not suggest that the 'social note' be excluded; indeed, it is the *creator
spiritus* of this poem, as of MacLeod's best work. I mean simply that it should be
subjected to an artistic discipline.

MAGAZINE REVIEWS 337

Robert McAlmon and Horace Gregory, is first of all a poet: which means that he is usually successful in the artistic assimilation of his material, and that the passage I have quoted above is no more than an illustrative lapse. But the lesser contributors to these magazines are not so fortunate. In most cases, they suggest no craftsmanship whatsoever. Their poems, like their stories, are no more than manifestoes very thinly disguised as 'creative literature'; and the disguises are worn without skill, — cast-offs, for the most part, of the extremists of *transition*. Nevertheless, typographical eccentricity and downright bad writing can not make a poem out of a social report, however much Vladimir Pillin ('O battalions! O disaster!' [1]) and Edward Dahlberg (why, in *Pagany* or anywhere else, must Mr Dahlberg rewrite the epigraphs to *Manhattan Transfer?*) may desire it. Briefly: for most of MacLeod's poems, for Dos Passos' *The Man who said his Name was Jones*, for *Left's* excellent movie-criticism (the best I have seen), for the stories and poems of Kay Boyle, Mangan, and Williams in *Front*, as well as for the intense sincerity of both magazines, *Front* and *The Left* are to be valued. For Calverton, verbosely trite; for Zukofsky, whose critical artillery seems to be composed exclusively of the *ipsius dicta*, apt or inept, of Mr Pound, and who contributes to *Front* IV a badly written review of *XXX Cantos*, adding nothing to his earlier (and badly written) french review in *Échanges* III; for the race-riot plays and the packing-house prose: — what need be said, except that the best fighting-steel is tempered?

In *Nativity*, which is more frankly a 'literary' quarterly, I can find little to recommend. A story by DeJong, inferior to his usual work; MacLeod's poem, from which I have quoted above. The rest is a sufficiently bad aping of the Paris Gang, rising to a transpaludian flight with a Miss Eva Pratt (hitherto unpublished), who drinks gin, speaks french, knows about Life, & concludes:

> It was a long winter, Spring came up the Connecticut
> in mid April, but we were a hard lot,
> we were a hard lot.

Of all these magazines, the oldest and most distinguished is *Pagany*. It has published some of the best stories (*e.g.*: Dos Passos, Erskine Caldwell, Mary Butts) of our time, and its occasional critical articles have been exceptionally good. A magazine that has brought out Dos Passos' *Eveline Hutchins* and Dr Williams' *White*

---

[1] *O saisons! O châteaux!*

Mule (which, however unpleasantly, is solid merciless guts) has achieved an eminence that it must not relinquish. At the same time, the boys and girls *will* break in to turn parts of every number into a pseudo-Triana *baile de máscaras*. The current number is representative: here are Dos Passos' and Williams' stories; here are six poems by Cummings, who can still get away with crooning *if i love You;* three more *Cantos* by Mr Pound; a stylized savagery by Mangan; at least one original poem by Conrad Aiken; some real things by MacLeod. But here also are Mr Dahlberg, having a hell of a good time with the compositor; Basil Bunting, who once wrote a fine poem about Villon,[1] agreeing with F. P. A., in a distressing version of *Carm. I, Od. xiii,*[2] that Horace was the Roman equivalent of Walter Winchell; and Mina Loy, who is certainly experienced enough to know better. . . . And why is it necessary to continue (and, worse, to announce yet another instalment of) Mr Halper's parody of *Farewell to Arms,* — a parody which was amusing enough at first, but which tired soon, forgot it was a parody, and has now become weakly pathetic, and frequently even touching, *quâ* Hemingway? Yet one number of *Pagany* is worth volumes of the others. It is, of this collection, the single solid force.

The others . . . *Hesperian,* typographically pretentious to the point of unreadableness, suggests the vigour of the West Coast. There is an interesting colloquy by Diego Rivera, and, in the Winter issue, some extremely good translations, by Yvor Winters, of Corbière, du Bellay, Vielé-Griffin, and Mallarmé. The magazine is purely literary; acceptably amateur; generally unexciting. The same is true, in diminution, of *Procession.* There are some pretty album-verses by Yvor Winters, a long and informative discussion of Russian music, by Carl Gehring. Little more . . . *The New Review* is at least stimulating: Pound's penetrating illiteracies and Antheil's musical notes see to that. In the second number there's a grand sculpture of Mr Hoover, done in cast iron with bathtub-enamel finish. In the first number, Maxwell Bodenheim, 'leading american poet' (!), appears staggering under eight pages of huge prose on a modest subject: 'Esthetics, Criticism, and Life.' Had Doctor Johnson composed the *Hisperica Famina,* he might have written so: 'Chaos is a massive struggle for birth, each separate

---

[1] In *Redimiculum Matellarum* (Milan, 1930); *R.M.* may perhaps be interpreted, *A Garland of Chamberpots.* It's an unerring sense, &c &c. . . .

[2] *Cum tu, Lydia, Telephi,* &c. It becomes 'Please stop gushing about his pink neck, smooth arms and so forth, Dulcie: it makes me sick', *k:t:l.*

MAGAZINE REVIEWS   339

part of which is too antagonistic to the other part to permit the
release of broader and distinct units within this birth, whereas the
disorders of esthetics are infinitely friendly toward each other and
employ myriads of means to develop, circumvent, and surpass
myriads of contrasts, extensions.' And so on, without even a para-
graph-break, to the end. If Mr Pound's prose sounds as though its
author were trotting in his nightshirt through a cobbly street,
prodding an ancient typewriter suspended upon his bosom; if Mr
Dahlberg's prose seems to be waging a lost battle with a calliope; if
Mr Zukofsky's prose is stylistically reminiscent of the tabloids'
Vox Populi columns: what shall be said of this marmoreal diction,
except that, in Ovid's careful phrase, *ad metam properavit simul*?
Mr Bodenheim's extended detumescence wears itself out finally
in the third number — a number which opens with a lulu by Michel
Arnaud, *Onan or Love is Born Perfect* *, and closes with an essay
aptly entitled *Fungus, Twilight, or Dry Rot*, by Mr Pound. 'Remains
aht and licherchoor'; 'Very possibly true but is no excuse for
reprinting the god damn book [i.e., *The Golden Treasury*, with the
jury's comments] in a popular edtn. Some corpses shd. be allowed to
stay buried. For real cloacal obsessions apply to the Bri'sh critics.
One has just done a book about (guess who)'; 'Incitement to . . .
such disorder outside a given state is just as criminal as breeches
[*olé!*] of peace inside the state . . .'; 'Alfonso of Spain appears to
have been the typical king, a grafter. Like the french Bourbons before him'; — it is increasingly difficult to understand Mr Pound's
conviction that English is an unfit vehicle for criticism. The same
number contains an agreeable essay by Miguel de Unamuno, and an
excellent story by Wambly Bald. Otherwise, there's little of any
value, and much that is definitely bad. After an encouraging start,
The New Review seems to have cast in its lot with such organs of
high-school radicalism as *This Quarter*: professionally 'modernist',
it is apparently content to keep the usual battered signals floating
in the backwash of *après-la-guerre*, and it will probably stimulate
the advance-guard element in New-Britain (Conn.).

 . . . One summer, years ago, I was so fortunate as to share rooms
with a gentleman who conducted the Lonely Hearts Column for
the now alas defunct *Boston Telegram*. As a sideline he ran Advice
to the Love-lorn; and whenever there was a paucity of queries,
he'd take another drink and write them himself. It used to worry

---

* "Author's Note: — I have not wanted to publish *Onan*, for the reason that this
work no longer means anything to me. &c &c" *Quisque sui criticus . . . justissimus.*

HOUND & HORN

him: he was always afraid that some day he would cease to be,
let us say, Francis X McGinsburg, and would wake up as an anxious multiplicity of Maybelles, Eighteen-Year-Olds, Doubtfuls,
and Alysses. Perhaps it has happened, though with a slight change.
I detect a familiar tone: perhaps (is it possible?) he has become
a multiplicity of Lesser Contributors, and as such is appearing once
in a while in *Pagany* and the established reviews; rather oftener in
the Left Wing; and is supplying the mad little magazines with
almost their entire content. Sometimes he hits it off; more often he
is lonely for the dead dear days when a pied line was Art because it
was pied, when outraged syntax was Art because it was outraged,
when everybody gathered in Sam Schwartz' place, or in Joy street,
and had the fastest time: because all the old Values were bumped
sky-high, and Lonely Hearts could meet and mingle and be strident
and oh very consciously Modern. . . .

Dudley Fitts

June 7 1932

Dear Bill:

Sure I want another White Mule. I want her right through to the end. Don't pay too much attention to rumors concerning Pagany. I don't know yet what will become of it myself. I shall stagger through the year somehow, not paying, stalling off the printer, making a goodly number of enemies. By the end of the year I should know whether or not I can afford to go on. If you hear of any soul who'd like to sink a bit of money, getting nothing out of it but thanks send him or her my way.

Clearing things up at home is more of a job than I imagined anything could be, everything tied up, messed. It all has to be done right away as there isn't money to keep the house open. My house isn't paid for yet, just gradually being caught up on. I can't come back to New York as my creditors are ready to attach the car. All in all it's a hell of a mess, and I continue getting hell from people who don't get checks for stories, answers to letters. If I hadn't come to Gloucester, gotten rested up, I'd have dropped the whole thing (magazine) with the Spring issue. I think when I get things paid up and am living in the country I'll be able to swing things all right. Just now they're so confused all I can do is try to get them more in line, hope for the best. I work all morning, swim or lie in the sun all afternoon. It's not bad.

Do shoot the Mule to Gramercy when you get a chance. Never get an idea that I'm one to get sore when a story isn't printed. Hope to see you soon. Best to Florence and the boys. Let me hear from you, when's the next Contact?

Affectionately,
Dick

NUMBER 2 *April–June*

Contents

PAGANY

THE SUMMER WITCHES
Benjamin Appel

One afternoon, she said: "Fetch the laundry." Her precise lips were thin with directions. One mile down the road. Then turn off. Even a fool could remember that. Even he wasn't such a fool, was he? She thought of the washerwomen who lived without a man and naturally had a bad reputation. Little drops of sweat glistened in the corners of his stubborn eyes. The fool wasn't crying, was he? She had to affirm her authority.

He set off. As he walked his flannels threw moving columns of glaring progress into his gaze. The white dust stirred in sultry clouds, browning the cuffs. He wiped his face—already burned the mongrel red tan of a man in his first week of vacation and determined to get all the sun he could. Gleam and faded glitter sustained an intense sweat-pouring heat. A field of corn shone like a garishly painted picture. A pasture sweltered in the identical slack resignation that enervated a few cows, whose tails hung limp like wet ropes. Every time he pulled out his handkerchief the sun made a sickening glare of it. How long was a mile, anyway?

Thick bunches of green saplings lined the side road. Perpetually sighing among the leaves of young trees, the docile breeze spilled into his ears like cooling drops. Shadows leaf-parasoled his head. He thrilled with the moss-dripping shivers that grip men who escape the hottest core of heat. What of the washerwomen? His mind was an ocean and they floated in the languid liquidity of his thoughts, prosaic mermaids. He saw their arms digging into solid soapy waters. He heard the flaky splashes they were always hearing. What a nice hot day.

A small frame house tattooed with nails, a young pine bending in the adoration of young trees, a big kettle on the porch, hens and a rooster cluttering about as if humans never fried eggs, and Silence. The door was half open, presenting that darkling gape of mysterious space, doors that are neither shut or open convey to strangers. He knocked. A voice slipped out.

He first saw a table laden with dirty dishes piled in an incoherent architecture of teetering circles. Three women, in a blend of eyes and skirts, warmed their femininity at this stranger male. Two brown hands plunged and plunged into foaming white suds. Someone was washing clothes. She stood strongly on her bare feet, buxom with forty years. Her blouse was open at the throat, her skirt flared out into a bell of light tan cloth. "Hello," she said.

He liked her unlined neck, soft as her bosom; the coils of her black hair, the sudsy gleam of her teeth. "I've come for Mrs. Gifford's washing."

"Well, it won't take me long to iron it. I've been so rushed." She dumped the contents of a basket on a table. The iron began to slide up and down Mrs. Gifford's things like some sort of locomotive.

The road back was an intense miniature in his brain, a concentrated essence like the burning ray of a sun glass. He heard the harsh voices of the sparrows. His bones melted. Time enough to arrive at the cottage of bawdy green, with curtains the color of crabapples. Time enough to enter the "abode" Mrs. Gifford described as "summery" and "so like the leaves and flowers." In this interior time wasn't so brassy and ruthless. "Do you mind if I wait?"

"No, no. Sit down. You must be warm."

Now, that he had her portrait in the gallery of this remembering afternoon, he turned towards the other women. They were young. They sprawled on a deep bed. The blue curtain sunlight painted gold specks on them. He was impressed by their lolling ease. One of the girls was sitting, her feet wide apart, her dress hollowing between her legs. She was precisely curved in slimness, one of those women who appear to be carved out of steel blades.

"I'm Mr. Gifford," he declared, as if his name might serve as a handle to his newness, a something to grasp.

"I'm Carmel."

They all laughed with the tender caution of strangers who are inclined to like one another.

Behind Carmel, the other girl rolled on her side, a plump olive of a woman, glossy with neat fat. The immense seductive contour of her hip drowsed up like a high hill. She was younger than Carmel, her charms were ampler. He found himself tracing outlines beneath her dress with the pleased abstract seduction of a man lured by one of those gaudy voluptuous girls who only live on calendars. Brown eyes, brown arms. She looked naked and brown and soft all over.

"And what's your name?" He wondered if he had a contented headache? Certainly, his head was tight, a pleasant numbness. When she said, Mary, he led the laughter. He heard his voice blurting hysterical chuckles. I really an cracked but it's nice.

Carmel had lazily taken up the washing. Suds foamed and foamed and the clean smell of soap cooly mating with water bubbled in his nostrils. She seemed to be idling. Her splashing hands threw up incessant gurgling fountains in the big basin. He listened to the fountains and then turned his eyes—he thought they were goggling like a frog's—to the woman pressing Mrs. Gifford's things.

"What's your name?"

"Marguerite."

"I'm Tom Gifford. I don't mind if you call me Tom." How pleasant it would be to doze, listening to the lullabies the dirty linen sang with the purifying waters.

"Tom," Marguerite exclaimed in an odd shrill voice, winking. The lid, a swarthy petal, closed over the gleam of her eye like a descending curtain.

I'll bet they like me. His pleasant headache was tighter about his temples. He sat down and let their names brighten his dull thoughts like insects glow—pointing against a black night. Glow names. Mary, Carmel, Marguerite. If he had married brook silver Carmel or Mary, the ripe pear, or good staunch Marguerite instead of Mrs. Gifford, lady of caloried carrots. Why did the woman tyrannize it over cauliflowers?

He imagined the vindictive pleasures that were now tormenting the cottagers. Men playing cards or holding fishing poles over the dead blueness of the lake. Women clacking their mean sexual spites. Children playing with the sticky stubbornness of kids on a vacation. The night would be even worse. Dancing; the silhouettes would engage in the charming fantastics of shadows; some of the men would daub their faces with passion and try to get up affairs. Too bad the swollen summer moon hung like a lamp, the night a cool great room of romance. The children would squawk, still hopelessly sticky. Wasn't summer an intense heedless maid not to be won by strenuous wooing? Come to me if you care to, dear summer. The slop slop of mauled water tinkled. Did the bare feet of the women prove anything?

Marguerite's half naked shoulders were made of robust middle-aged flesh. How delicious to girdle her waist with his stealing arm, to feel the contours of her back merge with the softening stone of his chest, to press his firm lips on the nape of her neck. What would the reaction be? A why-did-you-do-that, a lowering face, scowls and a lined forehead as if kisses were anti-feminine? No, not that. Would the earth be angry if he kissed its perfumed expanse, or a tree invoke the feeble word walls of honor and chivalry if he kissed its scaley skin?

"Mrs. Gifford has quite a few things," she said.

He felt so cool because he knew the sun was baking outside. His body seemed to put on layer after layer of coolness as if he were an apple on a bough, and was fresh in the delectable manner of ripening fruit. When he rolled tongue in mouth, he could almost taste the vagrant flavor of the luncheon lemonade. The tinklets of water were silent and Carmel was gone from the tub.

"It would be better," he answered, "if Mrs. Gifford wore less. When she goes swimming she wears sneakers." He walked over to the bed and sat down by the side of Carmel. Her smooth firm thigh bit into his with the ardor of an embrace. I wonder if she minds? It was as harmless as swimming in a lovely pool. Mary was lying face downwards, her calves faintly flirted with his back. He considered turning around and kissing the top of each calf. He had noted the worn areas, the hollow hinges where the lower legs are fleshed to the upper ones. She's firm all over. Such nice calves but it wouldn't do to kiss them.

Carmel's face flashed at him like a mirage. He was adorned by the brilliant gemmed expression of her eyes—shining like bright waters—and surrounded by the pleasantest brown flesh hands he had ever seen.

"Would you mind," he asked, "if I take off my shoes?" and he did, crumpling each sock into their warm leather caverns. His naked feet looked as if they were ashamed of him. " Ladies, I'm intoxicated. I'm cracked. I've never known what summer was until to-day."

"Once a year comes the summer." Marguerite ironed one of his shirts. He stared at its stiff eccentricity as if it were an old friend strangely mutilated.

"Good old summer time." Carmel winked at Mary.

"Most people don't know that." And all the while her hard thigh was kissing his own. The two of them were carrying on a secretive love affair unsuspected by the others.

"They must be fools." Her face was as calm as if no man's thigh was pressed against her own. Her attitude depressed him but when he glanced at his bare feet his pleasure was renewed.

Twisting his head, he saw Mary lounging on her face. The panorama of her body, curving from shoulder to hip and sweeping down to her calves, struck his eye with the fatality of a range of hills. Her face strained to look at him, she smiled, seeing upside down like a reflected image in water. How hollow was the hollow of her back, how round the haunched hillocks.

"I'll have your laundry, soon." Marguerite was ironing one of Mrs. Gifford's elaborate underclothes. It resembled a dried-up sea jelly, a pink one.

What a pity these three fine women and himself should gather for the one purpose of ironing Mrs. Gifford's things. Who was Mrs. Gifford anyway? If he beckoned to them would they come to him? their bodies nesting into his own. He would pluck their eyes of all their warmths, ruthlessly, as if he were picking rarer daisies. Hand in hand they would leave the house. He would kiss their round cheeks as their faces flailed warm against his own. And they would all laugh.

"Summer's a funny season," he said wistfully.

Mary was so full and plump she appeared to be asleep. Her curves fascinated him with the vanishing roundness of the unstraight. Carmel got up, stretched lazily. She leaned against the table and her hands and limp fingers dangled from her loose arms. She was negligent as a light summer rain. She partially sat on the table, the sharp edge made hardly any indentation in her strong haunches.

"I'll bet you're a grand dancer," he said. "Your heels are small and firm. Your legs are beautiful. You're lithe. You're a wind."

When he left that afternoon, the laundry under his arm, he was tired and happy. Thinking of the three women, the fragrant, short-lived afternoon, he felt as if he had lived months, known July and August and June.

It's been a grand summer, he thought as if it were all over and he were looking past the frontier of Labor Day. The dusty road stretched back to Mrs. Gifford and the green cottage "so summery, so like the leaves and grass." But the summer was really over.

ELECTRA-ORESTES

Choros Sequence.

H. D.

1.

Electra: To love, one must slay,
how could I stay?
to love, one must be slain,
then, how could I remain,
waiting, watching in the cold,
while the rain
fell,
and I thought of rhododendron
fold on fold
the rose and purple and dark-rose
of her garments;

her clothes
were purple
her way,
toward an open temple,
mine toward a closed
portico;
the sea beat high
and the Aegean rose,
the wave and the sea-wave and the salt-wave
of the Aegean rose
to beat down the portal;
no one knows
what I myself did not,
how the soul grows
how it wakes

and breaks
walls,
how, within the closed walled stone,
it throws
rays and buds and leaf-rays
and knows
it will die
if the stones lie much longer
across the lintel and between the shafts
of the epistyle;

no one knows
what I myself did not know,
that the soul grows in the dark
and outside one waits in the rain,
seeing her change from purple to dark-rose again,
seeing her choose
the reds and the sea-blues,
knowing the sting of her rose-of-Eos
scent in my brain,
hating and longing and still;

O God
if only someone would tell the child
how it loves—
but time goes,
no one knows
until it is too late
and the high-dead lie in state,
the heart—
the heart—
the heart—
how it thrives on hate.

2.

He marked the pattern of the sky,
but I
saw not the passing of the Wain,
saw not the Plough,
saw no bright Dragon
nor the Water-snake
saw not the great nor small Dog
nor the Bees,
saw not Orion nor the Pleiades,
saw not the glittering row

of that one's belt,
saw not star-angle or star-tilt
of that sword-hilt;

He traced the Archer
on one summer night,
light from the terrace,
faded out star-flight
of doves;
we moved
out toward the lion-portal
through the grove
of myrtle;
one cypress
made a column
like black smoke from incense;
Agememnon spoke:
the Sickle shines in winter
and the Maiden with the wheat-spike head
rules in the dead
heat of the summer;
a stream ran small and terrible and shrill;
it was so still;

the stream ran from the oak-copse
and returned and ran
back into shadow.

3.

Choros: *Lovers may come and go,*
there was the memory of blood,
the low call;
tread not in blood
on marble,
who would know
later fulfillment:

there was one cry
defilement;
one dull blow;
let no one say
the lustral vases will wash clean,
demean not your fair mind
with lies.

Mar . 14.   From:H.D.Aldington/Case Postale 72
============   La Tour
                                  Vevey
                                  Vaud
Pagany,   Suisse.
Dear Mr. John.   ======================

        Ezra Pound suggested my/sending you something,
I enclose some H.D. poetry.   Robert McAlmon also, some time
ago, said you might look at some of my prose.   I am
sending a 1920 Greek sketch to you, under the name,
Rhoda Peter. It is rather important to me that the H.D. and
the Rhoda Peter are not confused as I find it increasingly
difficult to remain MYSELF   when writing; the two
manners and personalities are quite distinct. However, as I am
anxious NOT to have Rhoda Peter incriminated with H.D. ,
will you please, if you want this PONTIKONISI (Mouse Island)
keep Rhoda Peter apart from H.D.

        I have the Pagany bound and always look
forward to it.   I have followed your work closely, and like
Robert McAlmon's contributions so much.   You have been
fortunate too, to have Mary Butts exquisite stories.

        With all good wishes,

                    H. D. Aldington.

WORK WAS NOW IN PROGRESS at the house in Redding; a well was being drilled and the carpenters were busy making the old place habitable. Time for Johns was now divided between keeping tabs on this work in progress while staying at the Chapmans' place in nearby Bethel and keeping appointments necessary to the continuation of *Pagany* at 9 Gramercy Park.

But cash for Johns was now tighter than ever, and he was in a constant state of embarrassment for obligations to the printer as well as writers and agents who trusted him with writing he had promised to pay for as soon as he was able. Johns was not happy to be under this financial pressure, for he had always prided himself on paying for each item of work as soon as it was accepted. It was a new and uncomfortable experience to know that he was holding money back from those who had more need of it than himself, yet who were gracious in their requests that they be paid only as Johns might be able to meet such needs.

And now it was time for the third issue to be printed. Fortunately, the small print shop on Lafayette Street which was doing this production work so reasonably and so well was willing to chance it on credit even though the balance on the Spring issue was not yet paid in full.

Which were the entirely new names to be added to the roster of contributors? The name Rhoda Peter looked new but in actuality it was H. D. again, asking that the two names used in writing poetry or prose be kept wholly separate since "the two manners and personalities are quite distinct." This was certainly true, but "Pontikonisi (Mouse Island)," a prose work, was richly poetic in itself. *444*

The name of Louis Zukofsky was not new to the pages of *Pagany*, but now he had submitted, "First Movement: 'Come Ye Daughters,'" from his highly ambitious long poem *"A"* and Johns felt it was a rich reward for *Pagany* to be able to include the first *460-464* section from what Johns felt sure would be the major work in Zukofsky's writing in later assessments of his quality.

Though Johns had already printed a story by Syd Salt, he was as excited to have four poems by Salt to print as a unit as he had been in the last issue when he included a series of poems by Edward Dahlberg. He had met Salt in Provincetown on Cape Cod when he visited the Dahlbergs the previous summer. Johns was always pleased to receive a letter from Salt, who frequently gave his literary opinions on other writers and their work.

And at long last, Jack Conroy of the Rebel Poet group had come through with a fine story, "Bun Grady," which had the intricate texture of those days of depression and its effect on the old and incompetent. This was a skillfully directed piece of prose, worthy of one of the key literary spokesmen of the proletariat.

James T. Farrell would make his first appearance in *Pagany* with the story "Twenty-five Bucks" in this same Summer issue. Johns had read sections from *Young Lonigan,* Farrell's first novel, when they were sent to him the year before. He felt that none of those sections submitted should be printed as individual pieces, for the power of the book was in its day-to-day progression; isolation of one short piece of it reduced its power and drive. "Twenty-five Bucks" was a compelling story, complete in itself. For Johns it was both whole and good.

466

447-449

450

468-475

3/11/32.

My dear John--

I have reached that point
of departure -- the East here can no longer
function for me - or perhaps I for myself.
at any rate, I feel I have fought a
good little here, but it has become
too irritating: New York, etc. I near and
verge on the dawn of a new legend
(I wish you had seen my "Stranger")
and had been actually started on a
new mss "This New World" -- but
I cannot go on here, I am convinced
I must go. my wife and I have become desperate -- in the terrible
manner. Europe holds no lure for
me, as a "place" -- I've never
left the States, yet I've never
been Southwest. It is a hope: the
climate, an Indian, etc. and
then, it is close to Mexico. I feel
I could proceed with my new mss.
there.

2.

Frankly, then, there are two points I wish to confide (I have no contacts in any sense, and I am writing to you because I feel you may help me—the one other possibility is Harriet Monroe, whom I have never met but who has expressed interest in me). First, if it be no imposition, can you give me names or name of any people about Taos, New Mexico, or Santa Fé, who could, possibly, give me a lift getting adjusted there (you see, I really hope not to come back here any more). I cannot disappoint you or your friends in any way, please believe.

Secondly,— can you give me very earliest decision on my story and poems for two reasons; I have hope of a check from you to make possible our hitching southwest, so that we can, at least,

3)

get there. And the sooner, the sooner
we start on the road. It is that
bad! Besides, altho H. Monroe has
more poetry of mine for the future
I feel certain she will take more
if you to give me a ~~good~~ check. She
has done that before, and I will not
submit to her until
This is really all. I hear from you.

Yours

Syd Salt

56 W. 92 St.

NYCity

THE REBEL POET

OFFICIAL ORGAN OF **REBEL POETS**, THE INTERNATIONALE OF SONG
Edited by **JACK CONROY**

Address All Communications To:—   "Repot," 407 E. 74th St., New York City.
Moberly, Missouri, May 4, 1932.
Rural Route Four.

Dear Mr. Johns:

My agent, Maxim Lieber, writes me that you have
accepted my story BUN GRADY. Of course, I am happy to learn
this, all the more so because it is a chapter of my forthcoming
book, of which other chapters have appeared in THE AMERICAN
MERCURY, THE NEW MASSES, THE LEFT, etc. Of course I am anxious
to have as many chapters as possible printed before publication.

It occurs to me that you might find it advantageous
to exchange advertising with THE REBEL POET. I am sure that many
of our readers would be glad to buy copies of PAGANY in which
my story appears. We have exchanged, quid pro quo, with THE NEW
REPUBLIC, THE NEW MASSES, THE NEW REVIEW, CONTEMPO, etc., etc.

If you follow the example of THE AMERICAN MERCURY
in sending out announcements to a list of persons supplied by
the contributors, I shall be glad to supply quite a large list.
If you do not do this, may I suggest that an advance guard
Quarterly like PAGANY should profit fully as much by this as a
magazine like THE AMERICAN MERCURY.

If you care to exchange advertising, please send
me your copy, and I shall be glad to send you ours in return.

Sincerely,

Jack Conroy
Jack Conroy

88 Horatio Street
New York City
May 30, 1932

Dear Richard Johns,

The copy of **Pagany** arrived last week, and while
I haven't had an opportunity to read it in detail, it
seems very interesting. I'm impressed at the way you're
turning up talent in all manner of unexpected quarters.
Looking over the early numbers, I seem to detect a
clear development in **Pagany**: the early numbers were
evidently filled with fair contributions by well-known
writers, the later by more impressive contributions by
unknowns.

But this isn't the purpose of my letter. I am
writing to ask if it will be possible for me to be paid
for my story at once. I am in what is very nearly a
desperate situation; otherwise I would not appeal to you,
The desperate situation is due to a lack of work, the
reviewing business having fallen off badly, and increased
expenses, as our child is to be born in July.

Best wishes.

Robert Cantwell

June 21, 1932.

Dear Dick:

It was very pleasant to get your note and thanks
much for what you say about From Flushing To Calvary. I am
terribly pleased that Harcourt Brace are doing it, for they
are really very intelligent publishers. The publishing date
is September 22, 1932. Have already corrected galley-proofs,
and am very slowly and tortÿrously starting work on a new
novel. This is again a new scene, another milieu.
       Will have the publishers send you aa copy as
soon as they are ready.
       By the way, Dick, would it be a hardship for
you to send now what check you think is due me for the
poems to Sara. It's her birthday, and as the publishers
are giving me a very small monthly stipend I'm absolutely
busted all the time. If you can manage it, would you
please sent it to Sara Mazo Dahlberg, Care Of Refregier,
Woodstock, New York.
       Will be glad to get the Paganys.
       Again many thanks for printing the excerpts
of the book. It was an emotional help to have them
published by youҙ at the time.
       As ever, with friendship,

Lucerne Supply Company,   *Edward Dahlberg*
Victorville, California.

347 w.23 st;NYC

Dear Dick Johns,

I seem to be Indian dinner to you and maybe I am
an Indian giver in more ways than one;at any rate I was
glad to hear from you and of course will keep on shipping
you more "gifts" in the hope of getting away from
my recent role.My scripts even seem bad to me,that is,
most of them.I still haven't made up my mind as to style(chiefly)
substance and most of the other bugbears altho I've been
writing three years.

I'm satisfied you're settled in the country
as somehow you seem more fixed to me among "cows and chickens"
than at Gramercy Park,where you lived as the mystery
man.I've also shifted homes moving from the Bronx
country to above.Can be gotten up to three pm,and from
six to seven pm at Chelsea 3-7739.You see I'm not going
to let you slide out of dinner this time..

The thing I m enclosing deserves a bit of ex-
planation.I'm doing a novel constructed on similar
outward plan as March's soldier series.I can only add the
idea's been in my head a number of years.This is to be
a c ollege novel,each novel under the name of some
senior,the chapters to contain the all of college life
as well as have the impact of sh.stories.I've often
felt that no college man is really worth an entire book.
My plan seems fairer and perhaps more truthful.The chapter
headings are alphabetical and include the entire senior class.
The characters appear and reappear in one another's chapters.
This is more than a bit.I'm conscious of obvious
comparisons but let "the work speak for itself". Am
enclosing three short ones for your opinion.
And my best to you in your new settlement

Aug. 10, 1932

Dear Dick:

Writing to you is like signaling a star, a couple of light
years later the reply <u>may</u> come back . But it's all right, I love you
just the same,

Say. Floss just put an idea into my head. This White Mule
business is awful slow; going this way I ought to be half way through
the writing and printing of it by about 1950 . Would you consider
using two chapters at a time ? It would take a lot of your space, I
realize that,but it's really terrible this way .

I can send you another chapter right away for this issue
if you want it . Come on, be a sport. I'd like to see these next two
chpaters together anyway.

And the two after that won't be so bad either . And I have
a swell one after that.

Anyhow, let's have a now-do-you-do on the subject if you
will.

Yours as ever

Bill

Sept 18, 1932

Dear Dick,

    Send me a little money if you can (providing
I have paid the hundred buck bill)-----
Am broke in Rotterdam.
But after ten days in a French prison the country
seems good.

    I think you owe me a letter, butwhatthehell.
Anyway, I keep hearing rumors of marriage entanglement.
I hope that is a bad dream well awakened.

    Being bitter and philosophical, I naturally
have no faith in it or food.

    Please write me anyway:

    The bols in Holland is rotten.

Norman

*c/o American Express
Rotterdam, Holland*

NUMBER 3 *July–September*

Contents

PAGANY

"A"

First Movement: "Come ye Daughters"

Louis Zukofsky

A
 Round of fiddles playing Bach—
  The double chorus.
   "Come, ye daughters, share my anguish—"
  Bare arms, black dresses
   "See Him! Whom?—"
  Bediamond the passion of our Lord,
   "See Him! How?—"
His legs, blue tendons bleeding,
Tinsel over his ribs
   "O Lamb of God most holy—"
Black, black full dress in the audience—
Dead century where is your motley,
Country people in Leipzig,
  Easter,
Matronly flounces,
   —starched, heaving,
Belly freighted—boom!

Cheeks of the patrons of Leipzig—
"Going to Church? where's the baby?"
"Ach, dort eilt sich der Kappellmeister—"
"Johann Sebastian! (twenty-two
      children!)."

          According to Matthew,
        Composed seventeen twenty-nine,
        Repeated here at Carnegie,
That was Thursday, 'twenty-eight, the fifth evening of April,
    April, and the autos honking outside, all those
    that were parked there.
            ("Hearts turned to thee")
        German lady
    Auch ich war in Arkadien geboren.
The lights dim, and the brain when the flesh dims.
Hats picked up from under seats.
Galleries darkening.
          "No suh!
Not past that exit, Zukofsky!"
"Agh, Satan! Agh—gh!"
Ecdysis: the serpent coming out,
                gradual molting,
Blood staining the floor as the foot stepped,
Bleeding chamfer for shoulder:
"Not past that exit, Zukofsky!"
"Devil! what!—?"
"Blood of your desire to graft what you desire,
Consider the Angels who sang in the boys' choir
God's cherubs,
If seen near the ocean, stripped white skins, red coat of the sunburn,—
They have mothers."
"No, Satan, not heart that bled
Over boys' voices, nor blood
Flowing for lost sons,—
I have harbored perfection."
And as one who under the stars
Spits free across the sand dunes, and the winds
Blow thru him, and his spit seems to drown worlds,
I lit a cigarette, and passed free

Beyond the red light of the exit.

Asmodeus fading to "Camel" smoke,
Greasy, solicitous, eyes longing minutes after,
Smiling, a tramp's face,
Lips looking out of a beard
Hips looking out of ripped trousers
                        and suddenly
Nothing.
But about me,   the voices of those who had
                        been at the concert,
Feet stopping everywhere in the streets,
Stopping of turned necks for chatter:
"Poor Thomas Hardy   he had to go so soon,
It was he who admired so our recessional
                        architecture,
What do you think of our new Sherry-Netherland!"
"Lovely soprano,
Is that her mother, lovely lines,
I admire her very much!"
And those who had perused the score at the concert,
The immature pants that filled chairs
Patrons of poetry, business temples erected to arts and letters,
                        The cornerstones of waste paper,
"Such lyric weather!" chirping
Quatrain on quatrain, empty and
The sonneteers when I consider again and over
                        again
                        Limp wet blanket pentameters,
Immured holluschickies, dead honor men
Persisting thru polysyllables,
Mongers in mystic accretions,
The stealers of 'melange adultere de tout,"
The Americanizers of the Classics,
                        Tradition!
(To them word of great contours).
And raping women with horses.

And on one side street near an elevated,
Lamenting contemporaneousness,

Foreheads wrinkled with injunctions:
"The Pennsylvania miners again on the lockout,
We must send relief to the wives and children—
What's your next editorial about, Carat?
We need propaganda, the thing's

                    becoming a mass
                        movement."

And I.
Upon the feast of that Passover,
The blood's tide as the music's
A thousand fiddles as beyond effort
Playing—playing
Into fields and   forgetting to die,
The streets smoothed over as fields,
Not even   the friction of wheels,
Feet off   ground:
As beyond effort, playing—
Music leaving no traces
Not dying, yet leaving no traces.
Nor any conscious effort,
Nor boiling to put pen to paper.
Perhaps a few things to remember
(Three there stealing in   thru the music
As pioneers moccasined stealing in thru the music).

Atheling—"There are different techniques ,
Men write to be read, or spoken,
Or declaimed, or rhapsodized,
And quite differently to be sung;"
Carlos—"I heard him agonizing,
I saw him *inside;"*
Estlang—"Everything which
We really are and never quite live."
Far into (about three) in the morning,
The trainmen the most wide awake

                "Weary, broken bodies," calling

Station on station, under earth
A thousand fiddles as beyond—

                "Cold stone above thy head—"

Trainmen chanting

And again:

"He came and found them—
Sleeping, indeed their eyes were
full of sleep."

Good night . . .

So the next day the reverses,
As if the music were only a taunt,
As if it had not kept, flower-cell in flower, liveforever
        before the eyes, perfecting,—
I thought that was finished, Zukofsky,
Existence not even subsistence,
Worm eating the bark of the street tree,
Smoke sooting skyscraper chimneys,
That which has been looking for substitutes, tired,
Ready to give up the ghost in a cellar.

Remembering what?
Love, in your lap, in a taxi, unwilling—
A country of state roads and automobiles,
But the greatest number idle, shiftless, disguised on streets,
The excuse of the experts
'Production exceeds demand so we curtail employment,'
And the Wobblies hollering reply,
Yeah! but why don't you give us more than a meal
        to increase the consumption!
While the great Magnus, before his confreres in industry,
Swallow tail, eating a sandwich,
"Road map to the stomach," grinning,
To a chart pointing, and between bites.

Dogs cuddling to lamposts
Lonely—look—what—maybe broken forged iron—
"We ran 'em in chain gangs, down in the Argentine,
Executive's not the word, use *engineer,*
Single-handed, ran 'em like soldiers,
Seventy-four yesterday, and could run 'em today,
Been fishin' all Easter
Nuthn' like nature for hell-fire!"

"Ye lightnings, ye thunders
In clouds are ye vanished?
    Open, O fierce flaming pit!"

PRELUDE

AND GOD SAID TO ADAM—

Conrad Aiken

Breath will be breath, the in the out,
    the cold the warm
word will be word, the agony
    the time the stone
I will stand here nor seldom move
    see nothing new
tree without root the unfixed thought
    wandering with the unmoving you.

Beach will be beach while sea returns
    meaning be nothing
nothing will mean what the world means, no more,
    the time the stone
I will wait here nor ever stir
    think nothing strange
while the heart's clock works round the dial
    of human and predicated range.
Where you have been, what seen, will mean
    but dark but bright
time but a dream, the seem but gleam,
    no time no stone
no bloodfilled heart that swarms with shapes
    no hands that clutch
only the lonely self that thinks
    of inaccessible to touch.

Stand there and wait stand there and think
    unbroken will
handful of light, delirium's brain,
    the strong the brave
seed left by light whose fading seed
    is darker light
o patient watcher whose faithful watch
    makes of the night more dreadful night.

FOUR POEMS
Syd Salt

I

Young lilting bough
with shaken crop of spray
distilling white loveliness
to the swift breeze,
the swinging sparrow
eyeing white fragrance
with strong delight,
and lovers beneath singing
to the lilt of spring and shaken loveliness—
lilting, swinging, singing bough.

II

Now I speak for the wind-cleansed breath
and the storm that leaves nothing.
Now that sparrows outnumber the leaves
there shall be dearth for many.
Only the quick small fire shall preserve.
And the sure touch of death shall be kind
to those who trace their fate on a last leaf.

III

I see these things as I say:
Low horses and chestnuts rolling on the road
A bright lake with burnished ducks
A far horizon that smells of hay
Children freshly planted near trees
A fork prodding the sky.

IV

TO FLORENCE

You walk like Egypt—
having seen you stand,
what makes you move?

I cannot write of Egypt.
It is a child's tale
of ponderous light and inscrutable mass,
a slow destiny I must visit.

I will say this:
your arm lifts with ancient grace
and I know no secret against such slow weight.

1929-1932

Harry Roskolenkier

Infants of Spring; lo—how the winds
sang; the small streams—arrogant,
hurled high from the mighty
bosoms; the fields were full
and we suckled at the overburdened breasts;
the saccharined fruits of the pompous years.

Progeny of the thunder!
who were your fathers and your mothers?
Who spawned you
against the bleak entrance to a factory:
you—whose history
comes to an end, on the minute tick of a dollar watch.
            You are dying,
            somewhere from Maine to California:
            nearby, a transcontinental Bus
            belches your requiem!
Your eyes lidded
by some rough shrubs of the Fall.
Under the stars, your sprawling decay
makes the new flowers!

TWENTY FIVE BUCKS
James T Farrell

Fifteen years is a hell of a long time to live in grease. Fifteen years is a hell of a long time to keep getting your jaw socked. Fifteen is a hell of a long time for a broken-down, never-was of a palooka named Kid Tucker. Fifteen years stretched back through a reeking line of stale fight clubs, of jeers and clammy dressing rooms, and lousy gyms, and cheap can houses where every bed sheet is filthy with the countless foot marks of nameless customers, of ratty saloons with sawdust floors—OH MEET ME TO-NIGHT IN THE MOONLIGHT—, of flop houses whose corridors are fouled with musty, lavatory odors of training camps, gyps, speakeasies—IT'S A LONG LONG TRAIL A-WINDIN' INTO THE LAND OF MY DREAMS—of mouldy dumps and joints, of crooks, pikers, louses, lice, the slaughter in Europe . . . fifteen years stretched all the way back through these things to a box car with Armour's Meats scrawled on its side in white, moving out of Lima Ohio, and across sweet Ohio landscapes on a morning when the world was young with spring, and grass, and the idiotic dreams of a good-natured adolescent yokel.

It was all over with Kid Tucker; and there had never been any shouting—only booes. His face had ben punched into hash: cauliflower ears, a flattened nose, a scar over his right eye. His greenish eyes were shifty with the fleeting, nervous cowardice of the sacked and broken man. He was flabby. The muscles in his legs were shot. There was a scar on one leg, the medal he had received for carrying an inarticulate, badly wounded farm boy through a wheat field near Soissons on a day when the sun was mad, the earth nauseous from the stink of corpses, and the wheat field slashed by ripping machine gun bullets. Kid Tucker was done for, useless. Toss him aside. Another boloney drowned in grease and defeat.

Sol Levison matched him K.O. Dane. It was for a six round preliminary bout at Sol's Arcade Boxing Club. Sol was a kike with a derby and a race track vest. He made money out of a mouldy dump of a boxing club. He made money off of a string of ham scrappers. He made money out of everything he touched. Dane was one of Sol's scrappers, a yokel in from the country. Sol was nursing him along on pushovers, building up a reputation so that Dane could be matched with a first-rater for a good purse. It did not matter that the big time boy would slaughter him in a round. Tucker was another set-up for Dane. And the Kid needed the twenty five bucks which Sol promised him. Tucker took the match. He earned his living by getting smashed on the jaw. But Sol told him that this time he would have to fight. No taking a dive this time.

"Lissen now that ring at the club ain't no swimmin' pool. See! No divin'. It ain't nothing like a bed or a park bench. It's a prize ring, and yere in it tuh fight. So don't act like yuh ain't seen uh bed fur uh month. Yuh gotta fight this time . . . or no pay. See!"

Tucker had heard that before.

He reported on time at the Arcade Boxing Club, a rumbly building near a tenement district. He dressed for the bout, putting on a pair of faded trunks. With his hands taped, and a dirty bathrobe thrown over his shoulders, he sat on a slivery bench waiting, watching a cockroach scurry up and down the wall. Two seconds sat on tilted chairs, one sleeping with his mugg opened like a fly trap, the other reading a tabloid. Tucker didn't have many thoughts any more. He never became nervous before a scrap. He had taken every kind of a punch. He sat and watched the cockroach on the poison-green colored wall, with its broken plaster. It moved up towards a window, turned about, scrambled sidewise, about-faced, then turned downwards, and moved across the floor to lose itself in the shadows of a corner.

Kid Tucker sat wishing that the scrap was over. He might manage to catch this kid off balance, and then put him away. But then, he mightn't get any more fights from Levison, because this Dane was one of Sol's boys. Sol wanted him to put up a fight, because he felt that he couldn't take Dane. Anyway, he wished the scrap was over, and he was sitting in a speakeasy with a glass of gin before him. He did not think much any more. Fools think. One day he had been a young ox, puking with excitement in a dressing room, waiting for the gong of his first fight. He watched a second cockroach scurry up and down the wall. Up and down it moved. His seconds started to converse; they lit cigarettes, and discussed the love nest suit which had put the abnormal relationships of a rich old sugar daddy and a young gold digger on the first pages of the tabloids. Tucker sat and recalled the lice in the trenches of France. Up and down the cockroach moved.

When he entered the ring, he received only a small dribble of applause. They knew the bum. Someone yelled out at him, asking if he had gotten his pants pressed for the tea party. Another wanted to know where his patent leather shoes were. Tucker never listened to the crowd and its razzberries. He was over the time when he heard booes. In France he had lost all concern and worry when shells landed. When he heard one coming, he just casually flopped on the ground. A guy can get used to anything, if he just hangs around long enough. He sat waiting, his eyes fastened on the ropes.

Dane entered the ring. The house came to its feet spontaneously, and roars rose from the murkiness of faces. Dane was an ox of a kid, a Swede with childish blue eyes, a thick squarehead, a bull neck, a mountainous pair of shoulders, and legs as hard as a tree trunk. Tucker did not look at him.

A Slit-Mouth of an announcer bellowed out the names of the contending fighters, pointing out their respective corners, as he described trumped-up reputations. They shook hands in the center of the ring, and returned to their corners. A gong clanged.

The arc lights glared down; the contrast they revealed between the two boxers seemed almost vicious. Dane was strong and full of youth; Tucker worn out, and with a paunch of a belly. The fight was slow; both fighters were wary; and the crowd was perfunctory. It wanted Dane to make a corpse out of the big fat ham. They faced each other, feinted, tapped, and blocked as they circled about. Tucker could see that the kid was nervous; but he had learned to be a little careful of shaky young fighters when they looked as strong and as powerful as Dane. Dane led with a few light lefts. Tucker caught them easily. It perked his confidence, and he retaliated with a straight left. It slid off Dane's square jaw. They lumbered, feeling for an opening. They clinched, and their interlocked bodies made one swaying ugliness in the white glare of the arc lights. The referee danced in and parted them. They clinched again. They broke. Dane made a hesitant attack, and Tucker clumsily skipped backwards.

Roars and booes grew out of the sordidness that surrounded the ring.
"Come on Kayo. He's only a bum."
"Lam one in the bread basket, an' he's through, Dane!"
"Hey you blokes! Fight!"
"This ain' no tea party."
"Hey! Will you gentlemen have breakfast in bed?"
"Look at 'em. They're fightin' like two fairies."
"And how about yere bawth gentlemen?"
"Siddown in front!"
"Siddown Tucker, and take a load off yere feet!"
"No guts."

"Murder the bastard!"

"Fight you sonofabitch!"

"Hey Tucker! Where's yere cane?"

"Kill the sonofabitch."

Dane connected with a few inconsequential lefts. He was clumsy, and stumbled about, repeatedly getting off balance. A good fighter, with a willingness to take a chance, and a heart to mix and trade punches, could have polished Dane off in short order. But Tucker kept backing out of range, pausing to jab out with a few untimed, ineffective left handed stabs. Dane danced about in his confusion, and when his opponent continued retreating, he stood in the center of the ring, a stupefied look on his face.

The crowd roared, and above the disgruntled roaring, there came the remark that sleeping quarters were upstairs. The bell saved them from further exertion.

The razzing continued during the one minute intermission. Tucker sat heedless of the mob. He washed his mouth out with water, and waited, puffing slightly. His seconds pointed out that Dane was leaving himself open; Tucker said he would watch it, and catch the kid in the next round. He waited. He had five more rounds to go. He wondered if he could catch Dane off guard, and stun him, or put him away. If he wanted to last, he couldn't take many chances, and the kid looked like he could take a blow from an axe. He glanced over towards the kid's corner, and the latter's handlers instructing him with emphatic gestures. He eyed the ropes.

Round two was more awful than round one. It was a clinching party. Someone called out that they were like Romeo and Juliet. A second fan called Tucker Daddy and Dane Peaches. A third fan suggested that they get a bed. Another wanted to know if it was a dance marathon, or a six day bicycle race. The mob muttered and grumbled.

And always, there was that repeated yell to kill the s—o—b.

One pimply faced punk of a kid stood up and yelled; "I'm goin' to uh Christian . . . Science . . . meetin'. It ull be more exciting."

The crowd laughed. He sat down.

Near the end of the round, Dane connected with a wild but solid right. The accidental wallop had echoed a thud, which brought the mob to its feet, yelling bloody murder. Dane hesitated a moment, and looked perplexedly at his opponent. Then he went for Tucker; a look of murderous if formal and melodramatic intent was stamped on his face.

The bell ended the round. There was buzz and excitement. Dane was not such a dud after all. That right had been a beaut. Now he was getting warmed, and he would do his stuff. He'd squeeze a lemon like Tucker dry; he'd put him away in a hurry. Watch Dane go now; watch him knock out that bastard of a Kid Tucker.

Tucker was a little groggy as the seconds started working over him. They whispered that he should fake weariness. That would bring Dane in wide-open. Then one solid punch, as the kid came in wide open, might do the trick, and turn defeat into victory. Tucker nodded his head, as if to say that he knew how he'd take care of his opponent. But when he was fighting, he found himself unable to put anything behind his punches. In France, he had gone through two days of a terrific bombardment. Then, he had caved in. He went on like an automatic man. He could not give himself. It was the same with fighting. He wanted to go in and take a chance trading punches. He told himself that he would. The haze was now cleared from his mind, and he was determined. But things had all happened like this before. Tucker, willing and determined, and then being unable to carry out his will, incapable of giving himself. He couln't go in and fight. The war and the prize ring had taken all the fight out of him. His nerves and muscles wouldn't respond to his will. There had been too many punches. He sat waiting for the bell, determining, but in vain. Tucker's state was called being yellow, having no guts. He sat out his final seconds of rest.

Just before the bell, Levison came up, and told one of the Kid's seconds to warn him that he must fight. Then, the clang of the gong. Some people noticed Levison, but their curiosity was drowned out in the spontaneous enthusiasm that shook the crowd, with the opening of the round. Dane would take the ham this time sure.

Tucker was tired, and he opened the round by withdrawing from Dane. The latter was determined. His handlers had persuaded him into a state of self-confidence. He unscrewed an awkward left that landed flush on Tucker's button. Tucker reeled backwards. The crowd was on its feet yelling for blood. Dane *grew far away from Tucker.* Gloves came at the Kid like *locomotives slowly rising from the distance, coming closer and growing bigger until they collided with him. One ran into his bread basket.* He experienced a heaving, weakening nausea, and *far, far away there was a din of shouting.*

Instinctively, mechanically, Tucker clinched. He tried in a hopeless, ineffective way to sew Dane up. His head swam in a daze; he was glassy eyed. Dane, *a billowing mass of flesh grew before his dimmed eyes. Something big closed his eye.* He went down. He was blinded for a few seconds. Then, he weakly perceived through his sick daze. He arose feebly. *There was a swinging of gloves, a going around of posts, ropes, and gloves.* He floundered forwards to clinch. He was off balance, and Dane came up with a haymaker that mashed him square on the jaw; the impact of the punch caused an audible thud. The lights went out for Tucker, and about him darkness crashed dizzy, like a tumbling nightmarish dream. His head snapped back suddenly. He tumbled backwards and bounced, head first on the canvas. He lay there, quivering slightly, while the referee tolled off the unnecessary count. He bled from the mouth; blood trickling out to run in tiny rivulets, and mix with the dust and resin.

The mob rocketed approval.

"That's the ticket Dane."

"That's the babee."

"Yuh put 'im off fur uh week."

"You got the stuff kid."

"Christ what a punch that was."

"He's out fer a week."

The punk kid, who had yelled out that he was going to a Christian Science meeting, evidently recalled Levison's visit to the ringside between rounds, and now, he shouted out "Fake!" As Tucker was lifted back to his corner, the cry of fake was taken up, and reverberated about the smoke hazy arena.

Tucker was a collapsed heap. His face had a sickly, quivering expression on it. His neck was snapped back, possibly broken. His breathing was heavy, spasm-like. Seconds worked on him, sponged his face, and the roar of fake grew increasingly louder.

Dane left the ring. He was cheered and booed.

The seconds continued working on Tucker, and the yelling persisted. Levison nervously spoke with some cops in the rear. Then, after giving hasty instructions to six burly bouncers, he came forwards.

"Take that bum back to the dressing room," he told the Kid's handlers, as he climbed through the ropes. He stood in the center of the ring. He waited, rasing his paw for silence.

"Silence pleez!"

They gave him relative silence.

"Ladees and Gents! Ladees an' Gents. I wanna sa-ay a few words to yah. I wancha tah know that I ain't never had nothin' tuh do with uh framed fight, or uh fake boxing match, or a de-frau-dulence uh any kind or classification. I wancha tuh know that anytime Sol Levison pro-

motes a fight, then that fight is on the square. A fight that Sol Levison *promotes is one hundred per cent on the level. Now tuh show yuh that I'm on the level I'm gonna offer one hunered dollars, one hunered dollars reward tuh the man that kin prove that this fight was a frame-up. Now some one in the audience had been so unkind as to insin-u-ate that this here fight was not on the level. Now I'm offring one hunered dollars to the man that kin prove that this or any fight that Sol Levison ever promoted was not on the level to the very best, to the very best of his knowledge and intention.*

There was a mingling of cheers and booes.

When one uh my fights is not on the level Sol Levison wantsa know about it. This fight was not faked to the knowledge of Sol Levison. Kid Tucker here, he asks me fur a chanct tuh go on so's he could make himself a little stake. I gave him a chanct, just as I always give a boxer a chanct. Now, when I came up here just before the last round of this here fee-asco, it was tuh instruct Kid Tucker that he hadduh fight or not get any purse. It was a square fight. Kid Tucker was jus' yellah. He was yellah. He was afraid of Kayo Dane. He refused to put up a resistance. He was too yellah tuh fight like uh man. He got what was comin' tuh him becuz he wouldn't fight like he agreed tuh when I agreed tuh pay him. He was yelluh.

There were cheers, and many cursed that yellow bastard of a Kid Tucker.

Now Ladies and Gents, tuh show yuh how I feel about this here matter, lemme tell yuh somethin'. When Sol Levison hires fighters, they fight. They fight, or Sol Levison knows why. I guarantee that each and every bout I stage will give yuh yere money's worth. If it don't, I guarantee that yuh kin get yere money's worth back at the box office. And when I hire boxers in good faith, they either fight . . . or they get no purse from Sol Levison. Now tah show yuhs how I feel and tah guarantee that youh'll get yere money's worth after the showing this yellah ham here made tuh-night, I'm gonna take his purse, that was comin' tuh him if he had stood up and fought like a man but which he won't deserve because he didn't carry out his part of the contrac', an' I'm gonna give it to the boy who puts up the bes' fight here this evenin'; and I'm gonna let you decide on that boy by general acclaim. Now I ask yuh is that fair? He was yellah and didn't earn his purse. So I asks yuh if that is not fair, tuh give it tuh a boy with uh real fightin' heart. Now is that fair or is it not?

The roars of the crowd approving Levison's speech sounded like far echoes down in the mouldy dressing room where the beaten Tucker lay unconscious. His handlers worked on him in vain, dousing him with water, using smelling salts, working in vain. Two bantams, one a dirty-skinned Italian, the other a bushy haired Jew left for the next bout.

"Jeez he musta got an awful sock," the Jew said.

"He looks pretty bad," the Italian said.

"We'll bring him around," one of the seconds said.

The seconds sweated for an hour. Cheers echoed from other fights while they worked. A doctor was called in, and he too failed. He called an ambulance. They carted Tucker out on a stretcher. As they were doing this, the crowd was roaring acclaim, shouting out its decision that the little dirty-skinned Italian bantam had merited Tucker's purse.

But Tucker did not need it. He was taken to a hospital, and he never regained consciousness.

THIS THIRD ISSUE of *Pagany,* Volume III, came out on time—the first of July—but from now on there was confusion, and from all directions. If Johns were in New York, there was the constant knowledge that he was surrounded by individuals who had written for *Pagany* and who needed the $3 per page which Johns felt he should continue to pay for material. But right now he did not have the cash to pay any but those for whom sheer existence had become difficult.

He owed his printers, too, but the two men who owned and operated the press were revolutionary in political inclination and were used to being owed money for running off tickets and leaflets announcing Party meetings. And they trusted Johns implicitly, which gave him the warm assurance that somehow the final issue of Volume III would be printed and distributed, although probably not in time to meet the proper October 1st deadline.

He also owed rent for 9 Gramercy Park, but here the agent was most businesslike. If Johns couldn't pay he'd be only too glad to terminate the lease and accept a more solvent tenant, one who would be able to pay two months' rent in advance. Johns was happy to stop paying what now seemed an exorbitant rent. He listed his Connecticut address at the post office, taking the few belongings he really wanted from the apartment and setting up temporary headquarters at the Chapman place in Bethel. He had no money for finishing his own place, but since he had paid a sizable sum on it prior to his father's death, he was able to add to the mortgage, and the work on the house could be finished quickly.

Redding and Bethel, Connecticut, were due north from Westport and very near to the industrial city of Bridgeport where Johns went to inquire about what sort of paying work was available. But thousands were unemployed in that city and there was no room for a man who had not graduated from high school, and who had lived a pretty undisciplined and unconventional life. No matter what he might personally feel about the literary quality of his magazine, he could not show any financial profit from it, and there was no magic from the names of Ezra Pound or Gertrude Stein in the depressed working world of Bridgeport.

However, through a friend who was making a comfortable living writing radio soap operas, Johns met a young man who was collaborating on these daytime serials, who not only knew *Pagany* well but was respectful of its contribution to literature. At that point, Johns needed a little encouragement for what he was trying to do for the literature of these early depression days of 1932. The man was Charles Kendall O'Neill, and he was filled with the excitement of the present-day world, no matter how deeply it might be scarred by the blight of poverty and insecurity. O'Neill was only two years out of Dartmouth, and after a long visit to his ancestral home in Ireland and almost a year on the island of Majorca, he was back in America to stay.

O'Neill had a fine stack of books and magazines from abroad and it was through him that Johns first read the prose of Henry Miller. O'Neill's ambition was already set on writing a novel of the years between the American Revolution and the formation of the Union. This dream was finally fulfilled in 1949 when Simon and Schuster published his novel, *Morning Time.* As for now, he had just completed a fine story about life in Majorca, and Johns was pleased to consider it for the final issue of Volume III.

488-494

At this point everything started to go to pieces. First, a suitcase containing much of Johns' own work as well as manuscripts of other contributors was stolen from his open Packard touring car while he ran into a drugstore for a package of cigarettes. Fortunately, all of the stolen manuscripts were kept in duplicate by their authors, but there was plenty of confusion in addition to the added expense of having copies retyped for the printer. As William Carlos Williams said in a letter taken up largely with his dissatisfaction with the way New York booksellers Moss and Kamin were handling *Contact:*

> Lord you certainly do run into hard luck with your scripts. I suppose next time it will be a hurricane that will carry the budget away, or a flood.

As for *Contact,* both Williams and his Assistant Editor, Nathanael West, had returned all manuscripts accepted for future publications. Williams stated this succinctly, adding:

> We have worked hard to make it worthwhile but recently we've felt that for various reasons we can't go on giving our time any longer.

This did not come as a surprise to Johns, who had been amazed at the amount of money both Moss and Kamin seemed eager to spend on the project of *Contact.* He had been to a number of their cocktail parties for their contributors, fresh into New York from other parts of the country or Europe. These parties were fun, with much lively conversation, imported canapés, and good liquor. Most of the guests, however, recognized that a couple of would-be booksellers with more money than literary judgment or personal taste were trying to get themselves accepted as men of distinction in the publishing world by using Williams and West as a front.

Neither man had the discernment of the other financial backers of little magazines, so that Williams and West became disillusioned with the entire project in a short time. Johns was deeply sorry that Moss and Kamin's *Contact* was not a renewal of Williams' earlier enthusiasm when he was editing his own original *Contact* out of Paris, while holding his cool physician's fingers on the rapid pulse of his co-editor, Robert McAlmon.

Johns knew, too, that *Pagany* had become very important to Williams, that all his creative enthusiasm as a writer was being summoned in the building of *White Mule* into a full novel. He dreaded telling Williams that this next issue of *Pagany* would probably be the last.

It was already November of 1932 and the fourth issue of Volume III, due to be printed and distributed by the first of October, was not yet organized. Letters kept coming in asking where the new issue of *Pagany* was, saluting its quality, hoping that it might continue, but all were written in a friendly tone by those who recognized a terminal illness.

Having no actual effect on Johns' decision to terminate *Pagany* was the burning down of the Chapman house in Bethel. A chink in the old chimney set the roof ablaze when a fire was started in the fireplace and within minutes the entire house was destroyed. Manuscripts and correspondence were burned, although these were few and mostly replaceable. Though a minor disaster for Johns, the fire was a major one for William and Louisa Chapman. It cost them not only the financial value of the house but the incentive to make a country home in Connecticut.

Now it was Johns who had the country house, in Redding, but not the money to turn it into the type of home he wanted. Johns moved into the empty, unheated place and, camping out in the middle of what was eventually to be a living room, lived out of two old suitcases crammed with a few clothes, books, running correspondence, and manuscripts for the forthcoming *Pagany.*

Slowly the final issue was assembled, proofread, printed, and around the first week of February 1933, mailed out to subscribers and bookstores. *Pagany*'s address was now given as Bethel, Connecticut, and the fourth issue of Volume III was listed as October–December, 1932; January–March, 1933.

In it *White Mule* was carried through Chapters X and XI, and Johns felt that he had dredged enough of it out of Williams in piecemeal fashion that it would be completed even if the vehicle which brought it forward, quarter by quarter, came to a standstill.

The longest piece in this final issue was William March's "The Unploughed Patch," which, though complete in itself, was being expanded by March as a part of his forthcoming novel, *The Tallons.* Since the first printing of William March's "Miss Daisy," in the second issue of Volume II, he and Johns had become good friends. He was born William March Campbell in Alabama and while in the Marine Corps during World War I had been both seriously wounded and gassed. He was now working as William Campbell for the Cunard Line and giving all his free time to writing. "The Unploughed Patch" demonstrates the looser construction of his novel writing as contrasted with the more precise style of his short stories.

This issue contained the first Charles Kendall O'Neill story, "Three Sisters"; a sensitive and realistic portrait, "The Doctor," by Albert Halper; plus a number of new, fresh names in fiction who

482-483

488-494
495-498

would now be printed in *Pagany* only once—Paul Brown, William Watrous Deats, Gertrude Diamant, Hazel Hawthorne, George F. Meeter, and Robert Cantwell.

There were new poets, too—Millen Brand (husband of earlier *Pagany* contributor Pauline Leader), J. V. Cunningham, Sol Funaroff, Merle Hoyleman, and G. H. Neiman. Millen Brand's poem, "Railroad Journey," had a lovely sense of motion toward an oncoming darkness when:

499

> Night gradually draws its curtains on the train
> which hands at every window raise in vain.

And Johns was sorry to know that the "Three Poems" of Etta Blum would be the last he would print. These three, "Early Dawn," "Where the Horses," and "Document," were among her finest.

Oct. 1, '32
R F D # 1
Bethel Connecticut

Dear Shapiro:

Am fairly well settled here, have set up a desk among the cows and chickens and hope within the month to stem the tide of letters swearing, quite righteously, at my procrastination and apparent general debility. In truth my spirits are high, I cut the cost of the last Pagany by well over $100 and no one has commented on the cheaper paper.

Your story will be in the coming issue. Forgive me for having vented any petty spleen on you. Trying to make ends meet and continue the magazine gave me for a time a small bitter feeling of bravery and martyrdom. You know me well enough to know it was not myself I hope and will forgive my waspishness. Definitely out of New York, connected there only by an occasional hotel room, with a house in the country which promises to be as lovely as I might wish, I trust to be nicer. And you must come up later, see for yourself. Will call you next week.

Regards,
Johns

Nov. 16, '32
R F D # 1
Bethel, Connecticut

Dear Shapiro:

Catastrophe! The Chapman home went up in smoke here, the editor escaping with nothing more than blistered feet and no clothes on a frosty morning. Unfortunately the subscription list went up in smoke and the corrected manuscripts for the coming issue. This, sadly I state, included your story. Should you have a copy ready, send to me at once and I'll get it in the issue to appear about Christmas time. It is imperative that I get an issue now even with no one to send it out to; otherwise I should ditch the whole thing, which would be a shame.

Hope to see you in New York soon. Should you wish a few quiet days in the country, do come up. It is a splendid place to work; and I should have to be a host bent over the keys for some time to come, so you would have to amuse yourself. Drop me a line as to when you'd like to come and I'll send you news about trains or pick you up if I'm in town.

Best regards,
Dick Johns

4 West 125th St [off 5th Ave)
N Y C
Nov 21 1932

Dear Johns:

Sorry to hear about that fire. I almost went thru
the same thing a couple of months ago: my old tenement caught
ablaze on the first floor, with me out, my script for my novel
in my rooms, but the firemen, those valiant and heroic boys,
conquered the conflagration.

Glad to hear you are continuing Pagany, though I know
the way you feel about it-- it is more or less a thankless job.
If you folded up, a lot of newcomers would feel it and would have
to nurse their scripts in solitude. Hound and horn print only
five or six stories a year-- and those by writers already on
the make-- while the other little magazines, like Midland,
Frontier etc.., while honest, are, for the most part, too
Christian and genteel. However, you have carried on for a long
time and have more than done your duty in helping to bring
out a lot of new stuff. Guys like Caldwell, Bragin, Chapman,
Rakosi, myself and a lot others owe Pagany a hell of a lot of
credit.

My book has been postponed to April or May, which is
all right with me. I am informed by my publishers that there are
big fireworks in store for me, which again is all right with me.
When the book comes out I'll mail you a copy.

Otherwise not much new. Yes, I would like to come out
to the country for a day or two. If you can arrange it, pick me
up if you come to town, otherwise, send me the details about
the train etc., and I'll come out by rail.

Please note my new address. I live, as a current song
has it, undeneath the Harlem moon.

Halpu

NUMBER 4 *October–December*

January–March 1933

Contents

PAGANY

THREE SISTERS
Charles Kendall O'Neill

We had just finished a late dinner and were smoking at one of the tables in the big room of the fonda when the miller came in. Maria was by the door and he talked to her for a minute and then came over to our table.

"Will you take coffee with me?" he asked in French.

We nodded, pointed to a chair and called Maria. She brought us three coffees without milk and we discussed the weather in a mixture of French and Spanish. If it hadn't been so long since the Romans were in Urba, the miller would have managed to work in a few scraps of Latin.

"Have you things to do tonight?" he asked.

At the next table three fishermen were shouting and beating the table in an argument. The miller didn't argue. He owned the town feed and grain store.

"We are closed for the day," I said. "What do you suggest?"

"You would like to see some girls?"

"What kind of girls?"

"Three sisters in a store and their mother."

We'd struck Urba de Mallorca during Carnival and there had been fiestas and dancing every night but for almost a week now the town had been deep in Lent. We were open for any proposition.

"I'd like to go," I said. "What do you say, Joe?"

"I don't think they'll fight," he said, looking at the next table. "Sure, I'd like to go."

We finished off our cups and went out into the street. It was dark and there were only a few people in the square. The miller led us by a side street and stopped in front of a small store. There were shirts and rope and shoes and jars of olive oil in the window. The miller knocked on the door. He put his face close to the glass and peered through into the darkened store front while we were waiting. He stepped back as the doorknob turned. A black haired girl with a dark face looked out through the half opened door.

"Bonanit," said the miller.

The girl saw us and changed the Mallorcan to Spanish.

"Buenas noches," she said. "Will you come in?"

"These are North Americans, Jose and Carlos," he said. "This is Carlota."

Her teeth were very white against the brown of her face. We shook hands.

"We will come in," he said.

We passed through the store under strings of little tomatoes, past counters piled high with boxes of goods. The mother and the other daughters were sitting around a pan of red coals in the room in back of the store. They stood up as we entered the room. The mother's face was fine-lined and beautiful under her black kerchief.

The miller seemed to have the standing of an old friend. He laughed at the youngest girl as she bent to pick up a piece of sewing that had fallen from her lap when she stood up.

"Jose and Carlos," he said, "this is Antonia and this is Teresa."

"We have pleasure," I said.

We shook hands with the three.

"This is your home," said the mother. "Will you sit down?"

The daughters drew up three more chairs and the seven of us sat down around the fire. Carlota was between the miller and me with Teresa, the youngest, on my right and Joe between the mother and Antonia. Carlota, the oldest, didn't look more than twenty-two. Antonia was more plump than the others and had the only light hair in the family. She would have been beautiful except for a slight cross in her eyes. She smiled often but with an embarrassment that I thought was from her eyes. Teresa hardly seemed Spanish at all. She was slender and her hair was brown rather than black. Her eyes were bright and lively and when she smiled it would be sudden and her eyes smiled too and then she would turn and look away from me to her mother. When she talked she lifted her face up and held her head cocked a little to one side. I liked her right away.

"I saw you walking the other night with Raphael's sister," I said to her.

She looked up and tossed her head.

"We were coming home from the sermons," she said. "Almost every night in Lent there are sermons."

"That is very depressing," I said.

She laughed and the mother clicked her tongue and shook her finger.

"Urba, do you like it?" asked Carlota. She had been saying something to the miller in Mallorcan.

"Yes," said Joe.

"Very much," I said. "You see we are here."

"It is too small for you," said Teresa.

"No, no," I said. "We can work well and the people have good hearts."

Carlota's smile broke for a moment.

"Do you find it that way?"

"Very much so."

"It makes me happy," she said.

Antonia pushed her chair back and went over to the corner for some more charcoal. She spread a few pieces over the fire and raked the ashes a little with the small shovel.

"And the girls here," said Carlota, "do you like them?"

"How can we save ourselves from it?" I asked.

"All beautiful," said Joe. "All beautiful."

Carlota tossed her head and looked at the miller.

"Jaime doesn't find them beautiful," she said.

Jaime laughed and winked at Antonia.

"He has a sweetheart in Puebla," Carlota said. "But to me there is no interest in this."

"She is very beautiful, this girl of his," I said.

"Have you seen her?" asked Teresa.

"What does she look like?" asked Carlota.

I looked over at the miller. He was grinning.

"Is she tall?" asked Carlota.

"Greatly tall," I said. "I saw her standing by his car one day in Puebla."

"Dark or fair?"

"Her hair is very yellow. She is also very beautiful. All her teeth are gold."

"All of them gold?" asked Carlota.

"I don't know whether I should tell all this," I said.

The miller shrugged his shoulders in resignation.

"Tell them everything," he said.

"She has a wooden leg," I said. "But you would never notice it she is so beautiful."

Carlota kicked her foot against the pan in annoyance.

"You have not seen her at all," she said. "But it is nothing. I have no interest in how she looks."

The miller pushed her and he and Teresa laughed. Even the mother smiled at her. Teresa said something and pushed her chair back. She came back from the other room with a tray. There was a wine bottle and some little glasses and a plate of galletas. We each had a little glass of the malaga and some of the cookies. The wine was a little sweet and we had to refuse the second time. Carlota had part of a glass but Teresa and Antonia didn't take any.

We talked some more and no one seemed to know what to do and Jaime suggested a game. It seemed to be the Mallorcan for post office or spin the bottle. They made Antonia lead it. She counted around on the knees singing 'peek-peek-poka-reek . . . gamma . . . gamma . . . ' and some more which I could't catch. It sounded like eenie-meenie-minie-mo.

"How do you say mere in Spanish?" said Joe. " I want to tell them I played this when I was a mere boy."

"Shut up," I said.

Whenever the count ended on a knee, the knee had to be drawn and it kept up until two knees of everybody had been touched. Teresa's left knee won.

We didn't know quite what was up but Teresa whispered something to the miller leaning across the fire and he took Carlota's hand and kissed it. Carlota blushed and everyone except the mother laughed at her. Then Teresa leaned across me to whisper to Carlota and Carlota slapped the miller a good one across the ear. We clapped and Joe shook hands with Teresa. I had to sing a song in Spanish and I got halfway through Donde Estas Corazon before Joe stopped me. Teresa tried to whisper Joe's forfeit to him but he couldn't understand and I had to translate.

"She wants you to declare your love for Antonia in English."

"That's a hell of a thing to have to do," said Joe.

He pulled back his chair and dropped down on one knee with his hand over his heart.

"Shucks, Nell," he said, "I'm not much of a hand for words."

He drew the words out and sighed deeply. Antonia blushed and shook her finger back and forth.

Teresa clapped her hands.

"What does he say?"

"He says he loves her as the waves love the shore," I said.

"Muy bien," said the miller. "I don't believe it."

Antonia's forfeit was to sing and she didn't want to at first but we all said she had to and finally she sang. She had been shaking her head and smiling her embarrassed smile while she refused but when she started singing she stopped smiling and looked down at the floor. Her voice was surprisingly low and clear. She sang Yira and Negra Consentida and then we made her sing La Paloma. It took her to the middle of a song to get any confidence in herself and then it was beautiful. After La Paloma we couldn't get her to sing any more.

The miller told about a German who tried to buy oats from him to make oatmeal. He couldn't understand oats being used for anything but animals. Teresa showed us some pictures she'd taken the summer before at the fiesta of the Virgin of Victoria. We recognized some of the young men and girls we'd met in town. In one picture, the zaranga was playing and some of the old people were dancing the old dances. There was some more talk and we saw that it was past eleven and we said we had to go. The miller said something to the mother about grain and we all stood up. We shook hands all around and Teresa and Carlota walked to the door of the darkened shop with the three of us.

"You won't come back," said Carlota.

"Without fail," I said. "You have been fine to us."

"Whenever you want to," said Teresa. "Our house is yours."

We found Erling next morning down at the port. He was out on the muelle watching the losbter catch being packed for the Barcelona boat. There were two of the big storing boxes drawn up to the key. They were almost submerged and full of water and kicking lobsters. I caught hold of Joe's shoulder and leaned out to look. The box was about eight feet by four and there must have been nearly a hundred lobsters inside. They weren't the kind that we were used to in New England, the ones with the big claws, but they were about the same size. They were more like giant shrimps. A prehistoric looking crab with long legs and a lot of sharp armor was pushing around on the bottom of the box. He looked lonely and confused.

The men were fishing them out of the box with a hand net and folding them into ice in the packing chests. When they handled them, the lobsters doubled up and kicked with a noise like creaking leather harness. One of them fell from the net and kicked around on the ground until Erling picked it up and put it into the chest.

"You've been up early," said Joe.

"Since before seven," said Erling. "They've had heavy luck this week. Good beginning for the season."

Erling was a Norwegian politician and ex-newspaper editor who had been living with the fishermen in the port for nearly two years. His hoarse, lusty English was almost faultless.

We sat down on some empty chests to watch the work. The man putting the lobsters in the ice was wearing a patched pair of faded pink pants. He had the chest nearly full.

"We were over at the three sisters' last night," said Joe.

"Up in Urba?"

"The ones who have the store. Carlota and Teresa and Tonia. Tonia is a little bit cross eyed. We went there with the miller."

Erling looked up at us.

"You know them, don't you?" I asked.

"Yes, I know them," said Erling. "Their father is a fisherman. He's in that boat over there now, unloading nets."

We looked over. A tall, thin fisherman with hair just going gray was pulling away at the brown wet pile of nets in his boat. His face was narrow and I thought I could see something of Teresa in his quick, abrupt movements.

"Teresa moves like that," I said. "But she isn't brown."

"Teresa hasn't gone out to sea all the days for thirty years," said Erling.

"I expect she'll get a good husband one of these days," I said.

"Why?" asked Erling.

"You can see yourself," said Joe. "She's a fine kid."

"She's pretty and she's bright, too," I said.

"And Carlota's putting out the nets for the miller," said Joe.

"There will be no wedding for them here," said Erling.

The words came out sharp and angry.

"Why not?"

He looked surprised.

"You don't know about Antonia?"

"No," I said. "Except that she's got a fine voice."

He lunged up and pulled me by the arm.

"We will walk out to the end of the muelle," he said.

We got up and walked along with him.

"No better girls are in town," he said, "and no boy here can make marriage with them. You were here during Carnival. Did you see them at the dances?"

"I don't remember them," said Joe.

"Because they weren't there," said Erling. "Carlota and Teresa went with their aunt one night to Puebla for dancing. One dance."

We stopped at the end of the muelle and stood looking down at the rocks. A school of tiny clay-colored fish streaked away as we came. Erling stood with his hands on his hips, looking across to the mountains on the other side of the bay.

"Two years ago, Antonia and a boy here were courting, were novios," he said. "I thought somebody would have told you. Antonia was too much woman to wait for marriage. It was early spring like now."

The sun was splintering into bits of light on the choppy water.

"That's not the average thing here. It surprises the man. I thought it was beautiful as hell in her."

Erling's voice seemed hoarser than usual.

"Then the boy spent a night with a woman over in Pollensa. Tonia found it out. There was an old gun of her father's. She shot herself in the head. The scar is on the left side, back of the ear. I don't think you can see it now. The father was the first to come on her. He shouted. There was a doctor here then and Teresa ran in her nightshirt to call him. When he came he found the father making heavy blows on Antonia with a strap. Much blood from the head had run down the back and the strap was red and wet. They say he tried to hit the doctor too."

He kicked a rock and it must have hurt his foot. We turned to walk back along the quay.

"Walls push people together," said Erling. "Whenever they tear down old houses in Urba they find closed up passages in the cellars. You can see all houses are built together with small windows at the street. If the Moors passed the walls they still could not get into the houses. With the passages between the houses, each street was a fort. There is no change. The town is still all one house. All things are known immediately."

It took me three matches to light my cigarette.

"Was she going to have a baby?" asked Joe.

"No," said Erling. "The boy must have been smart. They took her to the hospital in Palma. In two months she was better but all the world knew she had been with a lover without first going to the priests. All people think now that the three sisters are prostitutes."

"That goes for all three of them?"

"Antonia, Teresa, Carlota, the same."

"The miller goes there," said Joe.

"The miller is open for any deal. He goes to see what there is to get."

"What happened to the man?" I asked.

"He went to Palma that week to work in a hotel."

"Why didn't they do something to him?"

"How can I know?" said Erling.

The man in the faded pink pants dropped another lobster. It kicked around in the dust. I looked down the muelle. The tall fisherman was stooped over, unrolling the wet pile of net.

"The nets have to be mended two or three times a week," said Erling. "They are always breaking."

THE DOCTOR
Albert Halper

The tall, thin girl who had found out that she was pregnant put her hat and coat on and told her sister she was going for a walk. She went outside, walking carefully, because the street was icy, and turned north at the next corner.

Above the drug-store was the doctor's office and a big sign there swung in the wind. The tall, thin girl crossed over, made her steps slower as she came near the entrance, and walked by. Her heart was pounding. She walked around the block, seeing the hardened snow upon the front lawns, and when she came back to the doctor's corner the wind was blowing and her face was dry and red looking.

This time she stopped before the door, turned the knob and walked the flight up to the doctor's office. The doctor's wife, a small, plump woman of about thirty, answered the bell.

"Is Doctor Solin in?" the tall girl asked.

"Yes," said the doctor's wife and went into another room to call her husband who was reading the sports section of the newspaper. The doctor was a six-day bicycle race fan and grumbled often to his wife that he couldn't attend all the races because his patients needed him.

"There's a patient waiting," his wife said quietly.

The doctor put his paper down and got to his feet. He was a big, heavy fellow of about thirty-five and very settled looking. Laying his cigar aside, he put on his long white apron and stood still while his wife hooked it from the back. Then, frowning slightly, he walked briskly into his office.

"Come in," he said to the tall, thin girl who sat in the hall which served as the reception room.

The girl went into the office and the doctor closed the door.

The doctor sat silent and listened while the girl told him all about it. He could tell instantly she was a decent girl and came from a good family. At first she stammered a bit, but after a while spoke evenly. She sat with her hands in her lap.

When the girl finished talking there was a long pause. The doctor, sitting in the big, wide chair near the desk, leaned back and stared at the ceiling for a while. He told the girl it was against the law for him to do anything, there was a heavy penalty and perhaps imprisonment if he were found out.

"I can't do anything," he said. "I'm sorry," and he saw how disappointed and lonely she suddenly became.

But something in his attitude and the way he sat and looked sympathetically at her made the girl feel that the interview was not yet over. She began talking again.

The doctor sat without saying anything more, turning in his chair slowly, so that he could look out the office windows.

"I've got money of my own in the bank," the girl said. "No one will have to know."

The doctor continued to stare thoughtfully toward the windows. It was Saturday afternoon and the papers predicted a big jam at the bike races for the evening crowds.

The girl went on talking. Her tone changed and she began to plead. She was not accustomed to pleading and her face grew a trifle distorted with feeling as she spoke. Afterwards she blew her nose softly and sat staring at her knees.

Finally the doctor cleared his throat. He was sure of his ground now. He told her he was taking a big chance, it might mean jail for him, but he'd see what he could do. Then he paused and the girl asked a question.

"Oh, no," answered the doctor, "I'm sorry, but I myself can't do it. I have a friend, another doctor who lives on the South Side. I'll call him up and ask him if he'll do it."

The girl grew a trifle excited; she stood up and wanted the doctor to call his friend right away, but the doctor said he couldn't do that.

"Drop in tomorrow morning before noon," the doctor said. "I'll be able to tell you then."

The girl hesitated; tomorrow was Sunday and on Sunday morning she always went to church with her sister and her sister's husband, but, turning to the doctor, she said she would drop in before noon. As she stood up to go she opened her purse, but the doctor smiled.

"That's all right," he said, and she closed it again.

This made the girl feel so grateful that her eyes grew blurry and, speaking with a sudden rush, she thanked the doctor again and again, her voice breaking occasionally. He swung the door open for her, stood tall and heavy and sympathetic, and listened to her rapid footsteps as she went down the stairs to the street.

Afterwards he called to his wife to help him with the apron and then he sat in the parlor, reading the paper again. His wife went back to the kitchen where she had been preparing supper.

When the meal was ready she called and the doctor laid the paper down. His wife was a fine cook and he felt good as he drew up a chair and sniffed the food. Cutting a small corner from the piece of hot, browned steak, he told his wife about the patient who had just left a short while ago. The meat was good.

"If Doctor Alexander gets a good price from her he ought to give you more than he did last time," said the doctor's wife.

The doctor, who did not like his wife to tell him how to manage things, said nothing. Cutting another corner of steak carefully he continued to chew in silence.

The next morning was clear and cold. At ten o'clock sharp the bell rang and the tall, thin girl came up, her eyes a trifle shiny from the frost. The doctor himself answered the door and told her to sit down in his office while he finished answering a phone call from a patient who was suffering from violent head-aches. After he hung up he went inside the office where they sat talking for five minutes, and when the door opened again and they came out the girl thanked him once more, with feeling and warmth. She shook the doctor's hand and her eyes grew misty and finally she had to gnaw her lip, she was so grateful. Then she hurried down the stairs.

Three days later Doctor Alexander, who has offices on the South Side of the city and who employed two very efficient nurses all the time because business was good, mailed a check to Doctor Colin. Doctor Colin tore the letter open and was not satisfied with the amount, so he phoned Doctor Alexander and told him so. He spoke for twenty minutes with Doctor Alexander, while his wife came from the kitchen and stood near his elbow, listening. And in the next morning's mail another check came.

A week went by.

Then another letter arrived, a letter from the tall, thin girl. She wrote that because she had been so happy she had forgotten to write sooner, so the doctor must excuse her. "You don't know how relieved I am, doctor. My sister doesn't know anything about it. I'm so glad I came up to see you and for some reason or other I feel more grateful to you than I do to Doctor Alexander. Maybe it's because you told me you had to talk so hard to him, to get his consent. But I'm so very happy now, doctor, and I shall always be grateful for what you have done. Please, when you pass me in the neighborhood, don't recognize me. But I know you won't, anyway. You went through all that trouble on my account without taking anything so I know you'll never say a word about this to anybody."

There was no signature.

The doctor was alone in his office when he read the letter. He read it twice. Then he went to stand near the window and stared up the street, one fist holding the letter, the other in his trouser pocket.

A thin, fine snow was falling and two fat, old ladies were carrying bundles from the butcher-shop around the corner. The doctor stood there musingly, while the street grew whiter and whiter.

When the door opened and his wife, carrying groceries, returned from her shopping, the doctor felt a trifle irritated because she had forgotten to bring home the afternoon paper.

Along the curb, the wind coming from the west blew the powdered snow quietly forward, fanning it across the Kedzie Avenue car tracks.

RAILROAD JOURNEY
Millen Brand

There is serenity in this slow gliding
under deep hills.   The curve of train ahead
passes a few freight cars left on a siding
which now obscure the land view and the bled
sky which drains to night.   The curving train
straightens and goes clicking ahead.   A blare
of slow-drawn notes, three or four, stain
this total peace and touch the precarious air.
Near trees whirl fast and far more lovely far
trees eddy gently on the hollow space
above the sun.   Even steeples are
pointed to beauty on this hollow place.
Night gradually draws its curtains on the train
which hands at every window raise in vain.

Jan 26, 1933

#9 126 E 16 ST.

% Militant

N.Y.C.

Dear Johns,

  I wrote to you sometime ago in relation to a group
of poems that I had sent to you, and that was months ago. I think
the duty of an editor includes the necessity of answering letters, giving
a minimum of attention to contribs, in other words I want a bit of
information concerning the poems.

  A couple of us are getting out a magazine, strictly
if I can use that in a broad sense, PROLETARIAN. I dont believe in
the theory prevelant in the 'Marxist circles about the possibility
of building a literature PROLETARIAN, the vogue of the New Masses; if
you are acquainted with the theoryes laid down by Trotsky, expressed
in a book called LITERATURE and REVOLUTION, the fundement of Culture
of the old regime is examined, also the path the new Culture will take

  Will you let me know about my stuff; take what you
intend to use and send the other back!

      Sincerely
      Harry Roskolenkier

IT WAS A WRENCH to look at the pages of announcements for future publications. All writers listed had been published before, but not Mark Schorer. To know that he would not be printing "The Fair" by Schorer was a deep disappointment. He had not seen Schorer since after the early days of *Pagany* at 109 Charles Street, Boston. He remembered with nostalgia that lovely, long office with the wide fireplace, so very different from the bleak empty room in the middle of the cold Connecticut countryside. Mark Schorer, who had been at Harvard at that time, had always liked the place and Johns recalled their enthusiastic arguing about literature and writing when *Pagany* itself was young and Johns far younger in many ways. Now, when returning "The Fair," he was warmed by Schorer's thoughtful reply that *Pagany* "was doubtless the best of the American experimental reviews and needed to be continued."

502-503

And Sherry Mangan said, "It's still the liveliest, or as Pound would say, the 'briskest' paper in the country."

But Johns, though he talked hopefully of finding some financial backing to continue *Pagany,* knew that it was hopeless. Indeed, he was thankful for being able to print the full three volumes without going more deeply into debt. Now, slowly, the printers were being paid and the contributors and literary agents given the small amounts owed for the quality work submitted, accepted, and printed. The house in Connecticut had been closed for the balance of the winter to save money, and Johns was living very simply back in Boston until spring.

In the next few years, Johns completed work on the Connecticut house. On his marriage to Veronica Parker shortly after reaching his thirtieth birthday in 1934, it became his home. Both he and his wife took to the typewriter, and it wasn't long before the first of many Veronica Parker Johns mystery novels, *Hush Gabriel,* was published.

THE UNIVERSITY OF WISCONSIN
MADISON

DEPARTMENT OF ENGLISH

627 Mendota Court
11th March, 1933

Dear Dick:

I'm sorrier than I can say about Pagany's end, if, indeed, it must end now. Will a check for my subscription help at all? I'm being lured into taking my degree here by the bait of a better job for next year and several years to come, & think I can send you three or maybe five dollars next month if that will be of any use to you. I have yearned to return to the Coast & thought always that by next year I would be back in Cambridge, but unless I get an appointment to the new Society of Fellows, which is most unlikely, I shall not be there for several more years to come. And I have been so poor since leaving Harvard that even a short visit has been impossible. I have been fed too long on hope for the good of my soul! But I am writing a novel and a book on William Blake, both of which are rather fun when I find time to get at them. And there may yet be some reward for an exemplary patience

I am anxious to know what you are doing. Writing, I hope; for I thought

THE UNIVERSITY OF WISCONSIN
MADISON

DEPARTMENT OF ENGLISH

ii

the style of your short piece in the current
Pagany so rich and moving, & the talent it
displayed so real, that it would be unfortunate if both were not cultivated.
I wish you the best of luck or whatever it is you are doing.

Do you know anything about Mary
Butts? I am planning a study of
her writings, & should appreciate
any information or suggestions you may
be able to make. And if you have her
address, could you give me that?

Do let me hear from you now and then;
with Pagany's demise, it would be
very easy for you to withdraw
from correspondences that business
formerly made imperative. Don't.

Ever faithfully,
mark.

P.S. Did you know that Jean Toomer is
collecting Margery's letters? His
address is Portage, Wisconsin if you
have anything to send him.
m.

MILLEN BRAND

92 Monroe Place
Bloomfield, N. J.
May 12, 1933

Dear Richard Johns,

Pauline and I were certainly sorry to hear that Pagany
is suspending publication, and hope that it will be possible to continue some time in the future. To me, the
magazine was the best of the smaller magazines I've seen,
and was liberal without going to the frequently unsatisfying
extremes of other small magazines. It had life and not
"just writing." And this was particularly an achievement
because the magazine was "small" only in name, was actually
a large piece of work, in editing and publishing. I felt
always that it was solidly good, and I know how hard it is
to collect a body of work that is good all the way through.
It gives a kind of validity to fiction and poetry that
second rate stuff so easily and devastatingly upsets. The
loss of Pagany is, to me, really a great loss.

I can honestly say that, because I feel this way and
always have, about Pagany, it meant a great deal to me to
have you notice my work, and then publish it.

I was happy that Sherry Mangan liked Railroad Journey.
Would you send him the little note I'm enclosing to thank
him?

Pauline and I would accept your invitation to come for a
visit, but the arrival of Jonathan (he was Anthony) is
only two weeks or so away, so we can't travel. Even after
that, what with diapers and 10 o'clock feedings, we won't
be able to do much visiting as a family for some time to
come. However, I might try to get up for a visit myself
some week-end during the summer, that is, if I can bear to
leave my offspring. (Pauline interrupts here...

(I will send him up. He is taking his two weeks vacation
taking care of Elinor while I am in the hospital, and he
deserves some reward for this. I deserve a change too, by
God, but being a woman I am resigned. Horace Gregory has
read the new novel and thinks highly of it, but says it is
too long, that it really is two good novels and one long
short story, and it should be cut up. But I don't agree.

2

He says I will have a hell of a time getting it published
as is. But even so, I'm going to continue sending out as is.
To me it is one novel, all necessary.

(Millen has started a new novel that's damned good. He's
also writing some new poems. He writes his poems by rapid
transit on the good old Lackawanna and the not so rapid ferry
boat, but it doesn't seem to show.

(We are going back to New York to live October first,
thank heaven. I will go cracked living in this suburban
place. One should either live in the Bethels, Woodstocks,
etc. or take it straight in New York City.

(Do you know where Norman MacLeod is these days? I saw
him and Catherine two years ago. Millen wants to meet him.
We'd appreciate the address.)

All of us send warm and affectionate regards, particularly
Elinor.

Yours,

Millen Brand

P. S. This was written on the twelfth, but luckily wasn't
sent. I had worked all night the night before on the new
novel without going to bed, and the next few nights Pauline
and I talked the new novel over until we were satisfied with
it. On the morning of the sixteenth, Pauline began to have
pains. The pains were not bad, and she decided to take it
easy and not notify me. When I got home, I called the doctor,
and he said it was the first stage of labor. Still we were
not worried. Pauline put Elinor to bed, and I got supper
ready. We ate supper, Pauline lying on the open day-bed and
I sitting near her at our rough table. As we were eating,
the pains became more severe, and Pauline would hold my hand
and pull on it. I became really worried then, and called the
doctor again. He said to take her to the hospital. I hurriedly got her ready and took her to the hospital in a taxi.
She was in agony. They rushed her to the labor room, from
there to the delivery room, and Jonathan was born at once.
The birth, though, was very normal, and now, two days later,
Pauline has recovered splendidly. I'm hardly permitted to
see the baby, but Pauline has reported (1) it's ugly, (2) it's
handsome.

And so now Jonathan sends regards.

Dear Dick :

It was a mighty tough jolt to hear about the bad condition you're in, and tough, too, to learn that Pagany is wrapping the drapery of its couch about it.

It almost goes without saying that if I knew of some sucker who still had dough, I'd sew him up for you so completely that he wouldn't even be able to breathe without a document from you in writing.

But there are no more such people. Everywhere, one hears the same sad slow music. The word 'depression' infects from mouth to mouth as though it were the microbe of a contagious disease. The mindattitude is the worst symptom I've seen yet. The hangdog look; the supreme pessimism; the despair which has passed the stage of hysteria and has become the obstinate agony of a mouse playing dead six inches from the jaws of an alert cat in a sealed room.

God knows I'm no Pollyanna, but even that happy sort of thing would be better than the idiocy of a defeat which springs only from a tightness of money. Any old time is the artists' time; he should be the last hope, because in fact he is the only hope. Instead of that, they're Bill Williams' cannonballs plowing into a wilderness of dejection.

Excuse the anger. Or better, don't excuse it, for it's a good sign.

You say you're living in seclusion, but I hope you'll tell me your Boston address. I was there four weeks ago, and have to go again either this weekend or next. It would be good to know where I could look you up. Suppose you answer this right off and tell me where I can get hold of you. I promise, if you wish, to keep your address secret.

My best regards, as always. If there's anything I can do here for you, you should know by this time that all you have to do is ask me.

Looking ahead to seeing you soon, I am,

Yours sincerely,

Will talk to you about my story when I see you, or will write again about it if I find you'd prefer to remain out of the way.

Apr. 21, '33

Dear Julian:

It was good to hear from you, and to know that you may be in Boston in the near future. Be sure and call me up at Lafayette 2593, and if I'm not there leave your number. Maybe I can arrange to drive you back to New York, or at least as far as Connecticut. I did not mean to give you any hint of supreme pessimism. I am merely swamped in bills for the house and for living, while the estate is not paying anything in at the present. I expect things will iron out within a year or so, and not be too tight in the meanwhile. However, any altruism must go by the board and Pagany with it. I hope by Fall to find someone willing to put up enough cash to try starting from the country what would really be a fresh venture, in all ways but editorially. But more when I see you. Was tickled to see West's book received so very nicely.

My very best,
Dick

Richmond Road, R.R.2,
Grand Rapids, Michigan,
June 13,1933.

Dear Richard Johns:

I received your letter and the returned
poems the same day I was leaving Providence for Michigan,
where I am spending the summer motnhs. I expect to be back
in Providence by the middle of September, and would greatly
like to see you anytime you happen to be there, and shall
make all effort to do so. As I shall be no longer connected
with Brown University, and practically all my time shall be
my own, I expect to be visiting Ken White more often than
my only and frustrated attempt so far this year. May I drop
in to see you then? Knopf is publishing my novel this fall,
and is aying me in advance to finish it, hence my finanical
independence , meager as it is, for a while.

As to Pagany, I hated to see it fold up. And especially
since it did so, do I notice the very evident gap it leaves.
Somehow one started to take it for granted, but now that there
is nothing and seems to be nothing on the horizon to take
its exact place, I rather mourn for it. It was in my opbnion
about as excellent as it could be, and I shall be happy if
you see the chance of reviving it.

Yours,

David C. De Jong

NINETY·SEVEN NAHANT STREET · LYNN · MASSACHUSETTS

Dear Dick:

*It's rather a pity you didn't come to Boston sooner, for until the 24th of
August, we had the loan of a very nice apartment in Cambridge where we could
entertain decently. Now, after some weeks of influenza, Kate's in Maine, and
I'm at the melancholy address above. I can heartily sympathize with your hysteria at the thought of entering Lynn; had I not worse hysteria at the thought
of going without food, I'd not be here myself.*

*Where are you in Boston? And are you visible there? I'm generally in town every
week or so; and should like to see you.*

*As for us, we are much the same. I've been job-hunting; with what success you
can imagine. Our present project is to buy ourselves a $25 Ford, festoon it
with hot dogs, pack a sterno and frying pan, and bounce off to a certain Mix-
coac, some 15 miles southwest of Mexico City, where a fairly reliable rumor
has it that we can live for $30 a month. Unless, prior to October 21st, when
we start, we find someone with a better car/ who's going—in which case we
can offer the $25 for our share of the gas, and live on 25¢ barbecued chicken
instead of the frankfurters. Which would be maint luxurious.*

*I've had, as a matter of fact, a very good summer as a result of this apartment
loan; and, besides getting back a modicum of sanity, have written a good deal
of long-postponed poetry. A first book of poems is coming out this month, or in
October; the short-stories perhaps in the Spring, if the book-market improves
at all. In a word, I love my work, I love my wife, I love myself; all I need
is enough money to live.*

*I was very sorry to hear your confirmation of the rumors of Pagany's decease.
I hope it may rise again like Lazarus under the manipulations of our new prophet
in the White House. Though I have melancholy suspicions that, though he has
turned water into 3.2 wine, that is the limit of his miracle-working. Seriously
I'm very sorry. Though I naturally didn't agree with your choice in all things,
I yet saw no reason to change my opinion that it was the best magazine in America.
As I have often enough said publicly. I do hope you'll be able to start it again
later.*

Let me have news of you, where you are, and whether visible.

Affectionately...

9 September 1933

There were quite a few contributors to *Pagany* who became familiar with this home in the country, among them Manuel Komroff, Albert Halper, and Erskine Caldwell. Caldwell was then married to the noted photographer Margaret Bourke-White and living in nearby Darien, Connecticut. At this time the Caldwells had done their book of text and photographs, *You Have Seen Their Faces,* and had the following two collaborations in mind for the future: first, *North of the Danube,* and then their panoramic view of America, *Say Is This the USA?*

William Carlos Williams once brought American artist Charles Sheeler and his lovely new young wife, Musya Sokolova, who at fifteen was driven from Russia by the Revolutionists. Sheeler was interested in the photographs Johns was taking with an Automatic Rolleiflex, and it was at his suggestion that Johns first began sending out his pictures, which shortly found a place in weekly journals and in such magazines as *Coronet,* as well as the yearly *U.S. Camera.* Little did he envision that in 1940 he would be invited to include a number of his photographs in an Exhibition of Contemporary American Industrial Art held at The Metropolitan Museum of Art.

So *Pagany* was gone, but proudly remembered. Johns felt that it had had a healthy influence on the state of American letters.

Now and again enthusiastic notes would come from contributors who were making their mark on the literary scene in these first years of Franklin Delano Roosevelt's presidency. And when on a bright, warm morning of late June 1937, Johns received this letter from William Carlos Williams, he knew that, although there had been no issue of *Pagany* published in over four years, its influence was still alive and flourishing.

512

Aug. 23, 1933

Dear Dick,

You must have been eating green apples or something, what in Heck makes you so contrite? Anyhow it is a real pleasure to hear from you again and to know you are still walking the surface of the world - so far away!

Sure I'll come and see you. I'd love to see you in fact but where in Hell, R F D #1, Bethel, Connecticut is I still haven't the least idea. You're the limit, really you are. You told me a couple of years ago you'd send me a map. But I'll make a try at it next week if possible anyway .

I'm on my vacation now, at my Mother-in-law's , Monroe N.Y. c/o Mrs. Paul Herman. And is it raining! Floss and the boys are here with me. We're trying to build a tennis court but unless things clear up pretty soon I think we'll just have to lie down in the mud we've created and take the cure or something!

Poor ol' White Mule . I wish I could go on with it. Not a word have I written on it since Pagany busted . I have ideas of course but there seems no chance of getting published so I just stall along taking things as they come - and go.

Well, I've been practicing medicine since I saw you last, that's about all . I did plugged way at the poems in January getting them in shape for a possible publisher . None has as yet been found . Then I put in some time on an opera libretto. That too is stalled . I've roughed out one poem on the low life around Passaic , N.J. and I've just finished a re-review of H.L.Mencken's, The American Language which Munson plans to have published in England , The New English Review. Tha's about all .

Bill, as you may remember, has finished his first year at Williams College and Paul begins his last year at High School in September . They both say they want to be doctors. Imagine!

No, I haven't Carnevali's long poem; as far as I know I've never seen it . I did see some prose of his which I sent within the past three months to Kay Boyle who is assembling it into a novel for him . There is nothing we can do further for Carnevali though I still send him five dollars a month to which he is more than welcome .

I'm really delighted that you've written and if it's humanly possible, which# I'm not q uite sure of, you'll see me , if not all of us, pretty soon.

Sincerely yours

Bill

June 25, 1937

Dear Dick:

These are orders for you not to buy *White Mule*. As you may know it was released by Laughlin June 10 and has received a very good break from the reviewers, so much so that it looks like a winner.

If it turns out to be a big success I want you to realize that I realize the important part you have played in the matter from the first. Without your early appreciation and most generous backing it might never have been written. Your critical acumen in suggesting that I leave out another complicating element in the story is also appreciated by me.

Therefore, Mr. Richard Johns, it will give me the greatest pleasure in the world to send to you (as soon as I get it) the first presentation copy of the book outside of my immediate family—and good luck to you. In just a few days you'll have the book. It's well made.

I wish I could present it in person.

Sincerely yours,
Bill

A RETURN TO PAGANY

The History, Correspondence, and Selections from a Little Magazine

BY STEPHEN A. HALPERT WITH RICHARD JOHNS

In recent years, students of modern literature have come to realize the important role played by the "little magazines" in securing the recognition of major writers, and even in aiding their development. One of the most exciting of these little-known publications was *Pagany*, a quarterly devoted to American literature which was edited by Richard Johns and appeared between 1930–33.

Throughout the life of the magazine, Johns maintained a fierce devotion to the ideals of good literature; refusing to be bound by commercial pressure or editorial posture, he searched continually for lively and expressive writing and made his only criteria excellence of thought and craft. This attitude was appreciated and supported by the literary community — the pages of *Pagany* were filled with the work of such writers as Ezra Pound, William Carlos Williams, Erskine Caldwell, Gertrude Stein, Kenneth Rexroth, Dudley Fitts, Hilda Doolittle, Conrad Aiken, e. e. cummings, Jean Cocteau, Katherine Anne Porter, Horace Gregory, Louis Zukofsky, and James T. Farrell. Many of these early appearances present illuminating and unexpected aspects of the work of authors now solidly established.

The narrative section of *A Return to Pagany* deals with both the idealistic and practical struggles of the magazine: the growth of Johns' conception of *Pagany*, the search for contributors, the trials of finding and keeping a printer, the move from Boston to New York, the financial effects of the Depression, and — most interesting of all — the various meetings and friendships between Johns and the writers.

Since the quality of these relationships is reflected in the correspondence between editor and author, *A Return to Pagany* includes many of the letters that Johns received over the years from his contributors; nearly one hundred are reproduced in holograph facsimile. Depressed or exhilarated, practical or theoretical, these letters reveal the private reflections of their writers on their lives and writings.

The inclusion of some of the best and most interesting pieces that appeared in *Pagany* give the book a vibrant "workshop" quality; the concurrent presentation of the history, the works, and the correspondence allow the reader to absorb the interplay of ideas and opinions that surrounded the entire literary scene of the early thirties.

Stephen Halpert, following a career in Boston publishing, is intensely interested in the literature of the thirties. In writing *A Return to Pagany*, he enjoyed the close consultation and cooperation of Richard Johns, the editor of the magazine.

Publication date: May 26
512 pages; indexed; facsimiles; 7 x 10"; $12.50
LC #69-14600

Available from: BEACON PRESS
25 Beacon Street
Boston, Massachusetts 02108

A SIGNED COPY ON PUBLICATION!